STATISTICAL DECISION
AND RELATED TECHNIQUES
IN OIL AND GAS EXPLORATION

1960 Award Winners

Bernard H. Baum *Decentralization of Authority in a Bureaucracy*
Dissertation submitted to Department of Sociology, University of Chicago

Leon V. Hirsch *Marketing in an Underdeveloped Economy: The North Indian Sugar Industry*
Dissertation submitted to Graduate School of Business Administration, Harvard University

Bedros Peter Pashigian *The Distribution of Automobiles, An Economic Analysis of the Franchise System*
Dissertation submitted to Department of Economics, Massachusetts Institute of Technology

Martin Patchen *The Choice of Wage Comparison*
Dissertation submitted to Department of Social Psychology, University of Michigan

Fred M. Tonge *A Heuristic Program for Assembly Line Balancing*
Dissertation submitted to Graduate School of Industrial Administration, Carnegie Institute of Technology

1959 Award Winners

Kalman J. Cohen *Computer Models of the Shoe, Leather, Hide Sequence*
Dissertation submitted to Graduate School of Industrial Administration, Carnegie Institute of Technology

Bob R. Holdren *The Structure of a Retail Market and the Market Behavior of Retail Units*
Dissertation submitted to Department of Economics, Yale University

Frank Proschan *Polya Type Distributions in Renewal Theory, with an Application to an Inventory Problem*
Dissertation submitted to Department of Statistics, Stanford University

Andrew C. Stedry *Budget Control and Cost Behavior*
Dissertation submitted to Graduate School of Industrial Administration, Carnegie Institute of Technology

Victor H. Vroom *Some Personality Determinants of the Effects of Participation*
Dissertation submitted to Department of Psychology, University of Michigan

1962 Award Winner

THE FORD FOUNDATION DOCTORAL
DISSERTATION SERIES

1961 Award Winners

Geoffrey P. E. Clarkson *Portfolio Selection: A Simulation of Trust Investment*
Dissertation submitted to Graduate School of Industrial Administration
Carnegie Institute of Technology

Donald E. Farrar *The Investment Decision Under Uncertainty: Portfolio Selection*
Dissertation submitted to Faculty of Arts and Sciences, Harvard University

Richard S. Hatch *An Evaluation of a Forced-Choice Differential Accuracy Approach to
the Measurement of Supervisory Empathy*
Dissertation submitted to Department of Psychology, University of Minnesota

David Meiselman *The Term Structure of Interest Rates*
Dissertation submitted to Department of Economics, University of Chicago

George William Summers *Financing and Initial Operations of New Firms*
Dissertation submitted to Department of Management, Case Institute of
Technology

STATISTICAL DECISION

AND RELATED TECHNIQUES

IN OIL AND GAS EXPLORATION

GORDON M. KAUFMAN

*Assistant Professor
of Industrial Management
Massachusetts Institute
of Technology*

PRENTICE-HALL, INC.

Englewood Cliffs, N. J.

To My Parents

Foreword

Professor Kaufman's dissertation, one of five selected for publication in the fourth annual Doctoral Dissertation Competition sponsored by the Program in Economic Development and Administration of The Ford Foundation, was completed during the academic year 1961–62.

The dissertation competition, which is open to doctoral candidates in business administration, the social sciences, and other fields relevant to the study of problems of business, is intended to recognize and encourage excellence in research on business by graduate students. In this year's competition the selection committee chose five such dissertations, to be added to the fifteen outstanding ones that have already been published. Publication awards are made to persons granted doctorates in business and related fields whose thesis research is especially distinguished by its analytical content and strong roots in the underlying disciplines common to business.

The dissertations selected this year in addition to Professor Kaufman's include the following:

The Effect of Capital Structure on the Cost of Capital
Alexander Barges
Graduate School of Business
University of Southern California

Simulation of Information and Decision Systems in the Firm
Charles P. Bonini
Graduate School of Industrial Administration
Carnegie Institute of Technology

The Advertising Rate Structure in the Daily Newspaper Industry
James M. Ferguson
Department of Economics
University of Chicago

*Mathematical Programming and Analysis of
Capital Budgeting Problems*
   H. Martin Weingartner
   Graduate School of Industrial Administration
   Carnegie Institute of Technology

On behalf of The Ford Foundation, I wish to express my gratitude to the members of the Editorial Committee for the care and thought they devoted to the selection process. The members of this Committee, who made the final selection of winning dissertations, are: Professor Alex Bavelas of Stanford University, Professor Roy Blough of Columbia University, and Professor Robert Ferber of the University of Illinois.

The Editorial Committee's task was considerably lightened by the assistance of ten readers, experts in the wide range of disciplines covered in the competition, who carefully screened the theses submitted. The Foundation joins the Committee in acknowledging their debt to Professors Thomas L. Whisler and Harry V. Roberts of the University of Chicago, Paul E. Breer of Cornell University, Lyman W. Porter and Earl F. Cheit of the University of California (Berkeley), Robert B. Fetter of Yale University, Daniel M. Holland of the Massachusetts Institute of Technology, Bernard Karsh of the University of Illinois, Donald P. Jacobs of Northwestern University, and Joseph W. Newman of Stanford University.

Finally, my colleagues and I wish to acknowledge the important contribution of Prentice-Hall, Inc. to the publication of the selected dissertations.

CLARENCE H. FAUST
VICE PRESIDENT
THE FORD FOUNDATION

New York, N. Y.
January, 1963

Acknowledgments

This monograph is an outgrowth of C. J. Grayson, Jr.'s, investigation of how the methodologies of statistical decision and modern utility theory can be used to aid oil and gas operators in making drilling decisions.[1] I wish to express my appreciation to him for helping me to establish contact with industry personnel and for providing valuable commentary on the practicality of my ideas.

Professor Howard Raiffa directed the progress of this research. I value the writing of this monograph under his direction as the most rewarding apprenticeship I have served. He was extremely generous in the giving of his time to direct my efforts, and his remarks were always constructive, invariably helping to dispel the fog of unclearly expressed ideas. Discussions with Professor Ross G. Walker were particularly helpful in clarifying the nature of the human problems that arise when one attempts to introduce mathematical decision making techniques into business organizations. Professor John V. Lintner, Jr., offered many valuable comments on the general organization of this research.

I also wish to thank Dr. John Bishop for aid in removing me from occasional mathematical cul-de-sacs. Walter Falcon of the Littauer Computation Laboratory programmed the general algorithm for calculating optimal strategies for the games against nature analyzed in Chapter 8. The computations of this chapter were performed by the Computation Center at Massachusetts Institute of Technology.

I am indebted to many members of the petroleum industry for the hours they spent patiently discussing petroleum exploration with me, and I wish to thank each for what he contributed to my understanding of a fascinating industry. The executives of Eason Oil Company, in particular, deserve my gratitude for the open-handed generosity they displayed.

Part of the financial burden for this research was borne by the Ford Foundation, who granted me a dissertation fellowship for the academic year, 1959-1960.

---

[1]C. J. Grayson, Jr., *Decisions under Uncertainty: Drilling Decisions by Oil and Gas Operators* (Boston: Division of Research, Harvard Business School, 1960).

Sue Morrison, Ingrid Nitsche, Marie Puzzanghera and Madeline Wisnia typed portions of the rough draft. Mrs. William Ericson typed the final draft. I appreciate their perseverance in carrying out a long, arduous task.

The contents of this monograph are the sole responsibility of the author.

GORDON M. KAUFMAN

"Drilling in the Face of 9 to 1 Odds"[1]

"It is a clear day and a large transport plane hums five miles overhead. Look up and you can see it, appearing hardly bigger than a speck of dust on your glasses. Now focus your imagination on a spot an equal distance below the surface of the earth and picture a small hole punched straight down through a thin layer of soil and miles of solid rock. That will give you some idea of the technical accomplishment of the Phillips Petroleum Company in drilling an oil well more than 25,000 feet beneath Pecos County, Texas.

"To call this five-mile hole in the ground an oil well is more an act of charity than a statement of fact, for the hole was recently capped when it failed to produce either gas or oil. Known as 1-EE University, the well set a depth record, and, likely, a cost record.

"This staggering effort demonstrated once again what oil men have long known: that all the instruments and scientific knowledge used in the search for oil are imperfect; only drilling can prove or disprove the presence of oil."

---

[1]"Drilling in the Face of 9 to 1 Odds," Reprinted with permission of *The IPAA Monthly* (August, 1959), p. 21.

Contents

CHAPTER 4

APPENDIX 4

CHAPTER 5

Part II

CHAPTER 6

CHAPTER 7

Part III

CHAPTER 8

A SEQUENTIAL INVESTMENT PROBLEM *209*

CHAPTER 9

A SEQUENTIAL INVESTMENT EXPERIMENT *260*

APPENDIX 9A

THE EXPERIMENTAL PAMPHLET *277*

APPENDIX 9B

RAW DATA UNDERLYING GRAPHS 9.1–9.6 & TABLES 9.4 & 9.5 *287*

CHAPTER 10

FUTURE RESEARCH PROBLEMS AND CONCLUSIONS *295*

PART I

CHAPTER 1

Introduction

The primary purpose of this monograph is to explore two basic problems that arise in the analysis of petroleum exploration ventures. One is a problem in statistical methodology:

What is the appropriate functional form to use for the probability distribution of the random variable "size of petroleum deposit" when formalizing exploration decision problems under uncertainty in which deposit size is a key random variable?

The other is representative of a rather wide class of decision problems under uncertainty:

How should the oil and gas operator with limited funds select from the stream of inside prospects and outside deals which he must review each year?

An ancillary purpose is to investigate some of the administrative implications of the results of the research.

The petroleum industry was chosen as a vehicle to demonstrate the interaction between statistical decision theory and some prototypes of business problems, first because exploration problems are an exciting instance of a wider class of business problems, second because a nice mixture of subjective and objective information come into play in petroleum exploration, accenting the difficulty of melding objective data, personal feelings, and subjective assessments — difficulties faced in every business, and third because recent researches by Dr. C. J. Grayson, Jr.[1]

[1] C. J. Grayson, Jr., *Decisions Under Uncertainty: Drilling Decisions by Oil and Gas Operators* (Boston: Division of Research, Harvard Business School, 1960).

1

provide an excellent springboard for furthering the use of statistical decision theory in oil and gas exploration. He provides a taxonomy of decision problems faced in exploration, and he demonstrates that the expected utility criterion is an effective aid in making drilling decisions.

1.1. Plan of the Monograph

The monograph is organized into three parts: Part I is descriptive, Part II is normative, and Part III is a combination of both.

The purpose of Part I is to outline the complexity of the business environment from which the mathematical models of Parts II and III are derived. The problems described in Part I play a pivotal role in determination of the underlying assumptions of the models and serve notice that the models deal only with a small portion of a large group of interacting problems which must be solved *jointly* to arrive at truly optimal exploration strategies.

Part I is primarily intended for the person not familiar with petroleum exploration. The essential elements of an exploration program are described in Chapter 2, and, in addition, petroleum exploration methods and tools are briefly reviewed. In Chapter 3 common types of information used in making exploration decisions are listed and discussed from a decision-theoretical viewpoint with emphasis on the sources of uncertainty in technical information. To give a flavor of realism, an exploration program undertaken by a medium sized independent is described in detail in Chapter 4, and some important decision problems faced by management during the course of the program are abstracted from the description and discussed. Nongeological determinants of exploration strategies — funds limitations, timing, and geographical location — suggested by the program described in Chapter 4 are considered in Chapter 5.

In almost every exploration problem a key random variable is the size of deposits that may be discovered upon drilling. As a necessary prelude, then, to analysis of exploration decision problems, Chapter 6 of Part II discusses the question of what functional form to assign to the distribution function of this random variable. The Lognormal distribution is found to be a useful functional form; first, because it is a good empirical fit to histograms of reported field sizes in barrels of oil or MCF of gas; second, because it is shown to be in concordance with concepts of how mineral deposits are formed; third, because stochastic models of the discovery process built on realistic assumptions about the process are shown to lead to the Lognormal functional form; and fourth because the

Lognormal distribution is analytically tractable and rich enough to capture most reasonable oilmen's quantitative judgments about random variables such as reported field size. Chapter 7 develops the analytical properties of the Lognormal distribution needed in the analysis of decision problems under uncertainty involving this distribution and shows how these properties are used in making a drilling decision when the operator's utility-in-money curve is logarithmic.

The focus of Part III is on the problem of how an operator with limited funds should select from the stream of inside prospects and outside deals which he must review each year. Since he must judge the number of barrels of oil or MCF of gas that each prospect or deal will yield, the results of Part II are relevant. However, the structure of the problem rather than its relation to the findings of Part II is emphasized.

Part III's primary objectives are to formulate a series of mathematical models which capture the essence of the sequential investment problem just mentioned, to analyze the models, and to explore some of their administrative implications. Chapter 8 accomplishes the first two objectives. Chapter 9 reports on an experiment done with two groups of volunteers to determine whether the mathematical decision rules derived in Chapter 8 are substantially more effective than unaided judgement in attaining a preassigned goal. The results indicate that within the limits of the assumptions underlying the models used in the experiment, mathematical decision rules do not necessarily lead to great quantitative improvement. The administrative implications of the results are discussed in Chapter 10, together with future research problems suggested by those investigated in this monograph.

1.2. Methodology

This monograph stresses *applied* aspects of decision theory. "Applied" is italicized to emphasize that our primary concern is with the administrative relevance of decision theory in oil and gas exploration; that is, the writer went out into the industry with a basic knowledge of what mathematical tools were available for use, searching for problems and situations where the proper use of these tools might give the oil and gas operator keener insight into the way decisions should be made in order to achieve preassigned goals, e.g., "maximize expected utility" or "maximize net expected present value." Then, taking strong motivation from the field work, *normative models* for two problem areas were constructed to prescribe how the operator should act according to either the expected utility or the expected value criterion.

Much progress has been made in developing mathematical theories which lay down rules for achieving goals such as maximized expected utility. Statistical decision, designed to prescribe action in the face of risk and uncertainty, is one such theory. Utility theory can incorporate personal attitudes towards risk taking into the prescriptions of statistical decision. Such theories may prove to be of substantial aid to the operator in making consistent decisions, but they will *never* tell him how he "ought to feel" towards a particular venture. And they can never replace the operator as a decision maker. His feelings, preferences, and judgements must be allowed to play a major role in any scheme designed to aid him — or he will discard the scheme. The mathematical models of Parts II and III are built in this spirit. Each model will deal with a specific problem and will be used to derive strategies, or policies for decision making, within the context of the assumptions on which the model is built. It is useful to think of this approach as an attempt to construct a set of rules which guide the operator towards a goal such as maximized expected utility.

These models constitute the backbone of the research, so it should be emphasized that a substantial amount of mathematics is employed in their formulation. This does *not* imply that a deep understanding of the basic elements of mathematics is needed to interpret them. On the contrary, the writer hopes that the models will be easy to understand on a common sense basis. However, mathematics was found to be an efficient means for rendering precise the key variables and relations which constitute the core of the problems discussed in this work, and some knowledge in this area is needed to understand the derivation of the results discussed in the text. No new mathematics appears, but as far as the writer is aware, some of the models are new; i.e., the particular industry problems discussed here do not appear in the literature of the industry in similar form. A few of the models discussed are not currently amenable to rigorous mathematical analysis. This emphasizes that the models presented here should be regarded as guidelines for future research rather than a terminal representation of particular problem areas.

The models built in Parts II and III are structured according to the following principle: When analyzing a complex real-world problem, one must initially dissect it into pieces which can be independently examined. The manner of division and analysis is based on a mixture of personal preference for subject matter as well as a belief in the "divide your difficulties" philosophy; i.e., the more complex the problem, the greater the payoff in breaking it down into small parts and attacking each part individually before rerelating it to the whole. In this process one cannot simultaneously consider several vital questions without losing clarity of argument. For example, important questions for analysis are:

Can authority be more effectively delegated by using mathematical-analytical procedures?

What will be the effect of introducing mathematical analysis for decision making on the executive group of a particular company?

How can such tools be integrated with present methods for analysis of investments in a particular company?

But before such questions can be considered as valid research questions, we must be aware of *exactly what it is that* we wish to introduce into the management process. This can be determined only by initially concentrating on a careful, detailed formulation of the types of models that might be useful for attacking specific problems in a given industry. It is here that the emphasis of Parts II and III lies.

1.3. Scope of the Monograph

Perhaps a word should be said at the outset about the limits of the research reported here: As stated earlier, it is a *preliminary* investigation of some specific exploration problems. No attempt is made to present a full description of petroleum exploration — there will be gaps in the picture presented which can be filled by reading Dr. C. J. Grayson's work and related technical publications. An important abstraction in Chapters 6, 7, 8, and 9 is that the generic term "operator" will be used to denote the individual or group who "decides" what action to take in a particular problem situation. This abstraction has a descriptive shortcoming, for it fails to consider the effects of organizational size and structure on decision making, but it vastly simplifies the normative analysis. And, most important of all, the problems discussed in Chapters 6, 7, and 8 must be circumscribed with the understanding that we are suboptimizing when we analyze these problems independently of their interaction with other decision problems faced by and within the firm.

While the emphasis in this monograph is on the creation of techniques for analyzing business problems, once new techniques are created, their *administrative practicability* must be tested before heartily espousing their use by businessmen. A mathematical technique can be regarded as "administratively practical" if it provides a rational framework for guiding action which

1. Includes the important variables in the problem area being analyzed;

2. Provides relations among these variables which accurately characterize the problem;

3. Yields a solution or strategy which is easily interpretable in terms of managerial action, and which can *informally* be justified as a "best" course of action within the limits of the assumptions underlying the technique;

4. Improves upon competitive methods of analysis.

A rigorous investigation of all of the techniques suggested in this monograph is beyond its scope, but Chapters 9 and 10 do deal with aspects of the administrative practicability of the decision rules of Chapter 8.

1.4.   Administrative Relevance of this Research

The real administrative relevance of decision models lies in two areas. First, they serve as a device for generating understanding of the complex nature of managerial decision problems. Even though a model may be impossible to analyze rigorously, an attempt to understand the nature of the relations suggested by the model often gives added insight. In such intractable cases we can often gain indirect insight by modifying the model's basic assumptions — although this is fraught with the danger of misinterpretation, as we interpret the results of analysis in real-world terms. Alternatively, we may use simulation to give us insight and to help us avoid the pitfalls of oversimplification. Second, these models suggest techniques which can aid management in making decisions.

Hopefully, these introductory remarks indicate where the emphasis of this research lies: somewhere in the middle of a particular research spectrum which has at one end research aimed at creating new decision-theoretic mathematics and at the other end research concerned solely with testing the administrative practicability of present statistical decision techniques. It is based on the premise that meaningful insight into the nature of decision making can be gained while paddling a narrow strait between the Scylla of overcomplication and the Charybdis of overabstraction.

Petroleum

Exploration Programs

Chapter 2 describes how oil and gas operators analyze and plan the early phases of an exploratory play. Of course, every play is different in many respects, but the *thought process* of the operator as he weighs information and outlines courses of action generally maintains an over-all consistency. There are certain elemental factors which must be considered, and a particular operator will usually have a rough but ordered framework within which he considers these factors.

His planning efforts result in a scheme for taking action called an "exploration program." A more precise definition is given in Section 2.1 below. This is followed in Section 2.2 by a general outline of a typical program which delineates the major blocks of decisions faced by the operator during a program's course and indicates how they are related. Words unfamiliar to the nonoilman will appear in this discussion: "slim hole strat tests," "regional gravity survey," etc. To clarify their meaning and to acquaint the reader with some basic facts of petroleum exploration technology which will be needed in subsequent chapters, Section 2.3 reviews the major petroleum exploration methods and tools and relates them to the exploration program outline of Section 2.2.

2.1. What is an Exploration Program?

An oil and gas exploration program is a plan of action. If it is well formulated, it specifies what action to take on the occurrence of any event starting from a period of initial interest in an area to the drilling of wildcat wells. A program can range in size and complexity from consideration of a single prospect by a small independent to an undertaking on the part of a major to explore an unexploited virgin area at a cost of hundreds of millions of dollars. In this monograph an "exploration program" will be understood to embrace the planning and execution of a venture which involves more than the decision to drill or not to drill. It differs from the drilling decision process in that:

1. The temporal span of planning is longer;
2. A substantially larger set of consequences of a larger set of possible acts must be considered;
3. A number of complex decision problems under uncertainty arise from the interaction between the drilling decision problem and the problem of whether or not to obtain added information before making the drilling decision.

Thus it is the *scope* of considerations and the manner in which they interact that differentiates an exploration program from the drilling decision process and gives rise to a new set of problems, of which "To drill or not to drill" is an important member.

2.2. Outline of an Exploration Program

In the sequence of activities beginning with initial investigation of an area and ending with wildcat drilling, there are four main blocks of decisions that must be made:

1. The decision to begin investigation of the area;
2. Decisions about reconnaissance information-gathering methods;
3. Decisions about advanced (detailed) information-gathering methods; and
4. Wildcat drilling decisions.

Along with the blocks above, subsidiary decisions about leasing and trading arrangements to acquire acreage are necessary and will be understood to be included within each block.

What factors must be considered in making these decisions? How do the decisions above interact? In what sequence must they be made? Each of these questions is discussed below.

The factors analyzed in building a program are of three kinds: geological, economic, and personal.[1] Here are some queries which might run through an operator's mind as he considers each factor:

Geological   Is the area a marine basin of sedimentation?
             Is there a suitable reservoir bed?
             Is the structure of the region favorable?
             Is there a possibility of strat traps in the area?

Economic   Can we afford to take a suitable acreage position?
             How much can we spend on exploration information?
             What are well costs to the sands we're shooting to?
             What are our overall budget limitations?

Personal   What is the probability of finding oil or gas?
             Are the costs high and the odds of finding low?
             This may be a wild gamble — perhaps we shouldn't stick
             our necks out.

These factors are the same as those which enter the "procedure of evaluation, comparison, and selection"[2] among individual wildcat drilling opportunities. The details of how an operator might put them together to arrive at a decision are set forth in Chapter 7 of *Decisions under Uncertainty: Drilling Decisions by Oil and Gas Operators*. We will not repeat Grayson's discussion but refer the interested reader to his work. Rather, we will crystallize some interesting and important decision problems under uncertainty by outlining the content of a typical program and then suggesting how geological, personal, and economic factors such as those mentioned above give rise to these problems.

To help the reader along, the principal steps in a highly simplified version of a typical exploration program are diagrammed in Exhibit 2.1. The diagram is meant to go along with the verbal outline of these steps presented below. Details have been deliberately suppressed to concentrate attention on the program's major decision points. The reader who does not understand the terminology of the outline and diagram is forward referenced to Section 2.3 for a review of petroleum exploration methods and tools, and to Chapter 3 for a discussion of various types of exploratory information.

---

[1]See Chapters 4, 5, and 6 of C. J. Grayson, Jr., *op. cit.*, for a penetrating discussion of the part these factors play in the drilling decision.

[2]C. J. Grayson, Jr., *op. cit.*, p. 144, defines this procedure as the "[drilling] decision process."

Outline of a Typical Exploration Program[3]

1. *Initial Investigation and Assessment of Potential*

The typical program begins with a company geologist expressing interest in an area. If an initial investigation is initiated, it might include:

(a) A review of available literature to develop an understanding of the regional geology;

(b) Acquisition of logs, cores, cutting, scouting reports, etc., from the area;

(c) A quick surface reconnaissance of the area.

The information is integrated into a variety of regional maps which can serve as guideposts to more detailed study of the area. Meanwhile, company landmen survey the area to determine what acreage can be obtained and under what conditions.

Before making a decision to gather added information, the operator will generally assess the area's potential on the basis of the information acquired in the above steps.

Is the geological character of the area favorable for the deposition of hydrocarbon deposits?
What are the odds that hydrocarbons will occur in economic quantities?
Are company funds available?
Does the venture meet company criteria?

2. *Reconnaissance Exploration — the Decision to Gather More Information*

If the answers to the above questions lead the operator to continue the program, he must decide what mix of information-gathering methods he wishes to use before making wildcat drilling decisions.

Regional seismic surveys?
Regional gravity surveys?
Slim hole strat tests?
Aerial photos?

---

[3]The reader who wishes a more detailed picture of a typical exploration program undertaken by a major should read an article by E. A. Wendlandt, Chief Geologist, Humble Oil Co., entitled "Exploration Planning." The article constitutes Chapter 41 of *Subsurface Geology in Petroleum Exploration*, edited by J. D. Haun and L. W. LeRoy (Golden, Colorado: Colorado School of Mines, 1957), pp. 815–858.

The mix that he ultimately decides upon for this phase of exploration will depend on the cost of each of the methods, the information that he and his geologist feel is necessary to complete their understanding of the geology of the area, and the funds available for exploration.

3. *Advanced Exploration — Detailed Information-Gathering*

By this time company landmen will be shaping up acreage acquisitions over inside prospects in the area, and negotiating for favorable trading arrangements. The operator is still in an information-gathering re-evaluation cycle (Exhibit 2.1, loop 2), but now he will be considering the use of sharper methods for gathering information about particular prospects — methods such as detailed seismic surveys and core drilling.

4. *Wildcat Drilling*

Eventually, the operator must decide whether or not to drill the prospects he has developed. He will consider the merits of each in light of the questions posed when he began initial investigation of the

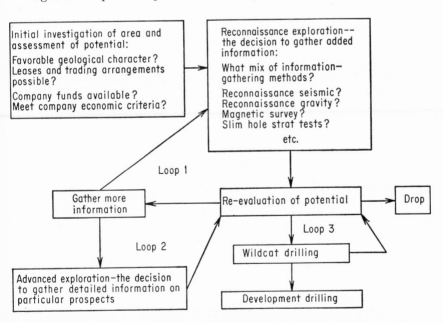

Exhibit 2.1

PRINCIPAL STEPS IN AN EXPLORATION PROGRAM

area, and if he makes a decision to drill a wildcat in an area where more than one prospect is involved, he will be in the drilling-re-evaluation-of-potential cycle of Exhibit 2.1, (loop 3).

2.3.   Petroleum Exploration Methods and Tools

Prior to the drilling of wildcat wells, almost all of the effort, time, and money spent in carrying out an exploration program is devoted to the collection, collation, and analysis of information about the area being explored. As shown in Exhibit 2.1, this information-gathering process can be divided into three main steps: initial investigation, reconnaissance exploration, and advanced exploration. No truly sharp distinction can be made between these stages, but for descriptive purposes each stage can be identified by the mix of information-gathering methods employed.

For the benefit of the reader not familiar with petroleum exploration methods, we will briefly review these methods. A petroleum exploration method is a procedure for making measurements of some physical characteristic of the earth by means of direct observation or by use of a prospecting tool and then interpreting the measurement data so as to draw conclusions about surface structure and composition, subsurface structure and composition, and the probability of finding hydrocarbon deposits.[4] The interpretation is portrayed in the form of surface and subsurface maps, or like representations. The mapping of structural and compositional features serves the same purpose for a geologist who wishes to understand the geology of an area that blueprints do for an architect attempting to understand a yet-to-be-built building: Structure is the geometry of the building, the manner in which materials are put together to give it form; composition is what the building is made of.

The tools which the geologist uses to measure the earth's physical attributes are of two general types: geological and geophysical. They differ in that geophysical tools are usually used to determine the geometry of subsurface structure, whereas geological tools give information about surface and subsurface composition as well. Operationally, the tools differ in that geophysical tools can be employed to make inferences

---

[4]Read Appendix to Chapter 2 for a brief description of the role structure and composition play in making inferences about the existence of hydrocarbons. This appendix is adapted from *Decisions under Uncertainty: Drilling Decisions by Independent Oil and Gas Operators*, doctoral thesis by C. J. Grayson, Jr., with permission of the author.

about the subsurface structure of an area *before* any wells are drilled, whereas there is no way to look at the area's subsurface composition until after drilling. "Geometry always precedes composition in a new area," according to a well-known research geologist. It is worth re-emphasizing that no presently known tool, geological or geophysical, other than the drilling of a well can give a *direct* indication of the presence or absence of petroleum in a particular locale. However, experience has shown that certain kinds of subsurface structure when associated with appropriate composition have a high probability of containing hydrocarbon deposits. Thus geological and geophysical tools serve to sharpen the geologist's inferences as to the location of hydrocarbons, complementing one another in that a knowledge of structure *and* composition is necessary for complete understanding of the geology of an area:

A realistic goal of the geologist is to discover prospects with an optimum combination of structure and composition — that combination favorable to hydrocarbon deposits which maximizes the probability of hydrocarbons being present.

One exploration method can be distinguished from another by noting (a) what tool is used, and (b) how it is used. Two methods obviously differ if they employ different types of tools. If both methods employ the same tool but it is used in a substantially different fashion to yield somewhat different data, then the methods can also be considered to differ. For example, a *reconnaissance* exploration method is often regarded as one whose goal is to help the geologist determine the petroleum-bearing potential of a large area in a short space of time. The tools or observational techniques used in reconnaissance exploration usually do not achieve the precision of measurement or "resolving power"[5] that the same tool or technique attains when employed as an *advanced* exploration method — a method whose goal is to study a small area intensely. Reconnaissance methods reveal regional attributes and anomalies which might be fruitful subjects for careful study by advanced exploration methods.

Our discussion of the role of geological and geophysical methods in

---

[5]J. J. Jakosky, *Exploration Geophysics* (Los Angeles: Trija Publishing Co., 1960), pp. 20–21, uses the expression "resolving power" to denote the ability of a geophysical tool to obtain "specific data diagnostic of subsurface conditions. The term 'resolving power' relates only to the *general* use and applicability of the methods, because a method which usually has a relatively low resolving power might under *specific* favorable circumstances become a method of superior resolving power."

the information-gathering process can be usefully supplemented by capsule descriptions of the major ones:[6]

The seismic method uses an instrument called a seismometer to record the travel time and intensity of artificially generated shock waves. The waves are induced by an explosion which causes them to travel downward into the basement rock, during which time they are refracted and reflected back to the surface by rocks of varying density. As the waves reach the surface they are detected by a series of detection devices placed over the surveyed area, and their intensity and distance in time from the instant of explosion is recorded on a graph called a seismograph. The time required for the wave to return to the surface is a reliable indicator of the depth of the refracting or reflection layer. By appropriate interpretation, seismic recordings can be used to trace the structural rise and fall of subsurface rock formations.

Gravimetric methods are based on measurement of variation in the gravitational attraction produced by rocks of differing density at varying depths below the surface. Such variations are measured with an instrument called a gravimeter, recorded, and then plotted on a map. Lines of equal gravitational intensity are joined to present a picture much like that of a topographical relief map. "Hills" and "valleys" indicate positive or negative gravitational anomalies. According to Jakosky, " . . . gravitational methods have been used more extensively and with greater success in mapping the relative topographic relief of the comparatively dense basement rock [than magnetic methods]. They are thus oftentimes valuable in locating associated structure in the overlying sedimentary formations as well as in finding major structural features such as faults, contacts, etc., in the overlying sediments."[7]

Magnetic methods require use of an instrument called a magnetometer to measure variations in the earth's magnetic intensity. Readings are plotted on a map. Then, just as with gravitational maps, lines of equal intensity are drawn to depict magnetic anomalies.

Electric methods are based on use of tools which measure the electrical resistivity or conductivity of the subsurface as an electric current is

---

[6]The following description of exploration methods has been drawn from a variety of sources, the most prominent of which are J. J. Jakosky, *Exploration Geophysics* (see above), and K. K. Landes, *Petroleum Geology* (New York: John Wiley & Sons, Inc., 1959).

[7]J. J. Jakosky, *op. cit.*, p. 25.

passed through it. Inferences about subsurface structure can be made; e.g., fault zones usually have high electrical conductivity.

Each method's resolving power, or sharpness, is dependent on the particular geological circumstances under which it is used. Jakosky points out that:

> Magnetic methods have several technical disadvantages which stem from a low degree of correlation between magnetic anomalies and structural anomalies in many instances. He adds,
>
> . . . compensating features in the use of magnetic methods are their relatively high speed and low cost. These are sufficiently pronounced to indicate a definite field of usefulness for magnetic reconnaissance, preliminary to further detailed studies by other methods. This is particularly true in areas where information is available on the controlling magnetic properties of the subsurface.[8]

Gravitational methods are subject to the same disadvantages as magnetic methods, although the degree of correlation between subsurface and gravitational variation is commonly higher than for magnetic variations. Gravity surveys usually require more time per unit area covered than magnetic surveys and are often more expensive as a result. However, the fact that they can be used for both reconnaissance surveys *and* detailed work is a compensating feature.

The use of electrical methods for petroleum exploration is still in the experimental stage, but they offer future promise; costs lie somewhere in between that of magnetic and gravity methods.

Seismic methods are the most expensive but by far the most successful of geophysical petroleum exploration methods. Seismic methods are widely used in both reconnaissance and detailed work and are generally successful in locating structural anomalies. However, like other geophysical methods, they have not been of much aid in discovering petroleum deposits which occur in stratigraphic traps, although recent progress has been made in this application.

Of those methods reviewed above, the seismic method is the most extensively used, accounting for over 80 per cent of all crew-months of geophysical activity in the past few years. As of June, 1959, for example, the *Oil and Gas Journal* showed the following breakdown of crew-months of geophysical activity in the United States:

---

[8]J. J. Jakosky, *op. cit.*, p. 29.

CREW-MONTHS OF GEOPHYSICAL ACTIVITY IN THE U.S. IN 1957 AND 1958[9]

	1957	1958	
Seismic	6283	5064	crew-months
Gravity	879	612	crew-months
Magnetic	80	55	crew-months
Other			
Total	7242	5731	crew-months

Although it is extremely difficult to specify the resolving power of a geophysical tool independently of the particular circumstances in which it is being used, most geophysicists would agree that seismic methods are sharpest, followed by gravity methods, and then by magnetic methods. This ordering is reflected in the costs of these methods: The sharper the method, the more expensive it is. Present-day costs might run roughly as follows:

GEOPHYSICAL EXPLORATION COSTS PER CREW-MONTH

Magnetometer	ground	$2000–$4000
	aerial	$6–$15/profile mile
Gravimeter	land	$4000–$8000
	marine	$10,000–$25,000
Seismograph	reflection	$8000–$80,000[10]
	refraction	$9000–$85,000

These are but gross estimates of the range of costs of geophysical exploration, for the cost as well as the resolving power of any particular method is highly contingent on when, where, and how the method is applied.

Whereas geophysical methodology is uniquely concerned with subsurface phenomena, *geological* methods are concerned with both surface and subsurface characteristics. However, geological methods can also be conveniently classified for descriptive purposes according to the tools each method employs.

---

[9]*Oil and Gas Journal*, Vol. 57, No. 24 (June 8, 1959), p. 188. The crew-month is used as a standard unit of measure of geological and/or geophysical activity by oilmen for two reasons. First, since geological and geophysical surveys are done by men in groups called "crews," this is a natural measure of information-seeking activity; second, crew-months are a more accurate indication of physical activity than dollars spent, as the cost per crew-month fluctuates widely depending on factors such as terrain, weather, etc. Both cost per crew-month and the number of crew-months of activity are carefully considered in planning programs.

[10]Estimates of the cost of offshore seismic surveys have run as high as $80,000–$85,000 per crew-month. See *Submerged Lands Productive Capacity*, A Report of the National Petroleum Council (1953).

Surface Methods

The most effective of all geological tools is the geologist himself. He is the observer, the recorder, and the interpreter of all that he sees about him in oil country. The oldest petroleum exploration method, geological surveying, nowadays consists of the geologist covering an area on foot, by motored vehicle, or by plane or helicopter for indications of petroleum deposits, such as oil seeps or tar lakes. At the same time he will be making observations about environmental conditions, the surface geology, surface stratigraphy, and surface structure — all of which are important clues to the location of hydrocarbons.[11] As with geophysical methods, if the survey's purpose is to determine the petroleum-bearing potential of a large area in a short space of time, only the grosser features of a surface structure and composition will be noted; such a survey is called a "reconnaissance survey." A reconnaissance survey may be supplemented by detailed geological surveys of selected areas, to " . . . determine the areal extent of a surface structural anomaly, its vertical magnitude (closure), and the probable depths to the potential reservoir rocks."[12] As Landes points out, field geology can be used effectively at all stages of exploration:

> It is doubtful that field geology will ever disappear as an aid to oil finding. It is used intensively in exploring new areas, in the reexamination of older regions, and in checking geophysical prospects.[13]

Field surveys can at times be profitably supplemented with aerial photographs. Very often features not evident from ground surveys can be observed. Modern developments in high-speed photography have rendered aerial photo surveys a useful exploration method, especially in regions which are relatively inaccessible from the ground and which are not well mapped.

Another technique which geologists use to infer the presence of petroleum deposits is known as soil analysis, or geochemical prospecting. While not highly enough developed to compare in efficiency with seismic methods, the theory underlying soil analysis is judged sound.[14] The basic

---

[11]K. K. Landes, *op. cit.*, p. 30, offers a comprehensive list of the observations usually made under each of these headings.

[12]*Ibid.*, p. 30.

[13]K. K. Landes, *op. cit.*, p. 29.

[14]D. Hager, *Practical Oil Geology* (New York: McGraw-Hill Book Company, Inc., 1951), pp. 299–300.

idea behind this method is that no rock is completely impervious, so that the lighter hydrocarbons imprisoned in the reservoir rock will escape through the cap rock and overburden into surface soil, where it can be detected by chemical analysis.

Subsurface Methods

In order to explore subsurface composition, a vital key to the location of hydrocarbons, the geologist relies almost exclusively on the drill.

Core drilling is a method whereby a light, portable drill is used to obtain corings, or subsurface rock samples, from depths up to a thousand feet. By virtue of their mobility and ease of operation, such rigs are easy to use and quite inexpensive by comparison with the cost of an exploratory well drilled with a rotary rig. A core drill survey of an area will give the geologist information about anomalies that may be obscured by overburden.

The slim hole drill is similar to the core drill but is designed to penetrate to much greater depths — up to 10,000 feet. It drills a very narrow diameter hole (1 to 4 inches) which is not usually designed to produce oil in commercial quantities but can give an excellent stratigraphic picture of the subsurface at much less cost than an ordinary rotary rig.[15]

Exploratory well drilling — wildcatting — is the best information-provider of all geological or geophysical methods. Not only does it tell whether oil or gas is present in commercial quantities, but, when supplemented by careful analysis of cores, cuttings, and logs, an exploratory well provides detailed information about subsurface structure and composition which can be correlated with the geologist's analysis of surrounding areas, correcting misimpressions and refining geological interpretations. However, it is the most expensive of exploration methods.

---

[15]In March, 1960, a $3\frac{3}{4}''$ diameter slim-hole wildcat was drilled to a depth of 20,603 feet! See *Petroleum Engineer* (May, 1960), p. B–19, for a complete report on this well.

Petroleum Exploration

and Production

Petroleum in the technical sense can occur naturally as a liquid, a gas, a semi-solid, or in some instances as a solid. Liquid petroleum is called "crude oil," petroleum gas is called "natural gas," and the semi-solids and solids are called "asphalt, tar, pitch, albertite, gilsonite, or grahamite." In this thesis, the term petroleum is meant to include only oil and gas.

Petroleum

Origin and Location. The origin of petroleum and the methods by which it accumulated into pools is still debated. Some believe that the primary source was organic (animal or vegetable); others say the origin was inorganic (hydrogen), with the weight of current belief on the organic side. Theories differ as to whether the petroleum was formed *in situ* or whether it originated in certain kinds of rocks called source rocks and later migrated into the present "traps."

Contrary to some public conceptions, petroleum is not found in underground lakes or rivers. It usually occurs in the minute pore spaces between grains of sand in a sandstone, the voids between crystal faces in

---

[16]This appendix is reproduced from *Decisions under Uncertainty: Drilling Decisions by Independent Oil and Gas Operators, op. cit.*, by permission of the author. Much of the general information for this appendix was obtained from a reading of A. I. Levorsen, *Geology of Petroleum* (New York: McGraw-Hill Book Company Inc., 1956).

limestone, and, in rare instances, along fracture planes in thick shale beds. The most common types of petroleum traps consist of a porous reservoir rock capped or overlain by a dense impermeable rock. Three traps frequently encountered are the *anticline, fault,* and *stratigraphic* traps.

An anticline is an upward fold in the earth's strata, forming an arch. A fault trap consists of a fracture in the earth's crust, resulting in a porous layer being cut off by a nonporous layer. A stratigraphic trap is formed when porous layers are pinched out between nonporous layers. These containers are spoken of as traps, while the portion of the trap that actually holds the petroleum is called the "reservoir." The term which loosely covers all types of traps is "oil structure." Within these structures, there may be oil, gas, and water. The gas and oil rise and are concentrated in the upper part of the porous rock, while the water is usually on the bottom and sides of the structure.

Reservoir Energy. When a hole (a well) is drilled into the trap, the petroleum can escape to the surface. The petroleum itself has no energy with which to produce itself, but there is usually a form of *reservoir energy* (gas and/or water) to sweep or flush the oil to the surface. The amount of such energy varies widely, both in degree and type, and there may be several types of energy operating successively during a well's life. If the amount of energy is small, the well may be quickly depleted of its primary oil. If the energy is large, a large percentage of the primary petroleum may be recovered before there is an appreciable drop in reservoir pressure.

The principal types of reservoir energy sources are *gas dissolved in oil* (dissolved-gas drive, solution-gas expansion), *free gas cap* (gas in excess of what the oil can absorb), and *water.* In the gas drives, the gas expands as it seeks to move toward the lower pressure at the well bore, and simultaneously it drags and drives the oil along. In water drives, the water moves toward the pressure drop at the well, flushing the petroleum from the pore spaces and driving it to the drill stem.

Gas drives are generally less efficient than water drive wells; i.e., the gas drives generally do not force as high a percentage of the total oil to the surface. Very roughly, water drive wells may recover up to *80 per cent* of the oil in place, whereas gas drives may more typically recover only *20 per cent* to *50 per cent* of the oil. The ideal combination is a well with a free gas cap initial drive that is replaced after its exhaustion with an active water drive.

When a well first begins production, it is very difficult to decide what kind of reservoir energy is present so that future production can be planned to make maximum use of the initial energy. For this same reason, it is very difficult to estimate the total amount of oil that can be recovered from a well until a production history over a period of months is available. Initial estimates can be made utilizing data from core samples taken from the hole, but much greater accuracy can be obtained after a production history of six months or longer is available.

Not too many years ago, when a well had depleted its original reservoir energy (primary production), it was abandoned. Sometimes as much as 50 to 85 per cent of the original oil in the place was left in the ground. Today, however, many wells continue to produce under *secondary recovery* methods. New energy is given to the reservoir by forcing down gas, air, or water from nearby input wells. These new energy sources force the oil toward the producing well in the same way as they originally performed. When gas is injected into the ground to maintain pressure or recover abandoned oil, the process is called "pressure maintenance" or "repressuring." When water is injected under pressure, it is called "water flooding." These methods are expensive, so most operators today try to extract as much as possible of recoverable oil through energy-conserving primary production practices. Secondary recovery has proved to be most profitable to date in recovering oil from older fields where original reservoir energy was quickly depleted, abandoning large amounts of oil in the reservoir.

CHAPTER 3

Information for Exploration
Decisions

As Chapter 2 indicates, the prime task of the petroleum geologist is to gather information which helps the operator to find oil and gas in commercial quantities and which can be produced at a profit. However, nature is like the shellman at a carnival who makes a man believe a pea is under a shell, when the shell really covers only air. Oftentimes the operator has the best of geological and geophysical information obtainable prior to drilling and still makes the "wrong" drilling decision because the best of pre-drilling information gives only a partial insight into a complex state of subsurface affairs. Yet such information is expensive. The typical small independent might invest from 10 to 30 per cent of his total exploration expenditures in geological and geophysical information; majors invest from 50 to 70 per cent.[1]

Since an operator's judgement is forcefully colored by the type of information he receives about a prospect and the manner in which it is presented, Chapter 2's description of exploration methods can be profitably supplemented by a closer look at information relevant for exploratory decision making. This is the subject of Chapter 3.

---

[1] C. J. Grayson, *op. cit.*, p. 79. In the Rocky Mountain area, a highly favorable one in terms of barrels discovered per exploration dollar spent, $60,000,000 per year is currently being invested in geology and geophysics. This constitutes about 20 per cent of the cost of finding petroleum deposits in the area, which in 1957 was $.70 per barrel discovered, according to R. E. Megill in an article entitled "The Cost of Finding Oil," *Oil and Gas Journal*, Vol. 57, No. 14 (March 30, 1959).

In this chapter the notion of "information" is used in its widest sense. It will be the generic label for any object or process which describes some aspect of the uncertainties of the problem. This will be made more precise subsequently. In discussing information relevant for decision making in this context, we will

1. Acquaint the reader with the more common types of exploration information;

2. Establish a point of view from which a number of exploration problems will be examined in Part II;

3. Examine some of the sources of uncertainty in technical data used in exploration from the vantage point of the operator as a decision maker;

4. Give some examples of how operators are attempting to refine the manner in which information is presented to make it more meaningful for decision making.

3.1. Types of Information

A wide variety of information helpful in making exploration decisions is available.[2] A loose classification might be

WRITTEN DOCUMENTS

Financial	*Technical*
Balance Sheets	Samples
Income Statements	Geological and geophysical maps
Return on Invest. Analyses	Logs
Budgets	Scouting reports
Reserve estimates	Journals
etc.	etc.

WORD OF MOUTH

Formal	*Informal*
Scheduled intra-company meetings	Day-to-day contacts
Association meetings:	Social contacts
American Petroleum Institute	etc.
Independent Petroleum	
Association of America, etc.	

The list above is a gross classification, and the reader unfamiliar with oil industry technology should realize that a great variety of significantly

---

[2]C. T. Grayson, *op. cit.*, Chapters 1–7, has amply documented how financial information is used in making drilling decisions.

different types of information are subsumed under each element; e.g., Landes[3] defines a "log" as " . . . a record made during or after the drilling of a well. It furnishes, directly or indirectly, a report of the geological formations penetrated." Then he discusses eight of the more frequently used types of logs:

Sample	Induction
Mounted Sample	Radioactivity
Time	Caliper
Electric	Mud Analysis

There are of course many important technical variations within each of these categories. Similarly, Landes[4] defines subsurface geological maps and sections as " . . . compilations of individual well records into geologic illustrations" and classifies them:

Geologic	Isopachus
Paleogeologic	Paleostructure, Paleotechnic
Paleogeographic	or Palinspastic
Structure Contour	Facies
	Cross Sections

The mix of various types of information that will be most useful for geological interpretation of a particular basin or prospect varies widely according to both the character of the basin or prospect and the predilections of the geologist doing the interpretation. The Recommendation reproduced below illustrates the kinds of technical-geological information a member of the geological staff of a large independent felt would be necessary to successfully pursue a major gas play:

A Recommendation for a Gas Play

Proposition. The X multiple sand gas play will ultimately develop into a size equal to or greater than most major producing areas, and the profits will yield returns averaging more than 5 to 1 on investments. It is proposed that we set aside sufficient funds to permit the undertaking of a long-range major program of acreage purchase, exploratory well drilling, and interest in acreage well deals in this area.

---

[3] K. K. Landes, *Petroleum Geology* (New York: John Wiley & Sons, Inc., 1951), pp. 69–85.

[4] *Op. cit.*, pp. 85–96.

Additional Study. We suggest this report be used as the basis for future study. It might also be worthwhile to explore the possibility of obtaining commitments of gas reserves of certain other companies not normally in the gas pipeline business.

General Conclusion. This multiple sand gas region covers approximately 6000 square miles. It is anticipated that approximately one half, or 3000 square miles, could be productive of gas in at least one sand horizon. It is also anticipated that the average square mile could have reserves in the amount of 15 billion cubic feet of gas, or more, which at 10 cents per MCF (a minimum price) would gross $1,500,000 per well section. Anticipated total reserves could be in excess of 45 trillion cubic feet of gas, or more than a gross value of four billion five hundred million dollars at 10 cents per MCF. It is believed that we could develop, and control, at least one fifth of this gas reserve by taking such action over several years. This would require total acquisition of at least 1200 sections, or 768,000 acres. We presently hold about 368,000 acres in this entire region. If our assumptions are correct, one fifth share of ultimate gas reserves in the region would amount to nine trillion cubic feet with a gross value of nine hundred million dollars at 10 cents per MCF. Note: The prospective area includes 6000 sections.

Recommendations.

1. Allocate approximately $4,000,000 for acreage purchases and acreage well deals during the next four years, and allocate $1,000,-000 to $3,000,000 additional to drill 10 to 20 exploratory wells to determine reserve possibilities. It is anticipated that one well to each 40,000 acre block would be the minimum requirement for exploratory testing, but some could undoubtedly be drilled under the acreage well deal program. All development wells are over and above these monies.

2. We recommend added funds as follows:

   To District A: $200,000 (or $400,000 total with the present money) for purchase of acreage in County B at a top price of $50 and $85 as outlined, or for acreage-well deals not to exceed $100 per acre tested and a maximum of $\frac{1}{16}$ override.

   To District B: $400,000 for acreage purchases as outlined above.

   To District C: $200,000 for acreage purchases at a top price of $50 and $100 and outlined, or for acreage well deals not to exceed $125,000 per acre tested and a maximum of $\frac{1}{16}$ override.

It is also recommended that $1,100,000 be allocated for eleven exploratory stratigraphic tests to be located and drilled approximately as follows:

District A: 1, 2, and 3
District B: 1, 2, 3, and 4
District C: 1, 2, 3, and 4

[Note: Each of these wells is specified as to location, depth, net cost, and month to commence.]

Supporting Data.

1. Regional map to illustrate the following:

   Contoured on top L sand.
   Acreage
   All wells (except shallow tests of no consequence).
   Fields, names, producing horizons (also for isolated wells).
   Important sand limit lines (not too detailed).
   Outline of authorized for expenditure areas, as recommended, with labels showing money spent to date, added amount wanted, and top price.
   Location of proposed strat tests, with labels showing depth and cost.

2. Larger regional map to illustrate:

   Number of known pay section and thickness of potential sand bodies by zones for each well.
   Known or anticipated areas of production for each zone to be indicated by suitable limit lines.

3. Six type logs, two from each district with potential pay zones, suitably named and marked.

4. Brief description and reserve estimate of chief pools.

5. Brief discussion of future potentialities.

6. Statistical summary — Actual ROI (return on investment) to date

	District		
	A	B	C
Total Wells Drilled			
No. Gas Wells			
No. Oil Wells			

No. Dry Holes
Per cent Productive
Est. ROI — Gas Wells
Est. ROI — Oil Wells
Est. ROI — Gas and Oil

7. Statistical Summary — *Productive Area Potential*

	A	B	C

Est. of Prod. Acreage
Sand L
    M
    N
    O
Others

8. Statistical Summary — *Estimate of Reserves (Gas)*

	District		
Sand	A	B	C

    L (20′)*
    M (30′)
    N
Others
*(Give average pay thickness and use 800 MCF per acre-foot and number of potential productive sections for each zone.)

9. Statistical Summary.

Brief statement of estimated total amount of gas reserves from 8 above with gross value at 10 cents per MCF and net value before taxes (by deducting acreage cost, well cost, production costs, or approximately $200,000 per section).

Technical and financial information overlap in that return on investment analyses, budgets, and related documents are based on assumptions which derive from maps and logs. Any inaccuracy or uncertainty in underlying technical information is projected into the financial information founded on it. The Recommendation reproduced above as well as the discussion of individual prospects by an operator presented in Chapter 4 illustrates this interdependency; e.g., the potential cash flow from a prospect is directly proportional to the barrels of reserves in it, which in turn is inferred from the picture of the prospect the geologist paints with maps and logs. There is a pyramiding of sources of uncertainty with the estimated cash flow from a prospect at the apex, feeling the impact of uncertainty from all sources:

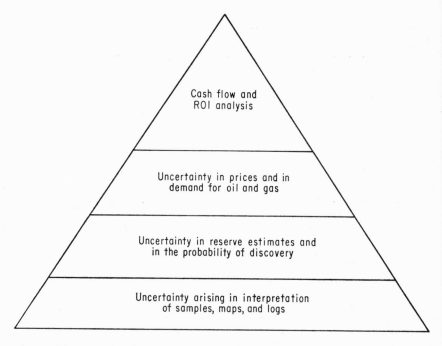

A graphic example of the effect of this pyramiding of uncertainty is the phenomenal amounts of money often "left on the table" after sealed bidding for oil lands:

> For two hours and 18 minutes one day last week, the U. S. Government ran an auction at high stakes. More than 500 oil men gathered . . . to bid for leases of Continental Shelf oil and gas rights in 1.6 million acres off the shores of Louisiana and Texas.
>
> John Rankin . . . presided as 441 sealed bids . . . were pulled out of some prosaic cardboard boxes . . .
>
> When the first Louisiana tract came up for bidding last week, covering 5000 acres in the West Cameron area, the highest of five bids proved to be that of Gulf, Socony Mobil, and Humble Oil & Refining Co.: $1,076,000. The next highest bidder was Pan American Petroleum Corp. at $325,600.
>
> This pattern varied even more widely at times. For Tract 611 off Louisiana, for example, the CATC combine . . . bid $7,630,-

000; the next highest was California Co. with $185,100.27. For Tract 628, CATC did it again offering $10,320,000 against the $751,000 of its closest rival, the Gulf-Socony combine. It was bidding generously for the leases it wanted most.[5]

Some majors are experimenting with techniques that will enable them to quantify the judgements of their technical experts in a fashion useful for bid evaluation. An experiment of this nature by the Albert Company[6] reveals how a judgement as to the economic worth of a tract is built up from a meld of technical and financial information.

Albert Company

The Evaluation of a Bid

The management of the Albert Company, a subsidiary of a major, was particularly concerned with the bonus that should be bid on some important offshore tracts up for sale. The tracts were to be sold at a sealed bid auction. Prior to evaluation, they had been shot. Albert's production manager evolved a scheme to be used for arriving at the bonus to bid on each tract. Its main features are outlined below.

The scheme centered on a graph which displayed the amount that should be bid to get a given discounted present value return conditional upon a given probability of hitting:

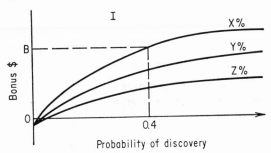

Once management selects a desired discount rate and decides on a point estimate of the probability of hitting on a particular tract, the bonus the company should bid can be read from the graph; e.g., at a discount rate of X per cent with a point estimate of the probability of discovery of .4, the bonus should be B dollars.

---

[5]"Wild Bidding for Oil Leases," *Business Week* (March 5, 1960), pp. 28–29. Reprinted with permission.

[6]Disguised name.

The primary factors considered in arriving at this graph were:

1. The size of field that might be discovered (in acres),
2. The production per acre in barrels of oil and/or MCF of gas,
3. The cost of drilling,
4. The cost of production.

Size of Field. The company geologists felt that the size of field that might be discovered was fixed by the subsurface structure of the area. They assumed one given size, and used this in their calculations.

Production. To get an estimate of recovery per acre-foot, company geologists and engineers did a careful analysis of sand formations similar to that which might be found in the acreage up for bid. This analysis was summarized in a graph:

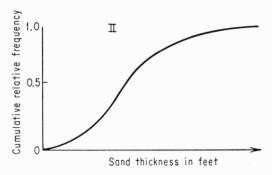

The expected value of net sand thickness was calculated using relative frequencies as probability estimates. This was multiplied by the yield to give an expected barrels per acre of recovery. The expected MCF of gas per acre of recovery was calculated in a similar manner.

Drilling costs. Company engineers summarized their estimates of potential drilling costs per well in a graph which took into account both vertical depth and horizontal drift of the bore hole:

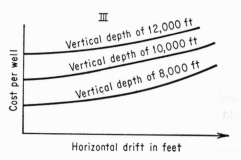

Total drilling costs were combined with platform construction costs. The cash outflows attributed to any one tract was a point estimate determined by interpretation of the geological traits of that tract; i.e., some platforms would be stationed in deeper water than others and hence construction costs and drilling costs would be more expensive, greater vertical depth of the bore hole would be required at some points than at others, etc.

Production Costs. Assuming a probability of discovery of 1.0, cash inflows were computed for a field; first, if the discovery should yield oil and then if it should yield gas. Expected recovery estimates such as those in Graph 2 were used together with estimates of allowables and of production decline curves to calculate the expected time pattern of production in barrels (or in MCF). These time patterns of production were multiplied by estimated prices per barrel (or per MCF) to give cash inflows over time.

Management assessed the probability of hitting oil conditional upon a discovery at $\frac{3}{4}$, and of hitting gas at $\frac{1}{4}$. These probabilities were used to weight the cash flow time pattern if oil were discovered and if gas were discovered, respectively, to give an expected cash flow time pattern:

Period	(Cash Flow if Oil Discovered)	$\times \frac{3}{4}$	(Cash Flow if Gas Discovered)	$\times \frac{1}{4} =$	Expected Cash Flow
1960	\$A $\times \frac{3}{4}$		\$C $\times \frac{1}{4}$	=	\$F
1961	\$B $\times \frac{3}{4}$		\$D $\times \frac{1}{4}$	=	\$G
1962	\$C $\times \frac{3}{4}$		\$E $\times \frac{1}{4}$	=	\$H
.	.		.		.
.	.		.		.
.	.		.		.

These cash flow patterns were summarized in a series of graphs like this one:

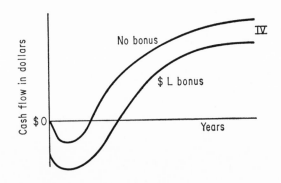

Finally, Graph 1 was plotted by:

1. Selecting a given discount rate;

2. Picking a probability of discovery and weighting the expected cash inflow determined above by this probability, assuming no bonus payments;

3. Finding the bonus payment which, when added to cash outflows, causes cash inflows and outflows to discount to zero;

4. Plotting this bonus payment as a point on the graph;

5. Repeating (1) through (4) for the same discount rate but different probabilities until enough points are plotted to give a smooth line such as for $X\%$ on Graph I.

6. Steps (1) through (5) were repeated for a number of discount rates $X\%$, $Y\%$, $Z\%$, etc., to complete the graph.

To stress the role uncertainty and judgement play in this procedure, the production manager likened it to "weighting hogs in Arkansas":

> What you do is to get a long straight board. You find a convenient place — a fence or a log on the ground — on which to balance the board at its middle. After placing the board so that it can be balanced, you tie the hog to one end. You very carefully weight the other end with different sized rocks until you get one so that the hog and the rock balance perfectly. *Then you guess the weight of the rock!*

3.2. A Point of View

Now visualize the operator as being at the center of a network of channels, each feeding information of a particular kind to him (see Exhibit 3.1). From one point of view the operator's job is to make a *sequence of decisions* based on this flow of information which lead to *acts* whose *consequences* are uncertain. He generally makes decisions so as to achieve some preassigned goal, e.g., maximize the expected net present value of the firm's capital or maximize his expected utility.[7] In fact, the operation of the firm can be thought of as one vast decision problem under uncertainty. However, it usually happens that there are so many decisions to be made and so many consequences to be considered that the

---

[7]These are two goals operators *might* attempt to reach. We are not implying that these are the goals adopted by most operators.

operator often restricts his attention to a small portion of this decision problem under uncertainty in making any one particular decision.

Borrowing from Leonard Savage,[8] we can state that the operator is concerned with "modest little worlds, tailored to particular contexts . . . " when he sifts and weighs information pertaining to a particular deal, province, or program. Savage's definition[9] of

the WORLD: as the object about which the person is concerned,
a STATE (of the world): as a description of the world, leaving no relevant aspect undescribed,
the TRUE state (of the world): as the state that does in fact obtain, i.e., the true description of the world,
an EVENT: as a set of states,

Exhibit 3.1

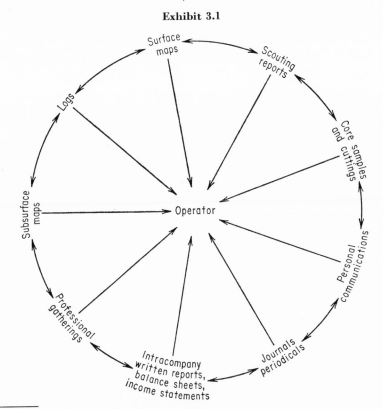

[8]L. J. Savage, *The Foundations of Statistics* (New York: John Wiley & Sons, Inc., 1954).
[9]*Ibid.*, p. 9.

provides a convenient and appropriate way of talking about the role of information media in making exploration decisions.

For example, Eason Oil Company, a small-to-medium-sized independent, has undertaken an extensive wildcat drilling program in south Louisiana. "South Louisiana" is one of the "worlds"[10] with which Eason's management is presently concerned — where the label embraces all economic, geological, and political occurrences of relevance to Eason's program. However, Eason's management is uncertain about the "true state of the world"; they do not know for certain

1. The number of barrels of oil and MCF of gas to be found in the five-parish region they are investigating,

2. The location of these hydrocarbon deposits,

3. Finding costs.

The successful drilling of British American's No. 1 wildcat on September 25, 1957, in Saint Mary's Parish is an "event" which undoubtedly modified Eason's judgement as to the "true state of the world."

The manner in which an operator uses information may be likened to the way crude inputs are processed through a refinery. The input is the information in the form of a written document or discussion. If the information is of enough import to change the operator's assessment of the true state of the particular world on which the information bears substantially, he will re-examine (some of) the possible states of the world obtaining. He then makes a decision to choose one of the available acts. This decision is his output. For example, if Eason were to decide to shoot a line of seismic[11] on one of their prospects, once the line was shot, the company would have to reassess its future strategy in light of the new information.

3.3. Sources of Uncertainty in Technical Information

Most operators will agree that subjective assessment and interpretation play a dominant role in molding the effect of even the most technical

---

[10]This particular "world" is a small part of a larger "world." Savage (*op. cit.*, pp. 9–10) explains how the notion of the smaller world with its restricted domain is arrived at by "neglecting some distinctions between states, not by ignoring some states altogether."

[11]"Shoot a line of seismic" is to explode a series of charges along a line traced over a region and to record the results of these explosions with the aid of a seismometer. It is akin to taking an indirect look at a cross-sectional slice of subsurface structure.

information on an exploration decision. It follows that the usefulness of information can be increased by carefully presenting it so as to clarify for the decision maker the sources of and magnitude of the uncertainties inherent in it.

Another way of stating the same point is that the usefulness of any particular set of data increases to the degree to which it brings the decision maker's opinions about a state of the world into correspondence with the true state. This correspondence can be made more exact in three complementary fashions:

1. By refining the techniques of data gathering so as to increase the probability of the data revealing the true state of the world;

2. By refining the manner in which the data is presented to the decision maker so as to increase his ability to interpret accurately the *degree* to which the data reveals the true state;

3. By refining the way in which the decision maker processes the information presented to him in order to arrive at a decision.

We will not discuss recent improvements in the design and usage of the technical tools of geology and geophysics — drilling bits, seismometers, magnetometers, etc. This is a subject to be reviewed by experts in oil technology for experienced oilmen. Most oil company managements are engaged in a constant struggle to render information more useful for decision making by constantly reappraising and refining methods of *gathering information,* so there has been rapid progress in this area in recent years. It is not clear, however, if the same rate of progress has been maintained with respect to the manner in which data is *presented* for decision making, or with respect to the way in which such information is processed by the decision maker to arrive at a decision.

An improvement in the presentation of geological and geophysical data can be conveniently labelled as either an *analytic* improvement or as an improvement in *risk specification.* Those which increase an operator's understanding of the geological processes at work in an area are called "analytic" improvements.[12] Those which increase the precision with which an operator can assess the sources and magnitude of uncertainty inherent in the data are called "improvements in risk specification." Both increase the operator's ability to interpret the degree to which the data reveals the true state of the world, and thus lead to a reduction of

[12]See for example W. C. Krumbein, "Measurement and Error in Regional Stratigraphic Analysis," *Journal of Sedimentary Petrology* (June, 1958), p. 176.

uncertainty about the true state. To give a flavor of the difference between analytic improvements and risk specification improvements, here is an example of each:

The Entropy Concept — an Analytic Improvement. The concept of entropy can be defined in several ways. Which definition is used depends upon how the concept is to be interpreted. The definition of the entropy of a finite scheme as proposed by A. I. Khinchin[13] suffices for the subsequent discussion.

Suppose we have a system of mutually exclusive and collectively exhaustive events $A_1, A_2, \ldots, A_n$, and suppose that we are given the probability of occurrence of each of these events at each trial: $p_1, p_2, \ldots, p_n$.

$$\left(p_i \geq 0, \qquad \sum_{i=1}^{n} p_i = 1 \right).$$

Then

$$A = \begin{pmatrix} A_1 & A_2 & \ldots & A_n \\ p_1 & p_2 & \ldots & p_n \end{pmatrix} \tag{1}$$

is called a *finite scheme.* In Khinchin's words:

> Every finite scheme describes a state of *uncertainty.* We have an experiment, the outcome of which must be one of the events $A_1, A_2, \ldots, A_n$, and we know only the probabilities of these possible outcomes. It seems obvious that the amount of uncertainty is different in the different schemes.

Thus, in the two simple alternatives

$$\begin{pmatrix} A_1 & A_2 \\ 0.5 & 0.5 \end{pmatrix}, \qquad \begin{pmatrix} A_1 & A_2 \\ 0.99 & 0.01 \end{pmatrix}$$

the first obviously represents much more uncertainty than the second; in the second case, the result of the experiment is "almost surely" A_1, while in the first case we naturally refrain from making any predictions. The scheme

$$\begin{pmatrix} A_1 & A_2 \\ 0.3 & 0.7 \end{pmatrix}$$

represents an amount of uncertainty intermediate between the precedent two, etc.

---

[13]A. I. Khinchin, *Mathematical Foundations of Information Theory*, a translation (New York: Dover Publications, Inc., 1957).

For many applications it seems desirable to introduce a quantity which in a reasonable way measures the amount of uncertainty associated with a given finite scheme. We shall see that the quantity

$$H(p_1, p_2, \ldots, p_n) = -\sum_{k=1}^{n} p_k \lg p_k,$$

can serve as a very suitable measure of the uncertainty of the finite scheme (1); the logarithms are taken to an arbitrary but fixed base, and we always take $p_k \lg p_k = 0$ if $p_k = 0$. We shall call the quantity $H(p_1, p_2, \ldots, p_n)$ the *entropy* of the finite scheme (1), pursuing a physical analogy which there is no need to go into here.[14]

The notion of entropy was first proposed by Clausius (1865) in his researches in statistical mechanics. Boltzmann (1894) observed that entropy is related to "missing information" in physical systems. Gibbs[15] (1902) used the concept of entropy as a cornerstone of his formulation of a formalism by which the facts of thermodynamics could be deduced. Shannon[16] (1949) and Wiener[17] (1949) extended the scope of the idea, employing entropy as a building block in a theory of communication. As communication theory became better known to the scientific community, research geologists began to see the possibility of fruitful employment of entropic ideas in subsurface geology. In a recent article on quantitative mapping techniques, J. M. Forgotson, Jr., states that:

> As the patterns shown on some [entropy] maps commonly have an empirical relationship to oil-and-gas-producing trends or mineralized areas, experimentation with maps of these kinds may provide valuable prospecting information.[18]

Entropy is now used as a summary measure of an important subsurface trait called "mixing." One research geologist with whom the writer talked commented that the use of entropy in this fashion:

> . . . Was prompted by a feeling that the major field structures have been found. Now we need to find stratigraphic traps. We

---

[14]A. I. Khinchin, *op. cit.*, p. 3.

[15]J. W. Gibbs, *Elementary Principles of Statistical Mechanics* (New York: Charles Scribner's Sons, 1902).

[16]C. E. Shannon and W. Weaver, *The Mathematical Theory of Communication* (Urbana, Ill., University of Illinois Press, 1949).

[17]N. Wiener, *The Extrapolation, Interpolation, and Smoothing of Stationary Time-Series with Engineering Applications* (New York: John Wiley & Sons, Inc., 1949).

[18]J. J. Forgotson, Jr., "Review and Classification of Quantitative Mapping Techniques, "*Journal of the American Association of Petroleum Geologists*, Vol. 44, No. 1 (January, 1960), p. 99,

need accurate and meaningful subsurface information for this. This, I think, is the motive behind the search for a summary measure of subsurface information such as entropy. All geology is a sampling problem, and we are continually asking ourselves, "How can you show information and handle it in a fashion which is most useful for decision making?"

Entropy is a measure of the degree of subsurface mixing of sand, shale, and limestone. We use it as a device for showing on a map the variation in type and composition of rock.

The entropy map was described in detail by a petroleum consultant as:

... a contour map. Points of equal entropy are joined as to make a map that shows the degree of and change in subsurface mixing over an area on a particular horizon; or, the degree of vertical mixing in a given borehole can be measured in terms of entropy, and this measure plotted on a map.

Here is how the entropy of a particular horizon might be determined. First, to determine the value of entropy at a particular point we use a device like this:

1. Draw an equilateral triangle:

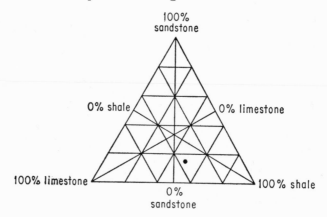

Label each corner as above. Cross hatch the triangle so that the per cent of each component at any particular point can be plotted as the distance from the side opposite the vertex labelled with that component; e.g., the plotted point represents a mixture of 50 per cent shale, 37.5 per cent limestone, and 12.5 per cent sandstone.

2. Now draw contour lines on the triangle according to the following scheme: letting

$f_1 \equiv$ per cent of sandstone,

$f_2 \equiv$ per cent of shale,

$f_3 \equiv$ per cent of limestone,

calculate the value of the entropy S which is defined as

$$S \equiv -\sum_{i=1}^{3} f_i \log f_i,$$

for a large number of combinations of (f_1, f_2, f_3).

Plot these values of S on the triangle and join points of equal value of S with lines. These are contour lines of equal entropy:

For ease in interpretation, the quantity $100S'$ is often plotted in place of S. The former takes on values from 0 to 100 and is related to S as follows:

$$100S' \equiv \frac{-100\sum_{i=1}^{3} f_i \log_e f_i}{H_m} = \frac{100}{H_m} S,$$

where H_m is defined as

$$-\sum_{i=1}^{3} f'_i \log {}_e f'_i, \qquad f'_i = \frac{1}{3} \quad \text{for} \quad i = 1, 2, 3.$$

Thus H_m is the constant $\log_e \left(\frac{1}{3}\right) = 1.09961$. The point of maximum entropy occurs at the center of the triangle, and the corners are points of minimum entropy.

3. As a visual aid to interpretation color the corners and the center of the triangle, as these represent the extremes of

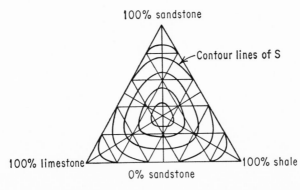

100% sandstone

Contour lines of S

100% limestone

0% sandstone

100% shale

low and high entropy respectively, as well as identifying the dominant rock. The degree and extent of coloring are dependent on personal judgement.

Now you are ready to make an entropy map of the horizontal variability over an area.[19] The next step is:

4. Take a sample log or an electric log for each point in the area where they are available. Calculate the per cent of sand, shale, and limestone at each point from the logs.

5. Go to the triangle and, for each point, find the value of S and the color which corresponds to that particular mix.

6. Plot the values of S and the colors on the map. The colors help you decide what the composition is at a particular point when you read the map.

You might get something like this on your map:

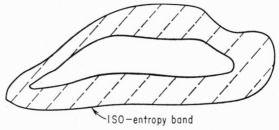

ISO−entropy band

An entropy map is useful basically because it relates to a theory of how hydrocarbons are formed. The position of ancient shorelines is important in the generation of hydrocarbon deposits and in the collection and deposition of porous rocks. All of these things are related to energy — and the point of greatest energy is where air and water meet — the shoreline. Here, there is maximum mixing of the three components. Usually this mixing forms a "halo" effect around the area most favorable for hydrocarbon deposits. Oil deposits themselves generally occur in areas of minimum entropy, where the mixing cleans up to a nice sand in a fairly small areal unit such as a bed or horizon in a producing area.

This is by no means a complete description of how the entropy concept is used in subsurface analysis (it is also used as a measure of vertical

[19]An example of an entropy map is displayed in an article by James Forgotson, Jr., *op. cit.*, p. 100.

variability in rock composition, for example), but it gives a glimpse of one of the new paths geologists are travelling in their researches. Two aspects of all geological and geophysical maps are spotlighted by looking at the entropy map from the viewpoint of an operator making exploration decisions. First, the entropy map results from a blend of theories of how hydrocarbon deposits are formed, empirical observation of a relation between mixing and hydrocarbon deposits, and the desire to summarize in one measure a set of geological facts. Thus the entropy map is a step in the geologist's logical progression towards more sophisticated forms of analysis and presentation of geological data. Second, in spite of the seeming mathematical precision of S, the personal judgement of the geologist drawing the map substantially affects the values assigned to each entropy point. Clearly, sophistication of analysis does not necessarily eliminate the sources of uncertainty inherent in information as subjective as a map.

Statistical Analysis of Maps — An Improvement in Risk Specification. The importance of *explicitly* recognizing the magnitude of uncertainty in maps used for exploratory decision making was emphasized by Professor William Krumbein of Northwestern University's geology department, when he said in an interview with the writer:

> The specification of the uncertainty inherent in maps is generally omitted in reporting to management. Yet a truly important question is, "To what extent do facies maps (geological maps) and structural maps (geophysical maps) reach the manager in a form so that he has an impression of the uncertainties in them?"

He describes the sources of uncertainty in stratigraphic measurements as either "compensating" or "noncompensating":

> Compensating errors do not affect the mean value of the attribute under study, but they do inflate the apparent variability of the observational data. Noncompensating errors affect the apparent mean value, and they may distort facies, gradients, or trends. The more important kinds of error that may enter facies maps are presented in a tabular summary.[20]

Table 3.1 on the next page lists the sources of error he discusses.

---

[20]W. C. Krumbein, *op. cit.*, p. 175.

TABLE 3.1. SOURCES OF ERROR OR UNCERTAINTY IN FACIES MAPS[21]

Source	Remarks
Miscorrelation	"Errors of Judgement." These may be compensated when uncertainty results in picking either too thick or too thin an interval. More commonly, perhaps, they are noncompensating, and may involve a cummulative effect.
Lack of Sufficient Control Points	"Error of Judgement." The subjective choice from among alternative ways of contouring a map may introduce incorrect trends or gradients into the map. Effects apparently are generally noncompensating.
Incorrect Identification of Lithologic Types	This type of error may arise in mechanical logs, where the initial problem is one of the classifying of the rocks as type A or not-A. In part, errors of judgement may be involved, although operational definitions are usually indicated. With good quality logs the errors appear to be mainly compensating, but where log quality varies, poor development of the SP† curve may introduce systematic errors.
Operator Effects	Some workers are liberal and others are conservative in measurement and rounding. Individual differences tend to be systematic. Data prepared by a single geologist are usually consistent. Strict adherence to operational definitions helps reduce operator differences.
Errors in Thickness Measurements	Assuming that the category of attribute to be measured is correctly chosen, errors of actual measurement are commonly small and compensating. These errors may rise to importance in very thin stratigraphic units.
Counting Errors	Number-of-sands counts are strongly affected by personal judgement unless an agreed-upon operational definition is explicitly followed. The definition itself needs careful statement in terms of the objectives of the map study. Counting errors may be compensating or noncompensating.
Computing Errors	Computation of percentages and ratios commonly gives rise to small compensating errors although systematic rounding errors may occur. Gross errors may occasionally occur.

[21]W. C. Krumbein, *op. cit.*, 178. Reprinted with permission.

†A curve appearing on a *spontaneous potential* log. It is a record of voltage potential measured in the mud along the borehole, and can be used to distinguish between permeable and nonpermeable formations.

Observe that five of seven sources of uncertainty are either "errors of judgement" or "operator effects." This emphasizes the subjective nature of uncertainty in geological maps.

Professor Krumbein[22] proposes a method of analysis which provides for an explicit statement of the amount of uncertainty in a prediction from a facies map: he describes how a polynomial regression analysis may be done over the map area in order to separate regional and local effects.

A squared grid is drawn over the map. This grid is used as a co-ordinate system for locating points (x, y) in the map area; e.g., the first element x of the ordered pair might locate a point along an east-west axis relative to some arbitrarily chosen origin, and y might locate points along a north-south axis relative to this origin. The regional effect at any point (x, y) in the map area A is postulated to be a polynomial function $f(x, y)$ of the grid co-ordinates (x, y). The local effect at (x, y) is assumed to be due to a random perturbation about the regional effect. For example, suppose we wish to describe variations in net thickness of a particular sand in the area. Let $z(x, y)$ denote thickness at (x, y), and assume that x and y assume discrete values. Then we postulate that $\tilde{z}(x, y) = f(x, y) + \tilde{\epsilon}(x, y)$ where $\{\tilde{\epsilon}(x, y), (x, y)\epsilon A\}$ is a set of mutually independent, identically distributed random variables with mean 0 and variance σ^2. The problem is now one of finding a good estimate $\hat{f}(x, y)$ of the function $f(x, y)$ based on our knowledge of net sand thickness $z(x_i, y_i)$ at a number of sample points (x_i, y_i), $i = 1, 2, \ldots, n$ in the map area. By performing a regression analysis we may find an estimate $\hat{f}(x, y)$ of $f(x, y)$, the expected net thickness at (x, y). The residual error variance about $f(x, y)$ is interpretable as the degree of variability due to local effects.

The variability of the local effects determines the magnitude of uncertainty in a prediction of the expected value of an attribute (such as net sand thickness) that may be encountered in a new well:

> The method is based on separation of the original facies map into its regional and local components. Such separation involves a large subjective element (Krumbein, 1956) in that a decision needs to be made regarding the terms assigned to each component. Once this decision is reached, with the aid of statistical reasoning if desired, the regional map can be made

---

[22]W. C. Krumbein, "Regional and Local Components in Facies Maps," *Bulletin of the American Association of Petroleum Geologists*, Vol. 40 (1956), pp. 2163–2194.

the basis for prediction of the expected value that may be encountered in a new test boring. This is done by computing the value of the regional surface at the proposed drilling point, or by interpolating it between the contours of the computed regional map. The local effects map, in turn, supplies an estimate of the uncertainty in the prediction, because the variability in the local effects map furnishes an estimate of the average magnitude of departures from the regional surface....

On the assumption that the parent distribution is essentially normal, the residual standard deviation is a measure of the uncertainty in any prediction made on the regional map.[23]

For example, "If we drill here, the expected net sand thickness is 80 feet, and there are about two chances out of three that the well will meet 80 ± 10 feet of sand."[24] A similar analysis can be done of other than facies maps, and in fact geophysicists have applied regression techniques to subsurface structure maps.[25]

Since regression techniques as applied to geological and geophysical maps can deepen a geologist's understanding of an area, it is an analytic refinement as well as a method for improving the specification of uncertainty in maps. High speed computers and standard regression programs make such quantitative analyses possible within reasonable cost and time limits.

3.4. Summary

In this chapter the reader was given a sample of the kinds of financial and technical information that an operator uses in making exploration decisions. The more informal sources of information — social contacts, association meetings, etc. — were neglected primarily because of the difficulty of ascertaining the impact on the operator as a decision maker. Future researchers might wish to explore these informal sources further.

Uncertainty in technical information was shown as being at the base of a pyramid of sources of uncertainty. In view of the pervasive influence of this source of uncertainty, two recent improvements in the presenta-

---

[23]W. C. Krumbein, *op. cit.*, pp. 183–184.

[24]W. C. Krumbein, *op. cit.*, see p. 183 for a discussion of a similar example.

[25]C. H. G. Oldham and D. B. Sutherland, "Orthogonal Polynomials: Their Use in Estimating the Regional Effect," *Geophysics*, Vol. 20 (1956), pp. 295–306.

tion and analysis of technical information were described to illustrate how oilmen are attempting to cope with it. These examples emphasized the highly subjective nature of geological information and led to the conclusion that the prime source of uncertainty in this information derives from errors in human judgement. The entropy map was mentioned as an analytic improvement in data presentation. Maps generated by regression analysis were discussed as an instance of both analytic and risk specification improvements. It was implied that such statistical techniques can be useful to the operator by increasing his ability to accurately assess the magnitude of uncertainty inherent in maps.

Finally, it was suggested that many aspects of the exploration decision process can be fruitfully viewed as a set of interrelated decision problems under uncertainty.

CHAPTER 4

Eason Oil Company†

Whereas Chapters 2 and 3 give the reader a simplified picture of the flow of decisions and activities that make up an exploration program, the nature of the decisions which must precede wildcat drilling is best illustrated by presentation of actual case histories. We will begin by describing a program being undertaken by a small-to-medium-sized independent — Eason Oil Company's "Louisiana Program." There are several advantages to using a small company's program as an illustrative vehicle: By virtue of its smallness, Eason is unencumbered by a welter of formal administrative procedures, and this simplifies the description of the decision-making process. In addition, basic decisions as to goals and as to policies for their achievement are traceable to one or two key

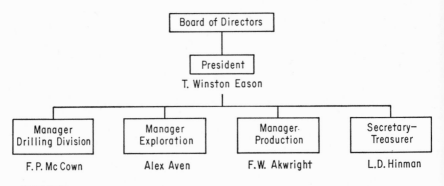

†The data of this chapter and the appendix to this chapter are reproduced with permission of the management of Eason Oil Company.

individuals, so that decision-making responsibilities can be easily pinpointed. For example, in Eason's organization the president, Mr. T. Winston Eason, and the exploration manager, Mr. Alex Aven, appear to be the chief architects of exploration policy.

Section 4.1 is general background material which is followed in Section 4.2 with a list of some important decision problems faced by Eason's management during the course of the Louisiana program. Section 4.3 is an interview with the exploration manager, Mr. Aven, which is supplemented by a long and detailed prospectus (reproduced as an appendix to this chapter) written by him, explaining many facets of the program. Section 4.4. is a summary of policies formulated by Eason's management to deal with the major decision problems which will arise during the course of the program.

Eason Oil Company

In August, 1957, Eason Oil Company began intensive study of a five parish area in south Louisiana. The study's goal was to determine if the Miocene Trend of oil and gas production in this area warranted a concentrated exploration program on Eason's part. Six months of analysis by Eason's technical personnel yielded favorable results, so it was decided to go ahead with the program.

4.1. Company Background

Organization and Size. Eason was a small-to-medium-sized independent, grossing about $3,000,000 to $4,000,000 per year in operating income. The company employed eighty people full time, including one landman and five geologists.

Activities. The Company's four major activities are oil and gas exploration, oil and gas production, natural gas processing, and contract drilling.

1. *Oil and gas exploration and production.* These are the company's most important activities, accounting for roughly 55 per cent of gross operating income in 1957–1958. As of 1 August 1958 estimated company reserves[1] were estimated at 5,700,000 barrels of oil and 51 billion cubic feet of gas.

---

[1]No credit is given for increases in reserves that will result from secondary recovery except where such operations are already in effect, and reserves are attributed only to drilled locations.

| | Wildcats[a] | | Development | Net Wildcat |
	Gross	Net	Gross	Discoveries
1958	13	6.50	28	2.10
1957	11	6.18	27	2.68

[a]A "net" well represents the fraction of the well and its proceeds owned by Eason.

The figures above do not include wells which were supported by acreage or dollar contributions. The company participated in twelve such wells in 1958.

	Net Crude Production	Net Gas Production
1958	627,826 bbls. or 1,715 bbls. per day	2.390×10^9 MCF
1957	672,596 bbls. or 1,840 bbls. per day	2.126×10^9 MCF

The company controlled more than 128,000 acres under lease, options, or royalty interests as of December, 1958.

2. *Drilling.* Drilling activities with the company's three rigs contributed roughly 30 per cent of gross revenues in the period 1957–1958. Price competition continued to be severe in 1958[2] with industry activity down 25 per cent from 1957. Partly as a result of this situation, 17 of the 20 wells drilled were on locations where the company owned or acquired an interest.

3. *Natural gas processing.* The company operates two small gas processing plants which contribute approximately 15 per cent of gross revenue. Gross income from both plants was roughly $631,000 in 1957 and about the same in 1958.

Financial Background. Eason is a publicly held stock company. Approximately 364,000 shares of common stock were outstanding at a book value of roughly $19 per share in July, 1958. Net income after taxes amounted to $1.41 per share in 1958 and $2.09 per share in 1957. The company has paid a cash dividend each calendar year for eighteen years (50 cents per share in 1957). Comparative balance sheets and income statements for the years 1952 to 1958 are displayed in Exhibits 4.3 and 4.4.

Investment Criteria. To aid their assessment of the economic worth of a particular deal or prospect, the management often uses their

[2]Well completions in the U.S. totalled 11,756 in 1957, 9582 in 1958, and 9977 in 1959. Source: *Oil and Gas Journal,* year-end issue.

"Handy Dandy Deal Analyzer," Exhibit 4.5. This is a three-page form which summarizes information necessary for a return on investment calculation. Page 1 lists estimated reserve figures, page 2 is for calculation of Eason's after tax share of the deal or prospect, and page 3 presents a variety of investment criteria: time adjusted return on investment, payout, etc.

In discussing how these criteria were interpreted, Mr. Eason said:

> We have an idea that we shouldn't go into a deal which involves more than 10 per cent of our cash flow, i.e., \$160,000 to \$180,000. Here I am talking about one particular prospect. We always keep this in mind in looking at return on investment figures.

4.2. Some Exploration Decision Problems

Before describing Eason's program, it may be helpful for the reader to keep in mind some questions which suggest decision problems faced by Eason's management during its course. Note that each of these problems can be related to the blocks of major decisions in Exhibit 2.1:

1. The optimum time of entry into an area varies with the state of development of the area and the activity of competitors. How should Eason time its entry?

2. What portion of available company funds should be allocated to this program? How many partners should be taken in to "share the risk"?

3. What criteria should be used to evaluate a prospect vis-à-vis other prospects and other investment opportunities?

4. As promising prospects are developed, in what order should they be shot and drilled — or dropped?

5. Seismographs, bore holes, etc., cost time and money. In addition, they are imperfect predictors in that they cannot reveal "for certain" whether or not oil or gas is present. What is the potential *economic* value of a particular combination of information-seeking devices? How should funds be allocated among prospects for intensive geological and geophysical study preceding a drilling decision?

6. What kind of trading deals should be pursued in the area — farm out, carried, interest, override, joint venture, etc.?

7. Where and when should leases be acquired, if available, and how much are they worth?

8. Should Eason employ consultants to aid in developing the program or create its own "Louisiana organization"?

It is important to recognize that these questions suggest a series of problems which interact very strongly. For example, the type of trading deal that can be negotiated in an oil province is partially dependent on the time of entry; if the area is highly developed there may be few open leases, and then most deals may have to come vis-à-vis a farmout or some similar arrangement. Or, the order in which a particular set of prospects will be screened depends on the state of information about each of the prospects. This in turn is a function of how much geological and geophysical investigation has been done on each of these prospects and raises the question: "Should we gather more information on some of the prospects before making a drilling decision on any one of them?" Or, a commitment of funds to the Louisiana Program decreases Eason's ability to participate strongly in outside and inside deals in other areas, and forces careful consideration of the effect of this allocation of funds on the Drilling and Natural Gas Processing Divisions.

The description of the Louisiana Program on the succeeding pages hopefully documents this interplay of decision problems.

4.3.   Interview and Prospectus

Eason followed up the decision to begin intensive operations in south Louisiana by retaining a consultant's firm to assist them in the initial stage of subsurface mapping. By virtue of their long experience in south Louisiana, the consultants were able to develop some immediate prospects for consideration. As of September, 1959, mapping was about one third completed over an area running 60 miles north-south and 168 miles east-west. Since the area is irregular in shape the mapping will actually cover only 70 per cent of this rectangular area, or about 7000 square miles, at a cost of roughly two man-years of time and $30,000.

4.3.1.   An Interview with Eason's Exploration Manager. When asked how he decides which prospects to include in a program such as this, Mr. Aven, Eason's exploration manager, replied:

Most of our subsurface information in South Louisiana comes from compiling and correlating data from wells in the area — principally electrical logs. Generally this work will reveal a number of interesting looking anomalies. We have done lots of mapping on the listed prospects and thirty other anomalies in the Louisiana area.

The first thing we do is to look at the anomalies generally to see whether any do not meet our requirements as to potential reserves. We do this by asking questions such as:

1. How big a surface area does the anomaly cover?

2. How far does the area of closure extend vertically? That is, how many lines of closure are there?

3. Can we expect a reservoir of the same "quality" as in nearby producing reservoirs?

When talking about the "quality" of a reservoir, the most important elements considered are, roughly in order of their importance:

POROSITY — the ratio of volume of pore space to total bulk volume of sand, limestone, or rocks;

PERMEABILITY — the ability of the reservoir rock to allow the flow of oil or gas;

PAY THICKNESS — the thickness of the producing zone;

RESERVOIR PRESSURE — pressure exerted by fluids and gases contained in the reservoir rock;

OIL SATURATION — percentage of pore space occupied by oil;

to which one might add as a sub-factor fracturing. The next question we ask is:

4. How apt are subsurface conditions to be as depicted on the map and as we have considered them?

Supposing that we have gotten relatively favorable answers to these questions; our next step in evaluation will depend on the nature of the information from which the anomaly has been recognized and the degree to which the information localizes the prospect. In general geological methodology leads to higher success ratios than geophysical techniques. But it often pays to obtain the added insight that shooting the prospect can offer.

In deciding whether or not to shoot the prospect, we try to keep in mind roughly three sources of uncertainty:

1. The location and existence of the anomaly,
2. The validity of the data on which our analysis is based, and
3. The presence of hydrocarbon deposits.

Basically, here is the way we handle them: Among the prospects meeting earlier criteria, let's assume that 90 per cent of the prospects you still like have sufficient acreage to justify an expenditure in excess of a well cost. Assume twenty prospects (anomalies) are left. Assuming also that we can get enough acreage, if an anomaly has greater than the minimum economic return, we turn our attention to selection of the prospects which have the least risk. Down here the spread of prospects with the risk factor left out often runs from 40 per cent to 250 per cent time adjusted return — with our cutoff at about 25 per cent.[3]

[Mr. Aven steps up to the map]

Let me give you some examples:

(A)   We can pin down this prospect with 2 miles of seismic for $2000 and have good well control. If seismic will confirm the faults and dip which seem to be present then we'll have a real prospect. We have all the information money can buy. We can only drill after that. We'll be betting that the faults will be a seal. There are fewer fields in this area where faults control accumulation than where relief on top of reservoir does. There's only a 50–50 chance of getting valid seismic.

(B)   If we go to another anomaly North, this one can swing around over several miles. We'll have to do at least eight miles of shooting at $20,000 cost. If it was confirmed, we would have a popular type of reservoir — one in which relief controls the accumulation. The chances are about 25 per cent of getting useable seismic records and we will find out if they are useable after spending around $5000.

(C)   Moving to this anomaly to the East, it would cost about $20,000 for twenty miles of shooting. The information is apt to be valid. There may be some faulting we can't

---

[3]"40 per cent to 250 per cent time adjusted return" *conditional* upon hitting a hydrocarbon deposit of a "typical" size. C. J. Grayson, *op. cit.*, Chapter 7, discusses the use of the risk factor in making drilling decisions, and how it is combined with present value calculations to yield a "risk-adjusted" present-value index.

pick up with seismographs and then we may have to drill two wells in order to locate the reservoir.

The accumulation of seismic information is aimed at helping us make the correct drilling decision.

As I mentioned earlier, if the prospects which we were examining exceed the minimum standards, then we would shoot the prospects with the greatest chance of success; that is, the one where we stood the greatest chance of the structure being confirmed and hydrocarbons being present when drilled. You should remember that we are now talking about the use of seismic devices to shoot a previously recognized anomaly, one which may have been recognized through the use of magnetic or gravity data or from subsurface geological studies.

There is another complicating aspect to the decision to shoot or not to shoot a prospect. We often contract with a firm specializing in geophysical services to do our shooting for us. Before going wholehog, we usually lay out a general line of seismic, evaluate the results, and then decide whether or not to shoot more. Since there are economies in the long term contract with these companies, we try to make up our minds at this point whether or not the new information warrants giving the prospect a really hard evaluation.

Whether or not we do a second round of shooting hinges strongly on the "quality" of the seismic records we get from the first round. You might divide "quality" into four categories:

Unuseable: this means no interpretable records. Some natural phenomena prevent reshooting, or there is not enough energy, or there is no proper return from the horizon.

Confirming: the records substantially locate subsurface structure or closure and type. They confirm the original idea as shown on the subsurface maps.

Nonconfirming: the records disprove the original basis for shooting. The prospect is "washed out."

Inconclusive: further seismic expenditure is required to derive data confirming or nonconfirming underground conditions.

Even if seismic confirms the existence of a structural trap as we visualized it, it's important to remember that there is an important difference in the risk of drilling a dry hole *between* various types of traps. For example, if we have an anticlinal structure in an oil province, the risk is very low of not having oil or gas. A faulted nose, on the other hand, has the problem of whether or not there is an effective seal — meaning higher risk. Thus, if we knew beforehand that a faulted nose was present, shooting seismic won't affect the faulted nose risk. However, seismic will confirm the existence of this type of trap.

Concurrent with our geological and economic analysis of the prospects in South Louisiana, we are looking to see how much acreage can be obtained over the anomalies we've found. A large company could afford to shoot this whole area and sit back and wait for ten to fifteen years for the leases to open up. This is because they can afford to sit on an investment and because if someone else drills it up it won't substantially affect their operations. But we simply can't afford to sit on our money for such long periods.

All of this time we're also thinking about how we are going to finance these deals. As of September, 1959, we have taken in five partners on this program. This is too large a thing to undertake all by ourselves. Generally, we don't go into a deal on a single prospect which will involve more than 10 per cent of our cash flow.

4.3.2. Eason's Prospectus. To aid in explanation of the Louisiana Program to prospective partners, Mr. Aven wrote a detailed prospectus. This prospectus is unusually complete in that, in addition to the terms of the joint venture and a description of the type of prospect being considered, it discusses in considerable detail the basis for the major assumptions underlying Eason's analysis of the geological merit and economic worth of the program. It is also atypical in another sense. The decision to include fourteen drillable prospects in the program is based on an analysis of the number of prospects that must be drilled to insure a 95.5 per cent or better chance of breaking even on cash outlays.[4] In the 1959 annual report, Mr. Eason commented on this analysis:

> A statistical approach to overall exploration planning was developed and applied during a recent study of producing areas by

---

[4]See pp. 60–63, in the prospectus, in appendix to chapter 4 for an explanation of this approach.

the staff. This technique, incorporating probability analysis with a thorough geologic and engineering evaluation, has been reviewed with interest by several groups. Too complex and lengthy to explain briefly, it is basically a device through which comparative and/or absolute economic evaluations can be made regarding prospective areas regardless of size. We are currently refining the technique to increase its value in the decision making process.

4.4. Summary

While the program is still in progress, the prospectus and the interview with Mr. Aven give a fair indication of how Eason's management proposes to proceed. They have a plan of action for dealing with the major decision problems that will face them as the program evolves. A portion of the policies or guides to action in this plan may be conveniently summarized as responses to the questions raised in 4.2:

1. Commence operation in 1959–60. Timing is appropriate because

   (a) Potential competitors are presently investing their money elsewhere, taking pressure off of South Louisiana,

   (b) There is high intrastate demand for natural gas, and

   (c) Current oil and natural gas prices are such as to favor a successful program.

2. Roughly 30 to 40 per cent of yearly cash flow is to be allocated to the program over a two-year period.

3. A set of five prospects are used as a reference for judging the geological and economic merit of prospects being considered for inclusion, no new prospect being included unless

   . . . each will have merit that, in Eason Oil Company's opinion, equals or surpasses those shown in this report [the Prospectus] as examples.

   Each individual prospect is evaluated against the economic criteria on page 3 of the Handy Dandy Deal analyzer: time of adjusted return on investment, payout in months, percentage reserves produced at payout, and cash income in the first year divided by the investment in the prospect.

4. The prospects standing the greatest chance of having their structure confirmed and hydrocarbons being present will be shot and evaluated for drilling first.

5. Most property acquisitions will be secured by farmout arrangements because:

(a) Most of the prospects under consideration are controlled by other operators and individuals;

(b) high lease bonuses and short term leases favor quick evaluation on the farmee's part; and

(c) the tendency of operators with large acreage holdings in Louisiana to invest their capital abroad also favors opportunities for farmout arrangements.

6. Consultants are employed to take advantage of their special knowledge of the area and to develop prospects more rapidly than could be done by Eason alone.

The preceding presentation is a purely descriptive effort, an example of the complex interplay of some of the decision problems found in oil and gas exploration — not an "evaluation" of Eason Oil Company's Louisiana program. No attempt is made to specify whether or not a particular policy is "efficient" in achieving management's "goals"; indeed, management's "goals" have not been presented!

The specification as to what constitutes an "efficient" policy can only be made precise as the definition of management goals is made exact. With respect to the broad and encompassing policies concerned with overall management of the firm, this is an open question, and shall remain so in this monograph. However, when specific problems are attacked, as will be done in Part II, the goal to be achieved will be carefully defined.

An outstanding attribute of Eason's policies, as interpreted here, is the wide latitude of judgment they leave to management. Their implementation with respect to any one prospect depends strongly on the subjective assessments and opinions of the management.

Copy of Oil and Gas Exploration Program, South Louisiana, of Eason Oil Company

This report covers a specific exploration program and describes the basis on which that program has been developed by Eason Oil Company. It is presented with the understanding that readers are aware of the nature of the oil business, the opportunity for capital appreciation, and the tax savings resulting from exploratory and development expenditures.

One of the basic ideas set forth herein originated in a conversation with Mr. C. J. Grayson. Mr. Grayson should receive acknowledgment for that contribution. However, as he has had no opportunity for further comment, his endorsement should not be assumed.

SCALE—MILES
10 0 10 20 30 40 50

----AREA OF INTEREST

CONTENTS

This report deals with a five-parish area in South Louisiana in the so-called "Miocene Trend" of oil and gas production. The conclusions of this report and the information contained herein were developed during a continuous study of known producing areas in the United States executed by the Eason Oil Company organization during a six-month period commencing in August, 1957.

The primary conclusion of the study is that a fourteen-well exploration program in the area affords the participants in the program a statistical probability of 95.5% of breaking even on their cash expenditure. The probability of its success as opposed to merely breaking even is somewhat less than the 95.5% and is primarily dependent upon tax considerations and greater success in the outlined plan of action than assumed in making the break-even calculation. The break-even conclusion is based upon the application of statistical techniques applied to certain conclusions and supportable assumptions regarding the historical record of success in the area and the actual nature of recognized prospects.

We have chosen to indicate the feasibility of the program by commencing an operation in South Louisiana that has resulted in the accumulation of some eighteen sub-surface geologic and geophysical prospects. Any one of these leads, if confirmed, will allow the program to succeed. A number of these leads are set forth in this report.

The area of interest is shown on the map included as the frontispiece and can be generally described as that covered by the five parishes of Plaquemines, Lafourche, Terrebonne, St. Mary's and Jefferson. The Miocene Trend affords operators a success ratio, as shown by historical results, of approximately one wildcat success out of each three wildcat wells. The success ratio in the balance of the state is significantly less than this.

There are two other prime advantages of the Miocene Trend. First, due to the high reservoir pressures, the wells can maintain their allowables at the current rate or at a higher rate for an extended period of time (the ratio of flowing wells to total wells in fields discovered since 1948 is 90%). Bottom hole pressures are generally above 5000 psi and active water drives are definitely the rule. The other important advantage of this area as compared with the rest of the state is the exceptionally high reserves. These reserves will range from 600 to 1200 barrels per acre foot and in the typical case the figure of 800 barrels per acre foot is appropriate.

As a state, Louisiana offers successful operators certain advantages that do not appear in nearby states. Those advantages arise primarily from the high intra-state demand for natural gas as a result of the industrial activity along the lower Mississippi River. This high demand tends to resolve the industry problems that have been created by the "Memphis decision," and by the F.P.C.'s authority to regulate the price of inter-state resale gas at the well head. That high demand results in rather rapid connections along with a price determined through negotiations between the buyer and the seller alone. Currently a figure of 23c per thousand appears reasonably typical of the contract price with the take being based on an eighteen or twenty year depletion of the well. The flat price for crude is $3.45 per barrel and the oil allowable compares favorably with other producing areas.

One disadvantage encountered in the area has been exceptionally high dry hole costs. When analyzed these costs seem to result from two basic factors; one, penetrations below 13,000' to 14,000'; and two, unexpected expenses due to location problems and, perhaps more frequently, mud problems resulting from high pressure water sands and/or heaving shales. Other disadvantages in the area are high bonus prices for some of the leases and high annual rentals.

Some of the disadvantages may be temporarily alleviated due to the desire on the part of certain operators in the area to expend a greater portion of their exploration money overseas. A portion of the disadvantages may tend to be resolved by the nature of the organization we propose. There should be a tendency to resolve the balance of the disadvantages by operating a program of the magnitude we suggest; hence, averaging out their ill effects.

* * * * * *

A basic problem in oil and gas exploration is whether the value of a discovery is sufficient to offset the costs related thereto. Those costs include losses represented by dry holes, seismic costs, geological effort, etc. If one can establish the value of a discovery, one can then calculate what costs can be incurred in making the discovery. Conversely, if the expenses related to the discovery can be estimated the required value of the discovery is established. The value, can be quoted as to some degree of profitability or as to its allowing the program to break even. We have chosen this latter approach.

Such calculations are often difficult because of the uncertainty of making a discovery. Rather than assume certainty we believe it best to deal with the probability of success and proceed from that basis.

There is a statistical tool available which will allow us to establish the size of a program, i.e., the number of holes that must be drilled in order for us to have a given probability of success. The tool is the standard distribution curve (sometimes called normal distribution curve or the Gaussian curve). This curve is a graphic presentation of the phenomena that events, or series of events, which vary randomly, will distribute themselves around a mean event, or series, in such a way that the resulting curve is bell-shaped. The vertical coordinate represents the number of events in the series (or the number of series). The horizontal coordinate as it leaves the mean line through the center of the curve shows the amount of deviation from the mean. This curve is illustrated on the following page.

We believe that success in an exploration program will vary randomly with different operators so long as all operators within the group being considered, approach the problem of exploration in the same general and scientific manner. An examination of the record in an established area will always show some few operators or some operator, who succeeded on his first attempt, or two or three attempts, at establishing wildcat production, despite the fact that operators in general in the area were finding only one success out of every, say, seven trys.

On the other hand, it is well known that operators proceeding in an equally prudent manner have been known to enter the same area and successively drill as many as a dozen or twenty unsuccessful wildcat prospects. Until such time as scientific cause for these failures and successes can be more accurately pinned down, it can be assumed that the difference in performance between equally prudent operators will be the difference in a random series of events. It is this feature that we believe allows the application of the standard distribution curve in exploration.

Our problem can be reduced as follows: how many wildcat prospects must be drilled to statistically assure us of a given probability of success on one of them?

To use the standard distribution curve one must make an arbitrary decision as to the degree of probability desired. It would be equally valid to make an arbitrary decision as to the number of wells to be drilled and solve the equations

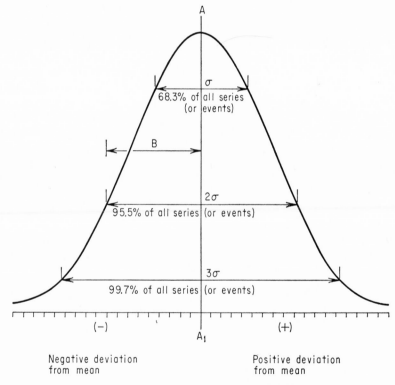

A₁ represents the mean success ratio consequently the success ratio occuring in the largest number of series

B represents a degree of negative deviation from the mean success ratio, between it and its positive counterpart lie 95.5% of all series

for the probability of having one success. We have arbitrarily chosen to seek a 95.5% probability for the success of this program.

In the case of South Louisiana our study has indicated an industry wide success ratio of one successful wildcat out of each three total wildcats. This same ratio can be considered as the ratio occurring in the largest number of

> Number of Series in Group, e.g., in S. La. Area, there may be 50 series with the mean success ratio (1 : 3), therefore the apex of the curve would represent 50 and other points smaller numbers.

Negative Deviation   Positive Deviation
From Mean   From Mean

A_1 represents the mean success ratio consequently the success ratio occurring in the largest number of series.

B represents a degree of negative deviation from the mean success ratio; between it and its positive counterpart lie 95.5% of all series.

series of wells, i.e., the ratio of the mean series. Other series in the area will have success ratios greater or smaller and will be composed of a smaller number of series per se. For example, assume that there will be 10 series with a success ratio of one out of three. Statistically, there will be a smaller number of series, say, seven, with a success ratio of one out of two (50% above the mean ratio). On the negative side of the curve there will be another group of seven series with a success ratio correspondingly poor, i.e., one out of six (50% below the mean ratio). These last two series can be considered as "deviations from the mean."

The formula for the value of one standard deviation is $\sigma = \sqrt{n \times p \times q}$. Exhibit B details the resolution of this formula and explanation of the various symbols. On the basis of that calculation we can say that there is a statistical probability of 95.5% of proving production on one prospect if *fourteen* prospects are evaluated, i.e., thirteen prospects may be drilled and dry, but the fourteenth should be successful. This information provides a logical basis for considering the economic merits of an area. We can now examine the likelihood of breaking even with a program, the potential profitability of the program and the minimum acceptable economic characteristics of a particular prospect or deal.

Having established the number of dry holes that might be drilled we have a basis for estimating the costs attributable to the discovery. A later discussion covers the factors considered in arriving at an average dry hole cost of $150,000; this figure and the estimate of thirteen dry holes indicates a total dry hole expense of $1,950,000.

Seismic costs can be estimated on the reasonable assumptions that: one week's seismic work will be required on each prospect, and, only one out of each three prospects will be seismically confirmed and available. Thus, we estimate that 42 weeks of shooting will be needed to develop fourteen drillable prospects.

Current seismic costs are about $5000 for one week's shooting. Hence, we estimate $210,000 for total seismic expense.

Land costs are not considered at this point. First, we estimate the major part of lease acquisitions will be by farmout with no cash consideration required. Secondly, in those cases where leases are purchased the cash is a capital expenditure and if expenditures of that nature need be included it is best done when calculating the margin on a well.

To cover contingencies, e.g., higher than average dry hole costs, more detailed shooting than estimated and errors in estimating per se, we have arbitrarily provided $250,000 (about 12% of the dry hole budget).

In total these estimates amount to $2,410,000. The value of the anticipated discovery must equal this amount for the program to be practical. Profitability will result partly from the discovery exceeding that amount.

To estimate the actual value of a discovery or impute a value thereto, the parameters of a typical well must be fixed. Our study shows the following characteristics to be reasonably typical. The basis for the actual values is spelled out in a later part of the report.

Depth		10,000' to 12,000'
Cost	Dry*	$120,000 to $150,000
	Complete	$190,000 to $250,000
Allowable		108 barrels per day
		(1 zone at 10,000')
Spacing		40 acres — oil
		320 acres — gas
Pay Thickness		40'
Recovery		800 barrels per acre foot
Working Interest Share of		
Gross Production		75%
Selling Price		$3.45 (Oil)
Net to Working interest		
after tax, lifting cost,		
and royalty interest		$2.19/bbl.

*This figure is net of dry hole contributions: dollar contributions are common in the area and we have assumed receipt of $200,000 in total dry hole money or less than $20,000 per dry hole.

We can impute a value for the typical well by considering the selling price of the reserves established by a *single* well either on the basis of so much per barrel, or on the basis of discounting future profits of the well and establishing the present value of that profit. For the latter type calculation the life of the well must be established (this method is the one used below). The profit margin on an *individual well* will, of course, be the difference between its calculated value and the cost of drilling and completing that particular well. Breaking even on the program will depend upon the margin from the successful wells equalling the whole dollars spent in drilling the dry holes, shooting the prospects and smaller operational expenses.

The reserves from a "typical" well are calculated by resolving the equation:

$$40' \text{ pay} \times 800 \text{ bbls./acre ft.} \times 40 \text{ acres.}$$

which gives 1,280,000 barrels of oil. At \$2.19/bbl. the total value to the working interest over the life of the well is \$2,800,000.

The life of this hypothetical 1,280,000-barrel well can best be calculated by dividing that figure by the annual production at the current allowable (39,400 barrels) indicating a $32\frac{1}{2}$ year life for the successful well. Correcting the working interest flow of net income to its present value one can assume a 6% discount factor for a 30-year life and use the working interest share of the annual income to be \$86,200 (\$2.19/bbl. × 39,400 bbls./yr.). At 6% for 30 years the present value of that annual income is \$1,218,000. Support for the use of that figure as the imputed sale value of the well is gained when it is recognized that this is tantamount to selling reserves for about \$1.00 per barrel. If the value of the well is \$1,218,000 and the cost was \$250,000, there is an imputed profit amounting to \$968,000 on that well. Corrected for capital gains taxes, if such were required, the after-tax imputed profit would amount to \$726,000.

Having established both the net value of the discovery well and the costs related to making the discovery we can proceed with break-even and profitability. The relationship between the post-tax margin on the one well above and the estimated costs of \$2,410,000 shows that in addition to the discovery well the discovery prospect must have three offset locations. This is in the event oil is discovered. Actually, when the per well margin is divided into related losses the quotient obtained is 3.32, indicating a requirement for three typical wells and a one-third interest in the third offset. Thus, each of our prospects must contain at least 160 acres which will be "proven" by the success of the first well.

In the case of a gas prospect the calculation, based on the same philosophy and tabular information, indicates that the individual prospect must be capable of supporting the discovery and one offset. More accurately stated, both oil and gas prospects must have as great a margin as that indicated in the break-even calculation or have a significantly higher probability of success to be included in the program.

The calculations on which both the oil and the gas conclusions are reached are presented in the appendix.

It is important to note that in calculating the break-even point we have considered the dollars expended in drilling dry holes and in seismic work as whole, or after-tax, dollars. The true situation, of course, is that that expenditure is offset by a saving that will be dependent upon the tax brackets of the various participants. Tax savings will lower the break-even point to the individual investor and increase his probability of economic success.

The potential profitability of the program can be exhibited in several ways. One is that stated immediately above. A second way is by the success ratio of the group being more closely akin to the industry average of one out of three. A third way, of course, is by the successful prospects being larger than the break-even size. It is important to remember that almost all fields in the area greatly exceed in reserves the size shown in the break-even calculation.

Using older measures of economic merit on a per well basis the potential profitability of the program is more than acceptable. On an individual well basis, an oil well such as the one we have projected will pay out in 2.85 years ($250,000 invested whole dollars divided by $86,200 annual income). The return (total income divided by investment) is $2,800,000/$250,000 or 11.2 to 1. For a gas well the payout is 1.35 years ($300,000 divided by $183,000), and the return is 20 : 1 ($3,700,000 divided by $183,000).

* * * * * *

No analysis such as presented above can be relied on to a greater extent than is warranted by the assumptions contained therein. Nor is such a concept valuable unless there is a practical means of following through on the program. A large part of our investigation was concerned with establishing a basis for the assumptions we have made. The validity of certain assumptions is indicated by historical records in the area. In the other cases, an illustration can be gained by examining the leads and prospects that have been developed.

In our so-called "typical" well, the allowable schedule shown in the appendix indicates that 108 barrels a day is currently the state allowable for wells of the minimum depth we are considering and, further, that this is from one zone. Actually, we will be dealing with a multiplicity of pay sections in an area where separate reservoirs can be satisfactorily proven. As a consequence, dual allowables are not uncommon. The matter of spacing is also almost statutory in its nature. Reservoir work in the area indicates that in the Miocene, 40-acre drainage for oil and 320 acres for gas is quite conservative. The $3.45 oil selling price is the current flat price for crude in the area.

As was previously pointed out, it was our early conclusion that one of the prime disadvantages faced by operators in the area was the high cost of dry holes. We further established to our own satisfaction that those costs were incurred primarily because of extreme penetration depths, e.g., below 13,500', and unexpected expenses incurred in the drilling of the well, especially those related to high pressure gas and water sands and heaving shales. It appears that the unexpected costs cannot be completely avoided; however, the utilization of engineering personnel experienced in the area including the services of specialized mud engineers, and the deliberate avoidance of areas of known high pressure sands and/or heaving shales, will tend to lessen the effects of those unexpected costs. Also, a program of the size contemplated will tend to average out any ill effects that are encountered.

The high dry hole costs insofar as they are contributed to by deep penetrations can, of course, be completely avoided if an acceptable operation can be prosecuted at lesser depths. The leads that are presented herewith do satisfy this depth requirement in that none of them will require penetration below

13,500' for evaluation of the primary target. It should be pointed out that as the program progresses, and these leads are supplemented, prospects may be included that have a deeper target. However, if such a prospect is included it will have a compensating advantage.

Through associates in New Orleans we have established the range of $130,000 to $160,000 for dry holes. Our own examination of the area, which involved consulting with several groups active in the area, indicated that if an intermediate string be required (as usually would be the case below 11,000') the dry hole costs net of salvage, would be approximately $15.00 per foot. A tabulation of the costs of dry holes on the leads recognized so far is presented with each lead and from this group it appears that the $150,000 average figure is adequate. (This figure includes an apportionment of $200,000 dry hole money, that amount being an estimate of the receipts over the entire program). It should also be pointed out that our contingency factor of $250,000 on the entire group of fourteen wells provides more than $18,500 per well which we consider as adequate.

The next parameter for which we established a value in our "typical" well is a pay thickness of 40'. It should be noted that this could be cumulative (double or triple) pay thickness. In a number of cases the leads presented herewith include a type log illustrating the potential pay thickness.

The recovery that can be anticipated in the area ranges from 600 to 1000 barrels per acre foot in the majority of cases. Experience in the area indicates that 800 barrels per acre foot is a reasonable and conservative estimate. Combining our figures of 800 barrels per acre foot, 40-acre spacing, and 40' of effective pay, shows recovery of 1,280,000 barrels per 40-acre well. Barataria, Lake Salvador and Barataria West are examples of fields in the area where 40-acre well reserves exceed that figure.

Our use of 75% of gross production as the working interest's share is based on several factors. First, the tendency in South Louisiana to have a standard one-sixth royalty on a lease immediately reduces the working interest to $83\frac{1}{3}\%$. Second, our arrangement with our group in New Orleans is such that a $\frac{1}{32}$ of $\frac{7}{8}$ths (2.75% of gross) accrues to them on each success with a calculated remainder for the working interest of 80.58%. As the major portion of our acquisitions will be by the farmout route, it appears that we will be faced in most instances by an override. The override will range between $\frac{1}{32}$ and $\frac{1}{8}$th; we have chosen to use a $\frac{1}{16}$ in making the calculation, which, when reduced to a percentage of gross reduces the working interest to fractionally less than 75%.

At our request T. M. Rodgers, the Petroleum Engineer in the group in New Orleans, has made a study of lifting costs in the area, the results of which are appended hereto, and which indicate the validity of the use of 23c as severance tax and approximately 22c as lifting costs. A portion of Mr. Rodgers' calculation is based on a large-scale operation which would require use of field camps and district offices. In those cases the allocation of expense has been deleted. The calculation reducing the $3.45 sale price of oil to the $2.19 working interest net before taxes is as follows:

Selling Price		$3.45/bbl.
Less		
Tax	0.23	
		$3.22
Royalty and Overriding Royalty	0.81	
		$2.41
Lifting Cost	0.22	
Net to Working Interest		$2.19/bbl.

The one to three success ratio is a matter of historical evidence. There is attached a tabulation showing the annual and cumulative success ratio in the area since 1951. It is, of course, this figure and the confirmation that is lent to it by its constancy, that causes us to rely upon it. Further support for that ratio can be gained by a more finite examination of the historical results. A spot check in calendar 1956 indicates that when the wildcat operations of major oil companies and those independents whose drilling is based primarily upon correlated geological and geophysical confirmation of sub-surface leads are considered by themselves, the success ratio is one to two. We would prefer to consider this latter ratio more as corroborating the validity of the industry-wide ratio rather than to use it either as a basis for our program or as the ratio of the program.

Concluding that the one to three ratio is an acceptable one, it becomes important to consider whether or not a contemplated program can be based on the projection of such figures. That is to say, can the Eason Oil Company organization anticipate performing as well as other prudent operators in the area? It is this factor that points up the necessity for experienced personnel.

To extend our technological and scientific organization we have retained the firm of Rodgers, Seglund and Shaw of New Orleans, Louisiana. The three partners are T. M. Rodgers, James R. Seglund and William Shaw. Their experience has been in engineering and law; sub-surface geology; and geophysics and stratigraphy, respectively. Their performance can be evaluated by the quality of the sub-surface and geophysical leads that are presented as a part of this report. Our arrangment with the firm provides for a satisfactory portion of their time to be spent working with our company. Their work in the general five-parish area is to be exclusively for the benefit of the participants in this program. An examination of their work load has indicated that they will have sufficient time to contribute their maximum potential to this program. By supplementing our own geological and engineering groups with these men and using Eason Oil Company's evaluation and management personnel to administer the program, we believe the projection of the 1 : 3 ratio is acceptable.

It should be emphasized that we have been dealing in the most frequent case with averages and, in individual instances, certain conclusions based on experience. As the program proceeds it is extremely doubtful whether any one prospect that is reduced to drilling status will parallel in all respects the "typical" prospect that we have set forth. Our intention has been to attempt to establish logically a planning magnitude and to ascertain what factors or parameters must be satisfied by a prospect before it can be included in the program. As is obvious from the leads that are presented in the subsequent portion of this report, none of them is minimal in all the factors we have set forth. It is important, however, to notice that each prospect well will exceed in its total reserves to the working interest, the total reserves of our "typical" well. Consequently, it will exceed our "typical" well in its value. Stated somewhat differently, these prospects that we have included in our group will have a greater margin than that required by our "typical prospect."

The availability of another operator's wildcat lease and the terms of an un-negotiated farmout are two of the most severe imponderables in any program. The prospects that are presented are, in the main, presently controlled by other operators and individuals. However, a potential farmee in South Louisiana has a group of basic economic factors that currently are working in his favor. The prime one may be temporary, but results from a tendency on the part of several of the operators having large acreage positions to invest their exploration and development capital in areas outside of the United States, attracted there by higher success ratios and reserves than they have encountered in South Louisiana. The resulting environment is favorable for our proposed operation since by farmout the lease investments are evaluated for the lessee. Similar effects may result from the imminent expiration (1959) of some 500,000 offshore acres. This situation is superimposed on a second group of general economic factors that should work in our favor. The latter factors include exceptionally high lease bonuses, rather short term leases (3 to 5 years) and rental payments greater than $5.00 an acre and that sometimes approach four times the bonus figure. These combine to create a desire for rapid evaluation of leases even among those operators whose principal area of exploration is the area under discussion. In the tabulation of specific leads, we have pointed out some of the specific farmout terms that have been proposed to us by the owners of the critical leasehold interest.

In the appendix you will find a number of the prospects that have been developed to date. One example is included in the body of the report. As previously pointed out these prospects will be supplemented by other internally generated leads as the program progresses, i.e., the program will be based on more than these leads. Currently work is proceeding on approximately 8 additional areas and we have recognized an adequate number of sub-surface and geophysical leads requiring further interpretive work. For planning purposes we have anticipated that only one out of three leads of the quality shown here will result in a drillable prospect.

The leads constitute the major part of the organization's tangible output to date. The next action is the selection of those leads deserving first attention and establishing the optimum procedure for their evaluation. These and subsequent decisions and actions ultimately will reduce the highest grade prospects to drillable status. In this area Eason Oil Company is prepared to make its greatest contribution.

* * * * * *

After our study showed the potential value of operations in South Louisiana, primary attention was directed toward creating an effective organization. The decision that the program utilize the management and evaluation procedures and concepts of Eason was immediate.

Concurrently it was decided initially to expand our scientific and engineering groups through use of consultants rather than creating an Eason Oil Company employee organization on the spot.

We believed that a competent consulting group would allow actual operations to commence at an earlier date than a newly created Eason staff. Experienced consulting groups with proven records of performance in the area appeared most likely to produce prospects immediately, based on prior work and familiarity with the region.

A further advantage of using consultants is that throughout the organization each group or individual contribution is direct and is based on applicable experience and talent. This is more than specialization. For example, the consultants' several years of personal experience in the region is brought directly to bear on the generation of prospects, not indirectly through others less experienced but accountable for the actual generation.

The overall management of the South Louisiana program will be by the Eason Oil Company. The Eason staff and the President will select the various prospects for further evaluation, establish and negotiate the terms of farmout agreements and lease purchases and, of course, oversee the operations in general. As needed, an Eason employee will commence direct supervision of drilling and producing operations.

Geological Basis:	Sub-surface well control establishes major fault zones and gives indications of south, east and west dip. Critical dip to the north is not satisfactorily controlled by well information and will have to be seismically delineated.
Similar Producing Structure:	One mile to the west. Field has three gas-distillate wells with reserves estimated to be 228,000,000,000 cubic feet gas plus 11,500,000 barrels distillate. Pay — 200' thick.
Acreage Involved:	1660 acres under lease to a major oil company. 1500 acres potentially productive.
Farmout Terms:	1/48 of 8/8 ORRI on 640-acre drillsite with 1/8 of 8/8 ORRI on remainder of leases or a 50% reversion right.
Estimated Seismic Costs:	Review of a major company shooting program should be sufficient with no seismic costs involved.
Estimated Well Costs:	Drilled — $110,000. Completed — $160,000.
Working Interest in Field:	70%

Farmee's Share of Field Reserves: 53%
Possible Well Contribution: $50,000 dry hole money.
Anticipated Depth of Production: 9500'–12,000'.
Recommended Drilling Depth: 12,000'.
Anticipated Production: Gas-distillate.
Anticipated Reserve Exposure: Per well: 96,000,000,000 cu. ft. gas plus
                                             3,800,000 barrels distillate.
                                  Field: 240,000,000,000 cu. ft. gas plus
                                             9,500,000 barrels distillate.

Our proposal may be outlined as follows: Eason Oil Company will manage the joint venture and will report each month on present and planned operations and furnish other information as requested by the other joint venturers. Eason Oil Company will assume all costs to date and all subsequent costs except seismic, lease acquisition, drilling and lease operations. We estimate that the costs absorbed 100% by Eason will approximate $100,000 per year. Costs of acquiring leases and/or options will be paid 25% by Eason and 75% by the other joint venturers. Seismic costs and the costs of drilling the first well on a prospect to the production casing point will be paid 25% by Eason and 75% by the other joint venturers. Development drilling costs and wildcat costs after the casing point will be borne 50% by Eason and 50% by the other joint venturers. Dry hole salvage income will be divided in proportion to the investment therein.

All Operations will be in the name of Eason Oil Company (but separate books of account will be kept for the joint venture) and all acquisitions of property will be shared 50% by Eason and 50% by the other joint venturers. Income and operating expenses on all producing wells will be shared, until payout of the individual well in proportion to the investment in the well; after payout, income will be shared 50% by Eason, 50% by the other joint venturers. Thus, in a discovery Eason receives and pays somewhat less than 50% of the joint venture income and expense respectively and the other joint venturers somewhat more than 50% until such time as that well is paid out; at that time income and operating expense will be divided 50%–50%. Prior to commencement of drilling, each joint venturer shall receive evidence of his interest in the lease in the same proportion to his share of the ultimate cost of that well. The delivery of the finite assignment or other document will be made after all expenses are calculated under the above formula.

The joint venture agreement will cover the entire series of fourteen wells. Prior to commencement of the program all participants will execute an operating agreement embodying the usual terms and conditions found in the area. Prior to commencement of any individual well Eason will distribute for attachment to the operating agreement an exhibit covering the particular prospect to be drilled. All dry hole contributions will be applied against the gross cost of the well prior to the determination of the expense.

The prospects to be evaluated through use of geophysics, geology and drilling will be selected by Eason Oil Company. Initially each will have merit that, in Eason Oil Company's opinion, equals or surpasses those shown in this report as examples.

Each joint venturer will agree that during the seismic and wildcat operations, his operation in the dedicated area will be only through this joint venture. Our agreement with the consulting firm carries this stipulation covering the area shown on the regional map included in the report.

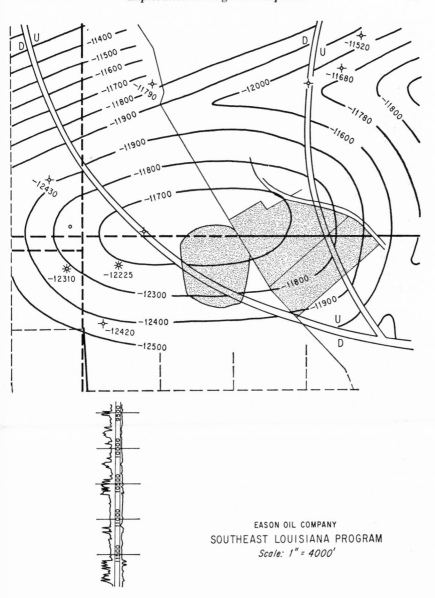

EASON OIL COMPANY
SOUTHEAST LOUISIANA PROGRAM
Scale: 1" = 4000'

All seismic and other geophysical or geological information acquired shall be the property of Eason Oil Company. Basic records shall remain in possession of Eason Oil Company but may be examined at any time by any joint venturer or his written designee.

Each joint venturer will agree that until such time as the fourteen-well program is complete, all his operations in the area will be under the terms of the joint venture. Eason Oil Company further agrees that for a three-year period subsequent to the completion of this joint venture each wildcat operation it intends to drill in the area will be submitted to the former joint venturers for their optional participation under terms similar to those set forth above.

Eason Oil Company will undertake to pay all rentals which in its opinion should be paid and will bill the other joint venturers 50% thereof. Eason Oil Company will make every effort to pay such rentals timely, but will not be liable for loss of leases and/or options through failure to do so.

The costs of statutory insurance, e.g., workmen's compensation, will be paid by Eason Oil Company. Hazard insurance to afford protection against loss of hole (if a market can be located), costs of controlling a wild well and underground damage will be shared by joint venturers as intangibles. Other protection will be available from the drilling contractor's insurance program.

Cash requirements will vary primarily with availability of leasehold interest in prospects suitable for drilling. We believe the fourteen-well program may be completed by mid-1960, approximately 24 months after commencement. The $210,000 estimated seismic expense is the cost most likely to average out through the period, an estimate of $8750 per month. For planning cash requirements, Eason Oil Company has used $9000 per month.

Land acquisitions may total $250,000 but are not likely to be expended in increments of more than $50,000 per month.

Wildcat drilling costs (for dry holes) have been estimated at $150,000 net of dry hole contributions. In an earlier portion of the report we assumed the total amount of dry hole money received would be $200,000 — $15,000 per hole on the average. Because two or more successive wells might not be subject to dry hole money, it should be ignored in estimating cash requirements. Consequently, we use here an estimate of $165,000. We may be further faced with a requirement to pay for drilling two wells in the same month despite efforts to avoid such a situation. In that event the cash requirement would include $330,000 for drilling.

Contingencies should also be provided for and probably $50,000 is more than adequate.

Summing up, it appears that joint venturers should be prepared for their share of at least $274,000 (one well) and perhaps $439,000 (two wells) in one month.

The total cash requirement for the entire program will be approximately $2,910,000 including the costs of a successful well.

Eason reserves the right to terminate the joint venture (as to the drilling of wildcat wells) at a number less than fourteen, upon the happening of events, which make the carrying out of the entire program inadvisable. One example of such an event would be the necessity to drill and complete in a short period of time, a large number of production (non-wildcat) wells on a proven lease.

While this joint venture contemplates the drilling of fourteen wells, no joint venturer of Eason shall be liable for the default of any other joint venturer.

Exhibit A

RESOLUTION OF $\sigma = \sqrt{npq}$*
(σ represents one standard deviation from mean ratio)

a	b	c	d	e	f	g
n	$\sqrt{n \cdot p \cdot q}$	σ	2σ	Mean for this n	$e - d$	Success ratio at 2σ
14	$\sqrt{14(\frac{1}{3})(\frac{2}{3})}$ $\sqrt{3.109}$	± 1.761	± 3.522	4.667	1.145	1.145/14†

*This is more accurately a presentation of the matrix for $n = 14$ — the matrix is composed of representations for all values of n. Mean ratio in the instant case is $1 : 3$.

n = total number of observations (statistically); total number of wildcat wells in the instant case.

p = mean success ratio $(1 : 3)$.

q = mean failure ratio $(2 : 3)$.

†As is shown by the numerator exceeding 1.0 the probability of one success in a 14 prospect program actually exceeds 95.5%. The accurate figure is found by solving 14. $(\frac{1}{3} \cdot \frac{1}{4})^{14}$ but does not materially affect the conclusion.

Exhibit B

DEVELOPMENT OF REQUIRED AREAL
EXTENT OF PROSPECT TO CREATE "BREAK-EVEN" VALUE
(Oil)

A. Annual Income to Operator
Report Page 14 and allowable schedule

Selling Price		$3.45/bbl.
Less: Tax	0.23	
		$3.22
Royalty & Overide		
($\frac{1}{4}$ of $\frac{8}{8}$)	0.81	2.41
Lifting Cost	0.22	
Net to Operator		$2.19/bbl.

Annual Production at current allowable: 108 bbl./day $\times$ 365 dys./yr.
= 39,420 bbls.
Annual net to Operator: $2.19/bbl. $\times$ 39,240 bbl./yr. = $86,329.80
(use $86,200)

B. Value of One Well to Operator
Life of well: total reserves/annual production 39,420 bbls.
              1,280,000 /   39,420   = 32.5 yrs.
      (use 30 years)
Present value of $86,200/yr. received monthly for 30 years at 6% discount
rate:
              $86,200 $\times$ 14.139 = $1,218,781.80
                (use $1,218,000)

C. Direct Costs of One Typical Well Completed: $250,000
Report on Pages 64 and 65

D. Margin On Individual Well

Value of Well	$1,218,000	
Direct cost of well	250,000[1]	
Operator's Margin		$ 968,000
Less Tax @ Capital Gain Rate		242,000
"Imputed Profit"		$ 726,000

E. Expenditures allocable to Discovery
From Report Page 63

Dry Holes	$1,950,000
Seismic	210,000
Contingencies	250,000
	$2,410,000

[1]In cases where a field dry hole was possible, an allocation of that cost
would be included at this point. Also where land costs were required, the
cost of the land which would be disproven if the test well were dry would
be included. In latter regard some adjustment would have to be made
for "un-disproven" acreage acquired in conjunction with other prospects

F. 1. Number of "Typical" wells required to cover allocable costs — using imputed profit figure — = E ÷ D

$$\$2,410,000/\$726,000 = 3.32$$

2. Number of "Typical" wells required to cover allocable costs using "Operator's Margin" = E ÷ \$968,000

$$\$2,410,000/\$968,000 = 2.49$$

(use 3.2)

Conclusion: Under this calculation and on basis set forth in report 3.32 "typical" wells (a discovery, two offsets and a partial interest in a third offset) are of sufficient value to allow the program to break even. On 40-acre spacing and with the balance of the variables as set forth, each prospect should have 160 acres proven by the first well.

Exhibit C

DEVELOPMENT OF REQUIRED AREAL
EXTENT OF PROSPECT TO CREATE "BREAK-EVEN" VALUE
(Gas)

A. Annual Income to Operator
    Selling Price (gas) $0.23/MCF
    Report Page 2
    Less: Tax   .0035
                                                  ――――――――
                                                                     $0.2265
    Royalty & Overriding
      Royalty (25%)   .0575
                                                  ――――――――
                                                                     $0.1690
    Lifting Costs   .0113
                                                  ――――――――
    Net to Operator (gas) $0.1577/MCF
                                                                   (use $0.15)
    Add: Distillate/Condensate
         at 20 bbl./MCF
    Selling Price $3.05/bbl.
    Less: Tax   0.23
                                                  ――――――――
                                                                     $2.82
    Royalty & Overriding
      Royalty (25%)   0.76
                                                  ――――――――
                                                                     $2.06
    Lifting Costs   0.00
                                                  ――――――――
    Net to Operator $2.06/bbl.
    Annual Production (gas)   960,000 MCF
    (1/20 of reserves)
    Reserves = 1,5000,000 CF/A-ft. × 40 ft. × 320 A. = 19,200,000 MCF
    Annual Income to Operator (gas):
      960,000MCF @ $0.15/MCF $144,000
    Annual Production (Distillate):
      960,000MCF @ 20 bbl./MMCF   19,200 bbls.
    Annual Income to Operator (Distillate):
      19,200 bbls. × $2.06/bbl. $ 39,552
    Total Lease Income to Operator Annually
                                                                     ――――――――
                                                                     $183,552
    (Use $183,000)
B. Value of One Well to Operator
      Life of Well: 20 years (depletion contract)
        Present value of $183,000/yr.
        received monthly for 20 yrs.
        at 6% discount rate — $183,000 × 11.782 = $2,156,106
        (use $2,150,000)
C. Direct Costs of one Typical gas/distillate
      well completed: $300,000[1]
    $250,000 (oil well cost) plus $50,000 increment

D. Margin On Individual Well:

Value of Well	$2,150,000
Direct Cost of Well	300,000[1]
Operator's Margin	$1,850,000
Less Tax @ Capital Gains Rate	462,500
"Imputed Profit"	$1,387,500
(Use $1,300,000)	

E. Expenditures Allocable to Discovery:

(Report on Page 59)

Dry Holes	$1,950,000
Seismic	210,000
Contingencies	280,000
	$2,140,000

F. 1. Number of "typical" wells required to cover allocable costs — using "Imputed Profit" figure E $\div$ D:

$$2,410,000/\$1,850,000 = 1.85$$

2. Number of "typical" wells required to cover allocable costs — using "Operator's Margin"

$$2,410,000/\$1,850,300 = 1.3$$

(Use 1.85)

Conclusion: Under this calculation and on the basis set forth in the report, 1.85 typical wells (a discovery and a partial interest in one offset) are of sufficient value to allow the program to break even. On 320-acre spacing and with the balance of the variables as set forth, each prospect should have 640 acres proven by the first well to be acceptable.

---

[1] In cases where a field dry hole was possible, an allocation of that cost would be included at this point. Also, where land costs were required, the cost of the land which would be disproven if the test well were dry would be included. In latter regard some adjustment would have to be made for "un-disproven" acreage acquired in conjunction with other prospects.

Exhibit D

HISTORICAL SUCCESS (Wildcats)
1952–1956

Parish	Year	O & G	Dry	Total
Plaquemines	1952	17	23	40
Jefferson	1952	4	1	5
Lafourche	1952	8	7	15
Terrebonne	1952	15	10	25
		44	41	85
Plaquemines	1953	16	29	45
Jefferson	1953	1	5	6
Lafourche	1953	12	5	17
Terrebonne	1953	22	4	26
		51	43	94
Plaquemines	1954	56	29	85
Jefferson	1954	3	6	9
Lafourche	1954	9	8	17
Terrebonne	1954	14	8	22
		82	51	133
Plaquemines	1955	9	25	34
Jefferson	1955	5	16	20
Lafourche	1955	10	32	46
Terrebonne	1955	15	23	38
		42	96	138
Plaquemines	1956	16	35	51
Jefferson	1956	12	14	26
Lafourche	1956	23	47	70
Terrebonne	1956	21	43	64
		72	139	211

Year	Totals	O & G	Dry	Success Ratio
1952	85	44	41	1 : 1.9
1953	94	51	43	1 : 1.8
1954	133	82	51	1 : 1.62
1955	138	42	96	1 : 3.29
1956	211	72	139	1 : 2.93
	661	291	370	

OPERATING COST ANALYSES — HYPOTHETICAL OIL LEASE — (5 wells × 100 bpd/well)

Cost Component	Early Years				Later Years			
	Per Bbl	Per Day	Per Mo	Per 2000 bpd	Per Bbl	Per Day	Per Mo	Per 2000 bpd
Superintendence	$.015	$ 7.50	$ 225.	$ 30.	$.015	$ 7.50	$ 225.	$ 30.
Engineering	.015	7.50	225.	30.	.015	7.50	225.	30.
Payroll Labor								
Pumper	.025	12.50	375.	50.	.025	12.50	375.	50.
Clerk	.005	2.50	75.	10.	.005	2.50	75.	10.
Roustabouts	.015	7.50	225.	30.	.03	15.00	450.	60.
Foreman	—	—	—	—	—	—	—	—
Contract Labor	—	—	—	—	—	—	—	—
Well Servicing	—	—	—	—	.10	50.00	1500.	200.
Clean-out and Swabbing	—	—	—	—	—	—	—	—
Artificial Lift Expense	—	—	—	—	.15	75.00	2250.	300.
Fuel and Water	.005	2.50	75.	10.	.02	10.00	300.	40.
Repairs — Labor & Parts	.01	5.00	150.	20.	.02	10.00	300.	40.
Supplies	.01	5.00	150.	20.	.01	5.00	150.	20.
Treating Crude Oil	—	—	—	—	.005	2.50	75.	10.
Gas Dehydration	—	—	—	—	—	—	—	—
Gas Compression	—	—	—	—	—	—	—	—
Automobile Expense	.005	2.50	75.	10.	.005	2.50	75.	10.
Boat Expense	.05	25.00	750.	100.	.05	25.00	750.	100.
Trucking & Hauling	.005	2.50	75.	10.	.01	5.00	150.	20.
Communications	.01	5.00	150.	20.	.01	5.00	150.	20.
Camp Expense	.005	2.50	75.	10.	.005	2.50	75.	10.
District Lease Expense	.01	5.00	150.	20.	.01	5.00	150.	20.
Other Direct Lifting Cost	.01	5.00	150.	20.	.01	5.00	150.	20.
Insurance	.01	5.00	150.	20.	.01	5.00	150.	20.
Taxes — Production	.23	115.00	3450.	460.	.23	115.00	3450.	460.
Taxes — Ad valorem	.01	5.00	150.	20.	.01	5.00	150.	20.
Other Miscellaneous Expense	.02	10.00	300.	40.	.02	10.00	300.	40.
Office Overhead	—	—	—	—	—	—	—	—
Depreciation	—	—	—	—	—	—	—	—
Depletion	—	—	—	—	—	—	—	—
TOTALS	$.465	$232.50	$6975.	$930.	$.765	$382.50	$11,475.	$1530.

Exhibit F

OPERATING COST ANALYSES — HYPOTHETICAL GAS LEASE — (3 wells × 3⅓ MMCF/day/well)

Cost Component	Early Years			Later Years		
	Per MMCF	Per Day	Per Mo	Per MMCF	Per Day	Per Mo
Superintendence	$ 0.75	$ 7.50	$ 225.	$ 0.75	$ 7.50	$ 225.
Engineering	0.75	7.50	225.	0.75	7.50	225.
Payroll Labor						
Pumper	1.25	12.50	375.	1.25	12.50	375.
Clerk	0.25	2.50	75.	0.25	2.50	75.
Roustabouts	0.75	7.50	225.	0.75	7.50	225.
Foreman	—	—	—	—	—	—
Contract Labor	—	—	—	—	—	—
Well Servicing	—	—	—	—	—	—
Clean-out and Swabbing	—	—	—	5.00	50.00	1500.
Artificial Lift	—	—	—	—	—	—
Fuel and Water	0.25	2.50	75.	0.50	5.00	150.
Repairs — Labor and Parts	0.50	5.00	150.	1.00	10.00	300.
Supplies	0.50	5.00	150.	0.50	5.00	150.
Treating Crude Oil	—	—	—	—	—	—
Gas Dehydration	0.25	2.50	75.	0.25	2.50	75.
Gas Compression	—	—	—	—	—	—
Automobile Expense	0.25	2.50	75.	0.25	2.50	75.
Boat Expense	2.50	25.00	750.	2.50	25.00	750.
Trucking and Hauling	0.25	2.50	75.	0.25	2.50	75.
Communications	0.50	5.00	150.	0.50	5.00	150.
Camp Expense	0.25	2.50	75.	0.25	2.50	75.
District Lease Expense	0.50	5.00	150.	0.50	5.00	150.
Other Direct Lifting Cost	0.50	5.00	150.	0.50	5.00	150.
Insurance	0.50	5.00	150.	0.50	5.00	150.
Taxes — Production	3.50	35.00	1050.	3.50	35.00	1050.
Taxes — Ad valorem	0.50	5.00	150.	0.50	5.00	150.
Other Miscellaneous Expense	1.00	10.00	300.	1.00	10.00	300.
Office Overhead	—	—	—	—	—	—
Depreciation	—	—	—	—	—	—
Depletion	—	—	—	—	—	—
TOTALS	$15.50	$155.00	$4650.	$21.25	$212.50	$6375.

Exhibit G

Geological Basis:	A gravity minimum is located in the middle of a structure postulated by sub-surface control. Two reconnaissance seismic lines give indication of north-south reversal. Seismic program will be necessary to delineate structure to drilling status.
Similar Producing Structure:	Six miles to the southeast. Field has three gas-distillate wells with reserves estimated to be 144,000,000,000 cubic feet of gas plus 4,300,000 barrels distillate. Pay — 100' thick.
Acreage Involved:	2880 acres. 640 acres under lease to an independent oil producer, 320 acres under lease to a major oil company, 640 acres unleased, 1280 acres unavailable, 2560 acres potentially productive.
Farmout Terms:	1/8th ORRI on drill site (640) acreage.
Acreage Costs:	$50 per acre bonus, $10 yearly rental, 3-year term, 1/6th royalty.
Estimated Seismic Costs:	Minimum — $7500. Maximum — $25,000.
Estimated Well Costs:	Drilled — $160,000. Completed — $210,000.
Working Interest in Field:	50%.
Farmee's Share of Field Reserves:	36.5%.
Possible Well Contribution:	$40,000 dry hole money.
Anticipated Depth of Production:	9000' — 12,000'.
Recommended Drilling Depth:	12,000'.
Anticipated Production:	Gas-distillate.
Anticipated Reserve Exposure:	Per Well — 48,000,000,000 cu. ft. gas plus 1,440,000 bbls. distillate.
	Field — 384,000,000,000 cu. ft. gas plus 11,520,000 barrels distillate.

Geological Basis:	Sub-surface well control indicating closure on the down-throw side of a major regional fault. Seismic program is necessary to delineate closure accurately.
Similar Producing Structure:	One mile to the north. Field has four gas-distillate wells with reserves estimated to be 96,000,000,000 cubic feet of gas plus 2,880,000 barrels distillate.
Acreage Involved:	1920 acres leased by major oil companies, 960 acres available on farmout, 1920 acres potentially productive.
Farmout Terms:	To be determined.
Estimated Seismic Costs:	Minimum — $10,000. Maximum — $40,000.
Estimated Well Costs:	Drilled — $120,000. Completed — $170,000.
Working Interest in Field:	To be determined.

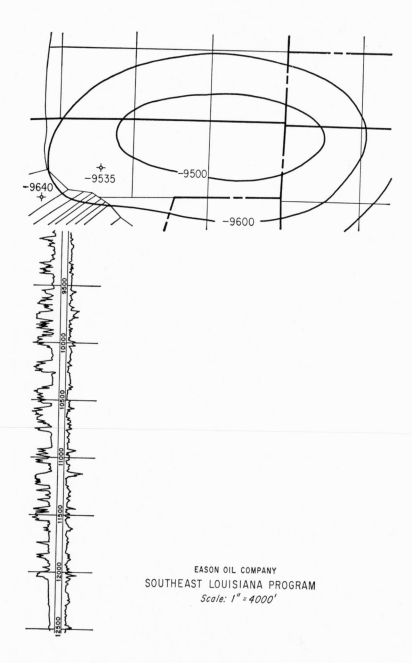

−9535

−9640

−9500

−9600

EASON OIL COMPANY
SOUTHEAST LOUISIANA PROGRAM
Scale: 1" = 4000'

Farmee's Share of Field Reserves: To be determined.
Possible Well Contribution: $23,000 dry hole money.
Anticipated Depth of Production: 8500' — 11,500'.
Recommended Drilling Depth: 11,500'.
Anticipated Production: Gas-distillate.
Anticipated Reserve Exposure: Per well—28,000,000,000 cu. ft. gas plus
720,000 bbls. distillate.
Field — 168,000,000,000 cu. ft. gas plus
4,420,000 bbls. distillate.

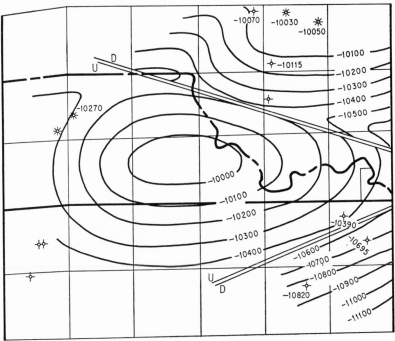

EASON OIL COMPANY
SOUTHEAST LOUISIANA PROGRAM
Scale: 1" = 4651+'

Geological Basis: Strong northwest dip from sub-surface control in area of recognized south dip. Partially controlled by seismic data. Require additional seismic program.

Similar Producing Structure: Six miles to the south. Field has 76 oil and gas-distillate wells with reserves estimated to be 100,000,000 bbls. oil plus 600,000,000,000 cubic feet gas plus 12,000,000 bbls. distillate. Pay — up to 200' thick.

Acreage Involved: 3500 acres held under lease by major companies, 1200 acres potentially productive.

Farmout Terms: To be determined.

Estimated Seismic Costs: Minimum — $1200.   Maximum — $50,000.

Estimated Well Costs: Drilled — $175,000.   Completed — $235,000.

Working Interest in Field: To be determined.

Farmee's Share of Field Reserves: To be determined.

Possible Well Contribution: $50,000 dry hole money.

Anticipated Depth of Production: 9000' — 13,000'.

Recommended Drilling Depth: 12,500'.

Anticipated Production: Oil and gas-distillate.

Anticipated Reserve Exposure: Oil Well — 2,000,000 bbls. oil.

Gas-distillate well — 62,000,000,000 cu. ft. gas plus 1,200,000 bbls. distillate.

Field — 10,000,000 bbls. oil plus 250,000,000,000 cu. ft. gas plus 5,000,000 barrels distillate.

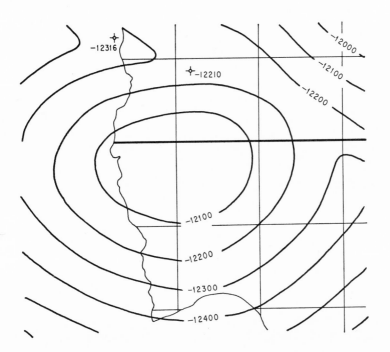

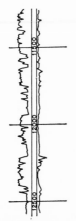

EASON OIL COMPANY
SOUTHEAST LOUISIANA PROGRAM
Scale: 1" = 4000'

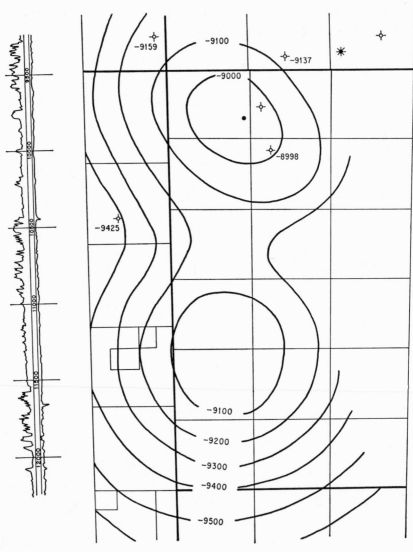

EASON OIL COMPANY
SOUTHEAST LOUISIANA PROGRAM
Scale: 1" = 4000'

Geological Basis:	Abnormally strong gravity minimal ridge indicating positive salt intrusion. On trend with faulted anticlines also on strong gravity minimum ridges. Sub-surface control sparse necessitating seismic reconnaissance.
Similar Producing Structures:	Three miles to the northeast. Field has 152 oil wells with reserves estimated to be 250,000,000 bbls. of oil. Pay — 800' net, averaging 200' per well.
Acreage Involved:	10,880 acres, all unleased. 400 acres potentially productive.
Acreage Costs:	$25 per acre, $5 yearly rentals, 3-year term 1/6th royalty.
Estimated Seismic Costs:	Minimum — $7500. Maximum — $25,000.
Estimated Well Costs:	Drilled — $160,000. Completed — $210,000.
Working Interest in Field:	100%.
Working Interest Share of Field Reserves:	80.5%.
Possible Well Contribution:	None.
Anticipated Depth of Production:	9000' — 13,500'.
Recommended Drilling Depth:	13,500'.
Anticipated Reserve Exposure:	Per Well — 4,000,000 barrels oil. Field — 40,000,000 barrels oil.

CHAPTER 5

Nongeological Determinants
of Exploration Strategies

An exploratory program undertaken by a particular company or group of companies may depart from the train of events suggested by Exhibit 2.1, *Principal Steps in an Exploration Program.* There are many nongeological circumstances which can cause a program to deviate from the initial investigation — reconnaissance exploration — advanced exploration pattern of this exhibit, or even to omit some steps altogether. The purpose of this chapter is to describe some determinants of exploration activities not discussed in earlier chapters. Rather than describe a large variety, only three of the most important ones are presented here — three which convey the spirit of the effect on exploration strategy of a broader class of determinants to which they belong:

1. Fund limitations or budget constraints,
2. Timing — time of entry into a region, competitive pressures, lease or concession termination dates,
3. Geographical location of the region being explored.

The influence of these determinants is evident in Eason's program. Entry into south Louisiana was timed to take advantage of a great deal of exploratory effort spent by other firms over the years. Eason did not have to undertake reconnaissance gravity, magnetic, or seismic surveys, for sufficient subsurface information was available in the form of maps, cores, samples, and logs from wells drilled by other firms to forego geophysical reconnaissance activities. The program's outlook was further improved in that potential competitors' attentions were focused elsewhere. Because the program requires more funds than Eason is willing to risk in one area in a relatively short space of time, the program is being undertaken as a joint venture with four other partner firms.

In this chapter the impact of funds limitations, timing, and geographical location on exploration information-gathering activities is illustrated by contrasting some real exploration situations with the "classical approach" to exploration.[1] To do this, instances of the effect of each of the listed determinants on exploration information-gathering and wildcat drilling activities are presented: "funds limitations" in Section 5.1, "timing" in Section 5.2, "geographical location" in Section 5.3. In reading the illustrations, a useful centripetal idea is to remember that each portion of the problem, "What is the best information-gathering mix to use?" is a component of the firm's over-all capital budgeting problem:

Given a limited amount of funds, how can we best allocate them among investment opportunities — taking into account those opportunities presently available to us and those which may be available in the future?

---

[1]"Classical approach" is a term used by one geophysicist to denote the typical sequence of information — gathering methods that would be used in exploration of a virgin area:

1. The cheapest method — aeromagnetic survey — is used first to obtain the grain of the country and to focus on major structural anomalies. It eliminates areas of noninterest, downgrades and upgrades broad areas, and helps to determine the depth to the crystalline basement.

2. If the time and money is available, a gravity survey may be run. The survey will reveal density gradients and give information on structural anomalies via density anomalies. Gravity work further eliminates areas, for by revealing more precisely the depth to basement rock it enables the geophysicist to determine where sediments are too shallow to be productive. Per unit area, gravity surveys are about 4 to 5 times as expensive as an aeromagnetic survey and take about 10 times as long to cover the same area.

3. The next step is to take land on the anomalies and to do a seismic survey. The choice of which locale to shoot is of course dependent on the combination of structure and sediment believed to be present. Both refraction and reflection seismic surveys might be conducted to give information about the depth, thickness, and character of the sediments, in addition to information about their attitude.

Clearly, the decision to purchase information is an investment which precludes using the funds so invested for some other activity. Although other determinants of exploration patterns draw attention away from fund limitations, the key economic constraint in a program's formulation, the information-gathering problem, is still primarily one of efficient allocation of funds.

5.1. Funds Limitations and Budget Constraints

Funds limitations or budget constraints shape the kind of program a company can undertake. Whereas no major or independent has unlimited funds, the difference in availability of funds between the major and the small independent results in quite disparate exploration strategies.[2] Without high risk of ruin, the major can take a large acreage position on general regional trends in an area, a substantial portion of which may be highly speculative. The small independent usually carries a small acreage inventory, most of which is on specific anomalies with a corresponding lower proportion of speculative acreage. The major has the financial ability to carry on extensive regional surveys over its holdings, or to "sit on" its acreage until lease expiration dates draw near. The small independent's need for a quick turnover of funds oftentimes does not allow him the same degree of latitude in evaluating his acreage. Majors can spend more to evaluate acreage prior to leasing, giving them the ability to lease more selectively and with less chance of leasing poor acreage. Clearly, the major has a greater variety of investment opportunities to choose from by virtue of its greater availability of funds. Illustrative of the pressure funds limitations places on the small independent is the Orange Company's Panhandle Program.

The Orange Company*

The Orange Petroleum Company is a small Midwestern company whose main activities are refining and marketing. During the past four years the firm has been accenting its exploration activities more actively than in the past. The firm is presently engaged in a program in the Panhandle area of Texas, Oklahoma, and Colorado.

---

[2]Cf. C. J. Grayson, *op. cit.*, pp. 80–85, for similar contrast of strategies. Grayson makes the important point that although majors do have some strategic advantages over independents, it does *not* follow that they are more profitable ones.

*Disguised name.

The Panhandle was picked from six areas which had been studied in detail by company geologists. According to the chief geologist:

> Orange gathered general information on several other areas also. But we picked the one in which we could best do three things: first, accurately determine the geological character of the area so that we could pick good prospects; second, get a sizeable amount of acreage by farmouts, and third, find prospects which meet our economic criteria.

> Economically, the most lucrative area in terms of potential net profit was not necessarily the best for us. For example, the net present value of prospects runs better on the average on the Gulf Coast, but due to allowables being higher in the Panhandle there is a quicker payout than on the Gulf. Had we been able to take a 1 or 2 per cent interest in ventures on the Gulf, it might have been a worthwhile area for us. But having to talk in terms of 50 per cent interest was too much for us. We could only get two or three well participations on the Gulf, but possibly ten to twenty in the Panhandle with the same funds because of the difference in well costs. Other plus factors in the Panhandle are:

> 90 percent of the production found is gas; gas is a better find for us because of its value in the heating market; we are suffering from oil imports.

> Our first well was drilled in this area back in 1957, and it was a discovery well. We had lots of money at that time, but this well showed that we needed more information before we could go ahead and exploit the area fully. Now that the program is underway, we're restricted on money. This happened because in '58 we ran into hard times in refining. This year (1959) is better but not good.

> Planning is difficult because when budget time comes around, marketing and refining are given first crack at funds. The money is allocated as if we were solely a marketing and refining company. Aside from our regular primary expenses, we in exploration simply get the leftovers, as there is no established pattern of cash flow allocated to production. From 100 per cent of cash flow in '53 and '54, we've gone down to 20 per cent. In those two years we had a program going with some outside participants, and we were compelled to come up with our share of development funds. Since that time, there have

been some years when we did nothing in production due to poor refining margins.

The key to the Panhandle's several hundred thousand square miles is subsurface geology. Seismic isn't any good, as most of the finds are stratigraphic traps. While gravity surveys may show the grain of large trends, we didn't have any of this information, but had only broad regional information. To delineate prospects, we extrapolated from the drilling history of the area — we bought every log in the country, both electric and sample, and employed a scout who records the information on every well that is drilled in the area. We put this information together, and made our decisions about prospects on the basis of structure maps on four horizons, isopac maps, and sand facies studies of eight different horizons.

Since starting the subsurface investigation, we have drilled six wildcats on hot prospects. Our first one hit; the second was a dry hole that told us to move; we moved and hit on the third; the fourth was a marginal producer; the fifth was a dry hole; and the sixth is now being drilled and looks encouraging. We have drilled four development wells on our first successful wildcats, and this has ruined our wildcatting for the time being — no more funds.[3]

$80,000 for a dry hole;
$120,000 for a single level producer; and
$160,000 for a dual producer.
The program is still going strong.

As a small company, there is constant reassessment of what we're doing in exploration. We jump from a rapid to a slow program very often because of the impact of refining on available funds. We are always faced with the decision as to whether money will be allocated to refining or to exploration and production.

While a major also must operate each of its programs within budget limitations, any one program is much less likely to be faced with oscilla-

---

[3]Capital for 1958–59 drilling was raised in the East. Orange Company's partners put up three-fourths of the needed funds in return for half of the profits. Orange came back in for half of the profits after the partners recovered their initial investment. (A carried interest deal.)

tions in funds available for exploration as violent as that experienced by the Orange Company. As one would expect, the scope of a major's program can be broader and can extend over a longer period of time than those of a small independent without putting undue strain on the company's financial resources. By way of comparison with the Orange Company, take the Ollen Company's Alaskan activities.

The Ollen Company*

The Ollen Company, a major, has been actively looking for oil and gas in Alaska for seven years. During this time the company has spent roughly $100,000 for 300,000 acres — an expense management regards as minor compared with what they estimate the total expenditures to evaluate these properties will be.

Very little surface reconnaissance was done initially, as there were few outcrops known to exist. After six years of investigation and one season of seismic work,[4] a decision was made to drill a well to determine the area's stratigraphy more precisely. Drilling a wildcat was expensive, but management concluded that they could spend $1,000,000 for a well, considering that they were looking for a field of 100,000,000 barrels of oil or better. In their estimation, this first wildcat was a long gamble; the odds of hitting were no better than 50 to 1.

While encouraging, the well was not a commercial producer, in spite of which it cost $1,500,000.

The first well was followed up by additional seismic surveying to get a more definitive picture of subsurface structure. The exploration manager stated:

> After our second round of surveying, we will drill another well and use the data from it and the first well to build up maps and cross-sections. At present we don't know what the odds are on how much oil is present, but if there is anything worth producing at all, it should be of fairly large size.

Clearly the low state of geological information about Alaska and the large expenditures necessary for extensive exploration in that region are far beyond the financial capabilities of the typical small domestic independent. As one geologist put the point:

---

[4] An Ollen Company geophysicist estimated reflection seismic costs in Alaska at about $3000 per crew-day for 20–25 miles of line.

*Disguised name.

There are companies who could go broke on a single trip to Alaska to look at the surface geology.

In spite of differences between a major's exploration strategy and that of a small independent, there are many methods for reducing the cost of exploratory information which are in common usage among both independents and majors when the cost of information is too high relative to its adjudged value and to the willingness of an operator to take financial risks. Three of them are: trading arrangements to gain information, pooling costs and sharing data, and exchanging information. The reader is referred to Chapter 8 of C. J. Grayson's book[5] for a detailed description of how trading arrangements are used by operators to reduce risk and to gain information. The latter two methods are frequently used in offshore exploration where the cost of exploratory information is prohibitively high. Technical problems greatly increase the cost of offshore exploration methods, doubling or even tripling the cost of equivalent methods used onshore:

ONSHORE VS. OFFSHORE GEOPHYSICAL COSTS[6]				
Exploration Method	Location	Onshore	Offshore	Cost per Crew-Month
Seismic	California		x	$100,000–$125,000
Seismic	California	x		$15,000–$30,000
Seismic	Gulf Coast		x	$35,000–$80,000
Seismic	Gulf Coast	x		about $15,000
Gravity	Gulf Coast		x	about $30,000
Gravity	Gulf Coast	x		about $12,000

Before bidding for offshore acreage sold by the Federal Government, it is common for interested companies to join together in surveying the acreage, sharing both the information accumulated and the costs of data gathering. Very often joint surveys are accompanied by information trades:

The Boscoe Company*

The Boscoe Company, a large independent, wished to survey some 3200 square miles of off-shore acreage before submitting a sealed bid on

[5]C. J. Grayson, *op. cit.*, pp. 189–230.

[6]Source of data: *Submerged Lands Productive Capacity*, a report of The National Petroleum Council, Washington 6, D. C. (1953).

*Disguised name.

those acres it considered desirable. Before bidding, Boscoe participated in a reconnaissance seismic survey with one group of companies and then in a deep coring survey with a different group of companies.

The reconnaissance seismic survey consisted of shooting the area with a grid 10,000 feet wide at the widest point and then crossing the grid lines at roughly 5000–6000 foot intervals. A Shoran system[7] was used for positional accuracy, so that shooting accuracy was approximately 25–50 feet. The personnel required in the off-shore party were:

Field Personnel   1 party manager
                     1 party manager's clerk
                     1 deck manager
                     1 observer
                     1 observer's assistant
                     2 surveyors
                     2 shooters
                     2 helpers
                     —
                     11

Office Personnel   1 party chief
                     4 data interpreters
                     2 chief computers
                     14 computers and computers' assistants
                     6 draftsmen
                     —
                     27

Their work took about three months at a monthly cost of $250,000 for a total cost of $750,000. After the seismic data were obtained, a drop coring through 300 feet of overburden was taken, to give a core sample of the offshore sediments.

The seismic survey was followed with a deep coring, done in conjunction with a different group of four other companies. The deep coring boats' survey required drilling 6000 feet into sediments, and then running a service casing with a 6-inch diameter hole. All the data from deep coring was pooled. The total cost of this work was roughly $1,100,000 which was shared among the five companies, three companies

---

[7]Shoran is one of four principal methods for obtaining the ± 100 foot positional accuracy needed for gravity and seismic surveys on the Continental Shelf. Two or more radio frequency transmitters are set up at known points on the shore. A radio receiver is placed in the survey boat. The round trip travel time of radio pulses are measured by electronic devices, the distance from each of the shore transmitters calculated, and then the location of the boat determined by triangulation. A Shoran system costs the user between $7000 and $9000 per month.

assuming a fourth of the cost each, and two companies sharing an eighth of the cost each. Boscoe pooled some of the information it had obtained in the course of the seismic survey, so that its fourth share of the costs of deep coring ($277,000) broke down as follows:

Valuation of Information
  Pooled by Boscoe:

Drop Coring	$ 46,000	
Seismic	171,000	
SAP	17,000	
		$234,000

Cash Contributed by
  Boscoe:

		43,000
Total cost to Boscoe:		$277,000

The examples above illustrate only a few of many ways in which funds limitations influence the planning and execution of an exploratory venture. The important point to recognize is that the size of a firm's financial resources is one of the strongest dictates of the kind of exploration program it can undertake. The effect of financial constraints is present in every stage of planning and execution, from initial investigation to the drilling of wildcat wells.

5.2.   Timing

The time of entry into an area is also an important determinant of the exploration strategy a company will follow. Grayson[9] points out that the time at which acreage is acquired, rentals, and lease expiration dates strongly influence an operator's information-gathering methodology and raises a host of questions. An operator might question himself about a venture like this:

> Should I buy in early here and then spend the money to evaluate acreage? I can get it at a few dollars per acre. If I wait until more information develops, I'll be able to select better acreage, but the price may be sky high, as much as two or three hundred per acre. On the other hand, maybe I should survey a few sections first and then pick the best acreage while it's available.

In Libya, for example, one major found rentals so high and had so many acres to evaluate that in place of careful reconnaissance surveys, it

---

[9]C. J. Grayson, *op. cit.*, pp. 85–87.

immediately moved in seismic crews who did "spot" shooting at 90° to the grain of major trends; interesting anomalies were drilled as they were discovered.

The Key Company's experience in the Cross Basin is typical of the way timing influences a small company's exploration strategy:

The Key Company*

In 1958 the Key Company owned 40,000 acres in the Cross Basin,* which they had acquired at a price of $25,000. Mr. Key commented on this acreage:

> There is some small activity by the majors who are backing up scattered leases. Leases are not valuable now, for the supply is plentiful. If, however, the majors continue to lease, our leases will rise in value purely because of scarcity of available acreage. Leases might go to $2 in three to five years.

The alternatives Mr. Key was considering were:

1. Sit and do nothing. We may have to wait ten to twelve years for someone else to drill near our acreage — if they ever do. This creates financial problems by tying our money up. The total investment that would be required to wait and do nothing would be about $160,000. However, leases will expire at the end of this period.

2. Wait for three years and if no interest occurs in the basin, drop it. We would lose about $25,000 if we had to drop it. If the majors were to start an evaluation program, they could be very liberal in supporting tests by us.

3. We could start on an exploration program ourselves. One way would be to fly the basin [aeromagnetic survey] at a cost of about $28,000 and then lease only the remaining promising structures.

In Mr. Key's opinion, a seismic survey would cost about $50,000 per month and would be unlikely to reveal more than two or three prospects. Core drilling was also a possibility, but a core drill survey would cost about $100,000, which Mr. Key felt was too expensive for his firm.

---

*Disguised name.

4. Go ahead and lease the entire basin and then go to the majors with a checkerboard deal.

5. Sit back and wait for the majors to fly the basin, then follow them around to secure information and possibly dry-hole contributions. Dry-hole costs should be about $125,000 for a 700 foot well.

His geologists felt that potential reserves could be anywhere from nothing to many hundreds of millions of barrels.

Timing shapes exploration strategy in other ways also; competitive pressures oftentimes combine with time deadlines to force a foreshortening of the sequence of information-gathering activities a firm would like to carry out, compounding the difficulty of making an accurate assessment of an area's potential.

The Arko Company

Geologists of the Arko Company, a major oil and gas producer, were convinced that there was oil in the X area, but that the area was too remote geographically from pipeline facilities to be profitably exploited. Many other companies bought land in the area at $7 to $10 per acre with rentals of 25 cents per acre.

Then one of Arko's competitors found a 250,000,000 barrel oil field in the X area. Arko was suddenly faced with the prospect of paying very high bonuses and rentals if it wished to take a position. Some Government tracts were coming up for bid about six months after the discovery, and Arko decided to enter the competition for the acreage. A similar sealed bid sale was to be held by the Government one year after this initial offering. Arko's exploration manager commented:

Since we had only six months we proceeded to shoot the area. We were really pressed for time, and so we didn't worry about money spent on shooting as much as time. Even after shooting it was difficult to differentiate the good acreage from the bad.

We computed the thickness of the sand, potential productivity, costs of drilling and the cost of production. Using this information, we figured a bid which would allow us a reasonable profit . . . and our bid was way too low. Five to six hundred dollars per acre low! Some of that acreage sold for $1100 to $1500 per acre. Yet our decision was good beforehand, because, as I said, it was very difficult to differentiate the acreage on the basis of the information we had available.

Even at that high price, the people who found oil on their acreage were very satisfied.

Pending the second sale, we kept a gravity and a seismic crew in the area and continued investigating. The decision to use only one crew was based on our ability to absorb information. We could have put ten crews in, but we couldn't have absorbed the information any more effectively in the time span of one year.

Everyone else who was interested did exactly the same thing. Everybody shot it. We found in a general way what people were thinking of bidding by looking for partners, and, as we suspected, the prices were way up high again. While we got a few relatively unattractive pieces on the second sale, no major fields were discovered.

In sum, competitive pressures, lease termination dates, and the state of development of the area combine to make timing an important consideration in planning an exploration program.

5.3. Geographical Location

The geologist who stated that there are companies small enough to go broke on a single trip to Alaska to look at the surface geology was emphasizing only one facet of the influence of geographic location on exploration planning. The nearness of an area to the company's main base of operations, the area's accessibility, the distance from pipeline facilities — all play a part in determining costs of exploration, the return on an exploration investment, and, consequently, the exploration strategy that will be followed.

As the reader has undoubtedly noticed in the illustrations presented earlier in the chapter, drilling and information-gathering costs are highly correlated with the ease of access, topography, and distance from supply sources of the region being explored; e.g., onshore exploration costs are much lower than offshore costs. Similar comparisons can be made as between Kansas and Libya, Oklahoma and Alaska, New Guinea and Texas, etc.

Other aspects of geographical location may determine the course of a program. Barton[10] points out that the use of high explosives for generating seismic shock waves may be forbidden in some foreign countries, or, if not forbidden, so highly controlled by the foreign government as to render a seismic survey impractical. Or, a landowner may not permit a geophysical crew to survey a tract which he owns.[11]

5.4. Summary

Chapter 5 has outlined the nature of some major nongeological determinants of exploration patterns. The examples cited serve to contrast the influence of funds limitations and timing on exploration strategies of the major with that of the small independent to give the reader a sense of the range of effects of these determinants. The impact of the geographical location of tracts being explored on exploration strategy was also briefly discussed.

Certainly, there is a variety of additional nongeological influences whose effects could also be fruitfully traced: Political considerations must be weighed in planning the exploitation of foreign leasehold concessions; the firm's organizational structure affects its ability to participate in widely dispersed ventures; and perhaps most important of all, a careful examination of the interactions between personal preferences in risk taking and the types of constraints on exploration activities mentioned above could be profitably done.

---

[10]D. C. Barton, "Petroleum Geophysics," *The Science of Petroleum* (New York: Oxford University Press, 1938), pp. 325–326.

[11]*Ibid.*, p. 325. Barton cites the early Texas-Louisiana Gulf Coast seismic campaign as an example. To overcome this difficulty, seismic detectors were set along public roads and large areas shot without obtaining shooting permits.

PART II

In Chapters 1 though 5 we acquainted the reader with aspects of petroleum exploration, highlighting the role uncertainty plays in the thought process of the operator as he weighs information and outlines courses of action.

In Chapter 6 we will focus our attention on a problem of statistical methodology which is implicit in every exploration decision problem — how should we characterize the probability distribution of "size of deposits" in a given petroleum province? Chapter 7 shows how the Lognormal distribution, a functional form which seems appropriate for such characterizations, may be used in the analysis of a drilling decision problem.

CHAPTER 6

The Size and Distribution of
Oil and Gas Fields

In any decision concerned with the strategy and tactics of oil and gas exploration, a key variable is the *size* of hydrocarbon deposits in barrels of oil or in MCF of gas. The size of pool or field[1] discovered in a particular wildcat venture determines the degree to which the venture is an economic success. Since the pool or field size that will be discovered is almost always unknown before a prospect is drilled, an important question is:

What functional form of distribution function should be used to characterize the probability distribution of field sizes in a petroleum province?

By "functional form" we mean a mathematical formula which defines a family of distribution functions.

That this is a question which has received too little attention among oilmen and in the published literature on petroleum exploration is

---

[1]For convenience we shall call a hydrocarbon deposit a "pool" or a "field," even though the terms differ in usage in that a new "pool" can be found within an already discovered "field." By convention, "size" will always refer to size in barrels of oil or in MCF of gas. The word "area" will denote areal extent.

emphasized by Charles J. Deegan in the 1959 petroleum number of *Mines:*[2]

> My own diagnosis is that our geological and geophysical data range from good to excellent, as far as they go, and that the same can be said for our techniques in routine application of these data. BUT, in my opinion, we have two basic weaknesses:
>
> 1. Not nearly enough exploration men know about and appreciate the significance of Mother Nature's basic SIZE pattern in distributing oil accumulations in the earth's crust.
> 2. Failure to grasp the significance of the size pattern results in undervaluation of the importance of the environment around the structure (or trap) as compared to the structure (trap) proper.

Deegan's pronouncement suggests that there may be a class of probability distributions which reasonably fit empirical frequency distributions of reported field sizes. If the functional form of this class is the same from province to province, varying only in the values of their parameters, the *sampling distribution* characterized by this form will be highly useful as a *data generating process model*. It will be explained why such models are important in the analysis of exploration decision problems, but first let us define what we mean by "sampling distribution" and by "data generating process model." In subsequent discussions it will be necessary to distinguish between conditional sampling and unconditional distributions, so we shall begin by defining them.

Definition of a Conditional Sampling Distribution. Imagine a random process which generates independent random variables $\tilde{x}_1, \ldots, \tilde{x}_i, \ldots$ with identical distribution functions $f(x \mid \theta)$, where θ is understood to be the parameter of the distribution functions. A sample of size n consists of performing n independent repetitions of the random experiment ϵ: Observe the value taken on by $\tilde{x}$. The composite experiment ϵ_n of performing n independent ϵ's gives rise to an n dimensional random variable $\tilde{z} = (\tilde{x}_1, \ldots, \tilde{x}_i, \ldots, \tilde{x}_n)$ such that z is the observed value of the sequence of n x's, each generated according to $f(x \mid \theta)$. The

---

[2]C. J. Deegan, "Incidence of Oil Occurrence," *Mines*, Petroleum Number for 1959, p. 127.

likelihood of z given θ is

$$f(z \mid \theta) = \prod_{i=1}^{n} f(x_i \mid \theta).$$

Since the distribution of $\tilde{z}$ is uniquely determined by $f(x \mid \theta)$, any number or statistic computed from $\tilde{z}$ has a distribution uniquely determined by $f(x \mid \theta)$. Let $\tilde{y} = h(\tilde{z})$ and let $f^*(y \mid \theta)$ be the likelihood function of y given θ. Then $f^*(y \mid \theta)$ is uniquely determined by $f(x \mid \theta)$ and is called the conditional sampling distribution of the statistic $\tilde{y} = h(\tilde{z})$:

$$\tilde{y} \mid \theta \sim f^*(y \mid \theta).$$

Definition of an Unconditional Distribution. By contrast, when θ is not known with certainty but is regarded as a random variable $\tilde{\theta}$ with range Θ and with a (subjective) probability density $g(\theta)$, we will talk about the unconditional distribution $\bar{f}^*(y)$ of $\tilde{y}$. Roughly speaking, the unconditional distribution of $\tilde{y}$ is the conditional sampling distribution $f^*(y \mid \tilde{\theta})$ "expected out" with respect to $\tilde{\theta}$:

$$\tilde{y} \sim \bar{f}^*(y) = E_\theta[f^*(y \mid \tilde{\theta})] = \int_\Theta f^*(y \mid \theta)g(\theta)d\theta. \qquad (6.0)$$

Definition of a Conditional Data Generating Process Model.
A conditional data generating process model is a conditional sampling distribution which is interpreted as a model of some real world random mechanism so that the sampling distribution may be used as a device for simulating data generated by the mechanism. As an example, consider a basin in which N fields have been discovered, and let the reported size of the ith field be represented by x_i, $1 \leq i \leq N$, $0 < x_i < \infty$. If we draw an empirical histogram of reported field sizes with class interval k, say, it might take the following form.

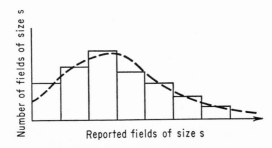

Suppose the dotted line is one member of a class of distribution functions $f(x \mid \theta)$. If we judge the fit of $f(x \mid \theta)$ to the data as excellent when $\theta = \theta'$, then given $f(x \mid \theta')$ and a table of random numbers, we can generate hypothetical x_i's whose relative frequency distribution will closely approximate that of the real x_i's providing N is large.

Definition of an Unconditional Data Generating Process Model. Suppose θ is not known with certainty but is regarded as a random variable $\tilde{\theta}$ with a (subjective) probability density $g(\theta)$. Let

$$J(x, \theta) = f(x \mid \theta)g(\theta).$$

Then $J(x, \theta)$ is the joint probability distribution function of $\tilde{x}$ and $\tilde{\theta}$, and it may be used to generate (x, θ) pairs. An unconditional data generating process model is a distribution such as $J(x, \theta)$ which is interpreted as a model of some real-world random mechanism so that it may be used as a device for simulating data generated by the mechanism.

In the application of this chapter it will be appropriate to visualize the generation of reported field sizes x_i, $i = 1, 2, \ldots$ as being done in two steps:

1. The unconditional distribution $g(\theta)$ of $\tilde{\theta}$ is used to generate a value θ.
2. The conditional sampling distribution $f(x_i \mid \theta)$ is used to generate a value of $\tilde{x}_i$.

Note that while $\tilde{x}_1, \tilde{x}_2, \ldots \mid \theta$ are mutually independent, identically distributed random variables distributed according to $f(x \mid \theta)$, $\tilde{x}_1$, $\tilde{x}_2, \ldots$ are identically distributed according to

$$\bar{f}(x) = E_\theta[f(x \mid \tilde{\theta})] = \int_\Theta f(x \mid \theta)g(\theta)d\theta$$

but are *not* in general independent.

As an example, suppose that an empirical histogram is drawn for each of a large number of well-developed basins. Using this historical data as a guide, a conditional data generating process model can be constructed for each basin. In general, it will not be possible to observe directly the true θ for each basin, but an estimate $\hat{\theta}$ of θ can be made and can be used for the parameter of the basin's conditional data generating process model.

Let there be M such basins, and denote the conditional data generating process model of the ith basin by $f(x \mid \hat{\theta}_i)$, $i = 1, 2, \ldots M$. In general, the value assumed by θ will vary from basin to basin. Just as for the x's within a given basin, an empirical histogram of the $\hat{\theta}$'s can be drawn which will give insight into the nature of the variability of θ.

If the number of basins M is large, and the number of observations on $\bar{x}$ within each of the basins is large, then the empirical histogram of $\hat{\theta}$ will be a useful qualitative aid in assessing a subjective probability distribution for the unknown θ of an unexplored basin with geological characteristics similar to those of the M basins used in constructing the histogram. If a geological evaluation of the unexplored basin together with consideration of the empirical histogram of $\hat{\theta}$'s leads the researcher to a subjective probability distribution such as $g(\theta)$, then the marginal distribution $\bar{f}(x)$ of $\bar{x}$ for the new basin can be found from (6.0).

Two reasons why the use of sampling distributions as data generating process models can be a fruitful aid in formulating exploration strategy immediately come to mind: first, when using simulation to test the economic effectiveness of a particular exploration strategy, the researcher's joint distribution over $\bar{x}$ and $\bar{\theta}$ can be made a part of the simulation model, infusing it in an explicit quantitative fashion with expert opinion about parameters which are not known with certainty. Second, if the conditional sampling distribution of $\bar{x}$ should prove to be analytically tractable, a limited number of exploration decision problems can be solved without resorting to simulation, e.g., the wildcat drilling problem solved in Section 7.3 of this monograph. This chapter demonstrates that there are two functional forms — Lognormal and Yule — which make reasonable conditional data generating process models of reported field sizes. These two functional forms were selected from among a wide variety of skew distribution functional forms because:

1. Each embodies a set of underlying assumptions which seem plausible when interpreted in real-world terms.

2. Empirical evidence justifies a Lognormal or Yule conditional sampling distribution of $\bar{x}$ with parameters which depend on the basin, or province.

Both points require considerable elaboration, and in fact we shall spend the rest of this chapter talking about them. In broad outline, the first point will be established by giving a probabilistic rationale for the fit of the Lognormal function form to empirical histograms of reported field sizes. (A similar rationale can be given for the Yule functional form, but it will not be given here.) The rationale sheds considerable light on the probabilistic mechanism underlying these empirical histograms. It will be shown to be in concordance with a theory of the geochemical process by which minerals are believed to be formed. The second point is established first by observing that one or the other of these two functional forms fits empirical histograms of reported field sizes well in the middle range of values and in the right tail and second, by noting that *the functional form of the frequency distribution of field sizes does not seem to change even over a wide range of values of field sizes:*

1. when it is noted that the ultimate recovery from a "young" field cannot be estimated as accurately as that from a long-time producer and that the data presented here are a mixture of "young" and "old" fields;

2. when comparisons are made between provinces where reserves have been estimated according to differing definitions of "estimated reserves";

3. when frequency distributions are compared as between a particular geological province and an arbitrary geographic area; e.g., the relative frequency distribution of field sizes in the Denver-Julesburg Basin versus the relative frequency distribution of fields of over one million barrels in the state of Oklahoma.

This invariance implies that one can use a given conditional data generating process model for many different areas, varying only the parameters of the model from one area to another. Such universality is highly desirable, for then an unconditional data generating process model of equally wide applicability can be constructed if the underlying conditional sampling distribution is analytically tractable.

In Chapter 7 we will show that the Lognormal distribution is particularly suited to interpretation as a data generating process model because it possesses nice analytical properties. These properties will be exploited in solving a wildcat drilling decision problem in which the operator has a nonlinear utility-in-money curve. However, in this chapter, we will restrict discussion to the probability mechanism which generates reported field sizes.

In Section 6.1 we shall briefly review the literature on the Yule and Lognormal distribution functions, with particular reference to the use of the latter in estimating the value of metallic mineral deposits and to the work of Arps and Roberts on reserve data from the Denver-Julesburg Basin. We shall also call attention to other functional forms which may prove useful for our purposes, notably distribution functions (such as the Pareto) which belong to the class of "stable" probability laws defined in Section 6.1.3. This is followed in Section 6.2 by comments on empirical data and on the method by which the Yule and Lognormal functional forms are fitted to the data. Section 6.3 is devoted to a derivation of the Lognormal functional form from basic assumptions about the probabilistic nature of the discovery process.

6.1.   Review of the Literature of Some Skew Distribution Functions

6.1.1.   The Lognormal Distribution

The Lognormal distribution in its simplest form may be defined as the distribution of a variate whose logarithm obeys the normal law of probability. . . .

We may indeed go further and state our belief that the Lognormal is as fundamental a distribution in statistics as is the normal, despite the stigma of the derivative nature of its name. It arises from a theory of elementary errors combined by a multiplicative process, just as the normal distribution arises from a theory of elementary errors combined by addition.[3]

This quotation is from a monograph by J. Aitchison and J. A. C. Brown entitled *The Lognormal Distribution* — undoubtedly the most complete coverage to date of the properties and applications of the distribution. The interested reader will find on pages 146–153 a reference list of two hundred and seventeen articles, monographs, and books dealing with aspects of the Lognormal distribution! A sample of the wide variety of observed frequency distributions that can be reasonably fitted with some form of Lognormal distribution includes the frequency distribution of:

sedimentary particles by diameter,
income size,
bodyweights,
number of fungal spores on organisms,
households by number of resident persons,
ages of men and women at first marriage, and
the radical component of Chinese characters by
number of characters containing the radical.[4]

Further references to usages of the Lognormal distribution can be found in *Statistics of Extremes* by Gumbel.[5]

Of particular relevance to this study are three articles on the use of Lognormal theory in the valuation of mineral deposits:

---

[3]J. Aitchison and J. A. C. Brown, *The Lognormal Distribution* (Cambridge: Cambridge University Press, 1957), pp. 1–2.

[4]*Ibid.*, pp. 20–27.

[5]E. J. Gumbel, *Statistics of Extremes* (New York: Columbia University Press, 1958), pp. 16–19.

1. D. G. Krige, "A Statistical Approach to some Basic Mine Valuation Problems on the Witwatersrand," *Journal of the Chemical, Metallurgical, and Mining Society of South Africa* (Johannesburg, December, 1951).

2. G. Matheron, "Application des Méthodes Statistiques à L'évaluation des Gisements," *Annales des Mines* (Paris, December, 1955).

3. M. Allais, "Method of Appraising Economic Prospects of Mining Exploration over Large Territories: Algerian Sahara Case Study," *Management Science* (Baltimore, July, 1957.)

Krige's paper applies Lognormal theory to the frequency distribution of gold values obtained in sampling a reef area on the Witwatersrand. The fit is astoundingly close. His opening comments are worth reviewing:

> The estimation of the tonnage and grade of payable ore in a mine and the correct policy of selective mining based on such estimates is of vital importance to the mining engineer. It is surprising, therefore, that more attention has not been devoted on the Witwatersrand to the scientific improvement of mine valuation methods. At present these methods consist almost entirely of the application of simple arithmetic and empirical formulae guided by practical experience and ignore the many advantages to be gained from a careful statistical analysis of the behavior of the gold values.

> The science of statistics has expanded rapidly during the last two decades and its value as a powerful and indispensable tool is now recognized not only by research workers and scientists but also, everincreasingly, by the commercial and industrial world. This being the case, it is noteworthy that in a mining field such as the Rand with its highly developed and advanced mining methods, singularly little attention has been paid to the analysis of mine valuation problems on a modern statistical basis. This omission is even more striking when cognizance is taken of the wealth of sampling data concerning the gold ore which is available and of the far-reaching decisions and deductions constantly being based on such data. . . .[6]

Krige's article is reproduced in full in the December, 1955, issue of *Annales des Mines*. The entire issue is devoted to the use of mathemati-

---

[6]D. G. Krige, *op. cit.*, p. 119.

cal statistics in estimating the value of mineral deposits. Matheron's article follows that of Krige; of special interest is Matheron's discussion of the law of proportionate effect as applied to the weight of a mineral deposit:

> Dans le cas d'un gisement on a bien l'intuition que le passage d'une teneur de 10% à une teneur de 11% est un phénomène equivalent au passage de 1% à 1.1%. M. Allais a remarqué que, dans ce cas particulier, la loi de l'effet proportionnel pouvait se rattacher à la physico-chimique d'Action de Masse. En effet, la genèse d'un gisement s'explique par un ensemble d'équilibres chimiques du type:
>
> $$\alpha A + \beta B = \gamma C + \delta D.$$
>
> Et la loi d'Action de Masse nous apprend que les variations des concentrations des différents constituants A, B, C, D, . . . sont liées par des relations du type:
>
> $$\alpha \frac{dA}{A} + \beta \frac{dB}{B} - \gamma \frac{dC}{C} - \delta \frac{dD}{D} = 0$$
>
> de sorte que l'élément différentiel significatif n'est pas dA mais dA/A.
>
> Toute variation fortuite d'une des concentrations se répercute sur toutes les autres suivant la loi de l'effet proportionnel.[7]

Matheron further remarks that it is not unreasonable to suppose that if the birth of a mineral deposit is explained by a chemical reaction of the linear type mentioned above, the frequency distribution of concentrations of the constituents entering such reactions should be Lognormal.

A conjecture of the same nature as Matheron's has been thoroughly investigated by a Soviet geologist, A. B. Vistelius, in a recent article in *The Journal of Geology*.[8] His work is an application of classical statistical techniques to the hypothesis that the frequency distribution of the concentrations of minor inorganic chemicals in rocks (11 minerals) has large positive skewness:

> . . . This skewness indicates that the deposition of small concentrations of the minor element by geochemical processes is, as a

---

[7]G. Matheron, *op. cit.*, p. 52.

[8]A. B. Vistelius, "The Skew Frequency Distributions and the Fundamental Law of the Geochemical Processes," *The Journal of Geology*, Vol. 68 No. 1 (January, 1960), pp. 1–23.

rule, more stable than the deposition of large concentrations of this element by the same geochemical process — the quantity of the deposited element in the form of large concentrations. It seems to us that prospecting and mining confirm our statements.[9]

While concluding that this skewness is in concordance with his conception of the fundamental law of the geochemical process, Vistelius states that, in his opinion, the data does not firmly establish the functional form of the frequency distribution.

Allais' article, first published in a special issue of the *Revue D'Industrie Minérale* (January, 1956) and then translated into English for presentation in *Management Science,* throws substantial light on the empirical frequency distribution of the value of mineral deposits of the world. The study was:

> . . . conceived as a part of a larger study in the field of operations research. Its purpose resides in the scientific detection of the best and economically optimal strategy to be used in prospecting for metal deposits in the Sahara.[10]

The published statistics considered only metalliferous and nonmetalliferous ores — fourteen of them. Allais' conclusion is that the Lognormal frequency distribution fits the distribution of values surprisingly well for most ores.

The ubiquitousness of the Lognormal frequency distribution in mining exploration would lead one to suspect that it might provide a good fit to data on the size distribution of oil and gas fields. In a very careful study of oil production in the Denver-Julesburg basin, J. J. Arps and T. G. Roberts divide 338 oil fields into fifteen groups according to their estimated average ultimate recoveries and then plot the relative frequencies on a log scale. Again a Lognormal frequency curve provides an excellent fit (see Graph 6.16). However, the authors state:

> It may be noted from graphical presentation of this "frequency-density" distribution . . . that it strongly resembles the typical bell-shaped normal Gaussian probability curve. Not too much significance should be attributed to its apparent symmetry, since obviously the physical reasons for the right- and left-hand slopes of this curve are quite different.

[9] *Ibid.,* p. 20.
[10] M. Allais, *op. cit.,* p. 289.

The diminishing number of fields with growing ultimates on the right-hand side of the mode are, as would be expected, the results of having fewer fields of larger size than of smaller size.

The tapering-off on the left-hand side of the mode, however, must be largely caused by economic factors. For instance, under 30,000 barrels ultimate per well it may become questionable whether an operator should run pipe at all, and many discoveries in this category which were found were probably never completed and therefore escape our statistics.[11]

The lack of information on discoveries of small size raises the question of whether a truncated or censored Lognormal curve might be more appropriately fitted to the data, or possibly even some *J*-shaped curve!

6.1.2.   The Yule Distribution. In one of a collection of essays entitled *Models of Man,* Herbert Simon analyzes:

> . . . a class of distribution functions that appears in a wide range of empirical data — particularly data describing sociological, biological, and economic phenomena. . . .
>
> The observed distributions have the following characteristics in common:
>
> (a) They are J-shaped, or at least highly skewed, with very long upper tails. The tails can generally be approximated closely by a function of the form
>
> $$f(i) = \left(\frac{a}{i^k}\right)b^i.$$
>
> where a, b, and k are constants; and where b is so close to unity that in first approximation the final factor has a significant effect on $f(i)$ only for very large values of i. . . .
>
> (b) The exponent k is greater than 1, and in the cases of word frequencies, publication, and urban populations is very close to 2.
>
> (c) In the cases of word frequencies, publications and biological

---

[11]J. J. Arps and T. G. Roberts, "Economics of Drilling for Cretaceous Oil Production on the East Flank of the Denver-Julesburg Basin"; unpublished paper (April 3, 1958), p. 10.

genera, the function [above] describes the distribution not merely in the tail but also for small values of i.[12]

In particular, Simon shows that this class of distribution functions, which he calls the "Yule distribution" after J. Udny Yule, nicely fits the distributions of:

words in prose samples by frequency occurrence,
scientists by number of papers published,
cities by population,
incomes by size, and
biological genera by number of species.

The literature on this particular distribution is not very wide, consisting primarily of applications in the biological sciences and in the study of the statistical structure of language. Some references to discussions of the Yule and associated distributions are offered on page 164 of *Models of Man*.

The fact that the Yule distribution is J-shaped with a long right tail and is defined for only positive values of the attribute being analyzed is of particular interest, for it offers a way of accounting for the conjecture that there are a great many discoveries of small size which go unrecorded. This point will be explored in more detail in Section 6.2.

6.1.3.   *The Pareto Distribution and Stable Probability Laws.*
The Pareto distribution is named after the Italian economist Vilfredo Pareto who discovered that if personal incomes are ranked by size, the proportion of incomes which exceed some positive number i_0 behaves like

$$\left(\frac{i}{i_0}\right)^{-p},$$

where p is a constant greater than zero, as i gets very large.

A vast literature on the use of the Pareto distribution in income analysis exists. Two good introductory articles are:

D. H. MacGregor, "Pareto's Law," *Economic Journal* (March, 1946);

E. C. Rhodes, "The Pareto Distribution of Income," *Economica* (February, 1944).

A mathematical anlysis of the attributes of the Yule distribution reveals that its functional form asymptotically approaches that of the

---

[12]H. Simon, *Models of Man* (New York: John Wiley & Sons, Inc., 1957), pp. 145–146.

Pareto distribution in the right tail. It differs from the Pareto distribution for values of i close to i_0 but maintains the same general form. It is this family resemblance which leads to consideration of the Pareto distribution as a candidate for fitting frequency distributions of oil fields by size.

Recently, Mandelbrot[13] has called attention to a wide class of distribution functions with members that serve well as stochastic models of the size distribution of income. This class is called the class of *stable* probability laws.[14]

Mandelbrot suggests that this class of probability laws is based on assumptions which lead to realistic models of the size distribution of income and furthermore that some members of this class fit income histograms better than distributions (such as the Lognormal) based on the "law of proportionate effect." Unfortunately, with the exception of the (strong) Pareto distribution defined at the outset of this section, nonnormal members of this class have intractable probability density functions.

Since, as we will show subsequently, the Lognormal distribution fits frequency histograms of the oil and gas fields by size to a degree that would make any further refinement of second order importance given the nature of the data with which we are working[15] and since it has the vital

---

[13]B. Mandelbrot, *The Pareto-Levy Random Functions and the Multiplicative Variation of Income* (Yorktown Heights, New York: I.B.M. Research Center Report, October, 1960).

[14]See B. V. Gnedenko and A. N. Kolmogorov, *Limit Distributions for Sums of Independent Random Variables*, Translated by K. L. Chung (Cambridge, Mass.: Addison-Wesley Publishing Co., 1954), Chapter 7. It arises as the solution to a problem which occurs naturally in the investigation of limit distributions of normalized sums of independent, identically distributed random variables: what is the widest class of *all possible* limit distributions of such sums? In order for a distribution function $F(x)$ to be such a limit distribution it is necessary and sufficient that it be *stable* in the sense that for constants $a_1 > 0$, $a_2 > 0$, b, and b_2, and for all x in the domain of F $(\cdot)$, there exist constants such that the convolution $F(a_1 x + b_1) * F(a_2 x + b_2) = F(ax + b)$. Hence the terminology *"stable law."*

[15]In an article on the size distribution of some geological attributes of minerals, "Distribution Lognormale de Certains Caractères de Quelques Phénomènes Géologiques et ses Applications," *Revue de Statistique Appliquée*, Vol. IX, No. 2 (Paris, 1961), p. 41, J. Y. Thebault points out that from a practical point of view, difficulties of measurement introduce enough error to invalidate the use of standard statistical tests such as the χ^2 test as a basis for accepting or rejecting Lognormality:

Mais, du point de vue pratique et appliqué, le seul qui m'intéresse ici, le rejet de la lognormalité mathématique est peu important, la sensibilité du test χ^2 est si grande qu'elle peut amener au rejet d'une distribution réellement lognormale mais où les difficultés des mesures et d'échantillonnages ont introduit des erreurs suffisantes pour faire rejeter la lognormalité.

virtue of being analytically tractable, we shall not investigate Pareto-Levy distribution functions here.

6.2.   Discussion of Empirical Data on Field Sizes

In the preceding section it was stated that a probability distribution function should be used as a conditional data generating process model of reported field sizes only if it is a good fit to empirical histograms of reported field sizes. An examination of data on oil and gas field reserves reveals that, for any given geological province or geographic area, the relative frequency histogram of reported field sizes has two basic properties:

1. It is defined only for positive values of the variate, reported field size.

2. It is highly skewed with a long right tail.

With proper choice of parameters the Yule, the Lognormal, and the Pareto distributions all possess these general properties. Graphs 6.1 to 6.16 (described in detail in Sections 6.2.1 and 6.2.2) indicate that both the Lognormal and the Yule distribution functions are good first approximations to empirical relative frequency distributions of reported field sizes. The Lognormal fits especially well in the middle range of values. In five of sixteen graphs the Yule distribution improves upon the Lognormal in the extreme right tail. (Graphs 6.1, 6.4, 6.6, 6.7, and 6.9). The Pareto distribution cannot be made to fit well.

6.2.1.   Sources of Data and Design of Data Presentation.
Exhibit 6.1 lists the sources of data in and the title of each graph. The graphs are grouped according to definition of reserves, range of field size reported, time of reporting, and type of area over which reserves are reported. Each group is homogeneous in these four respects, but there are wide differences between groups. In Exhibit 6.2 the aforementioned attributes are summarized for easy intergroup comparison.

These intergroup variations are introduced intentionally, as there are practical reasons for investigating their effect on the frequency distributions of field sizes. For example, the time of reporting influences reserve estimates in two ways. First, methods of production improve over time, so that recoverable reserves estimates based on, say, 1946 primary production methods may be substantially below those based on 1960 methods. Second, reserve estimates made in the early stages of exploration of a basin must usually be revised as it reaches maturity, as more knowledge about the basin accrues. The definition of "reserves" used has obvious significance — ultimate primary recoverable reserves in a field which has been producing for ten years may be many times the estimated *remaining* primary recoverable reserves, or, estimated remaining recoverable reserves if secondary recovery is taken into account.

However, suppose the functional form of the distribution function which best fits the empirical data remains invariant under wide variations in the definition of reserves and the type of area covered by the data. Then, as stated earlier, the operator will have a conditional data generating process model of wide applicability, which can be used in many different areas, changing only the model's parameters from area to area.

To test this invariancy informally, data from four different sources was selected — The Oil and Gas Conservation Board of Alberta Report to the Lieutenant-Governor-in-Council as summarized in *The Financial Post; Oil and Gas Journal* statistics on two states for 1946 and for 1960; an individual company's estimates of reserves in four basins; and the Arps-Roberts article on the Denver-Julesburg Basin. The graphs displaying this data tentatively suggest that:

1. Within a given area the functional form of empirical histograms of reported field sizes does *not* change
   (a) over time,
   (b) with changes in the definition of "reserves,"
   (c) with changes in the minimum size of field reported, or
   (d) from one geographic area to another.

2. The functional form is the same for a well-defined geological basin such as the Denver-Julesburg as for an arbitrary geographic area such as a state.

Although each of Graphs 6.1 through 6.16 is a plot of data from fields of varying geological ages and of varying length of production lives, the invariance in the functional forms is striking enough to warrant the conjecture that added data blocked on these two factors would not alter the conclusions stated above.

6.2.2. Methods of Plotting Data and of Curve Fitting.

Given a sample of reported field sizes $s_1, s_2, \ldots, s_n$ from an oil and gas province, can we assume that the population from which it was drawn is

Lognormal?   Yule?   Pareto?

With this question in mind, the data on reported field sizes were plotted on logarithmic probability paper.[16]

1. The data from each area were listed in order of size, smallest to largest, as in Exhibit 6.3, Column 1.

2. Fractile estimates were computed by considering the kth largest observation as an estimate of the $(k/n + 1)$st fractile of the underlying distribution, given n sample observations. (Exhibit 6.3, Column 2.)

3. These fractile estimates were then plotted on three cycle logarithmic probability paper. The vertical scale denotes barrels of reserves or MCF of reserves, depending on whether oil or gas reserves are being plotted. The horizontal scale on top of the graph denotes per cent of the number of observations less than or equal to the value on the vertical scale paired with that per cent; e.g., on Graph 6.1, 57 per cent of the observations are either equal to or less than 52×10^9. Since 52×10^9 is equal to or greater than a fraction .57 of the values of the arrayed observations and equal to or less than a fraction .43 of the arrayed observations, 52×10^9 is a .57 fractile estimate.

4. A straight line was visually fitted to the data.

If the sample observations are from a Lognormal population, then the plotted points should lie approximately on a straight line. The larger the number of sample observations and the closer the fit to a straight line, the more reasonable the assumption of Lognormality becomes.

In those cases where there seemed to be a substantial departure from the Lognormal in the right tail, the Yule distribution was fitted by manipulating this distribution's two parameters, a class interval and a free parameter ρ, by trial and error.

1. A class interval was chosen. (Exhibit 6.4, Column 1.)

2. The midpoint of each class interval was calculated. (Exhibit 6.4, Column 2.)

3. A particular value of ρ was chosen.

4. The Yule probability mass function

$$\rho\beta(s, \rho + 1) = \rho\frac{\Gamma(s + \rho + 1)}{\Gamma(s)\Gamma(\rho + 1)} = \frac{s + \rho!}{s - 1! \, \rho - 1!}$$

---

[16]J. Aitchison and J. A. C. Brown, *op. cit.*, present a detailed discussion of the theory and characteristics of this paper on pp. 31–36.

was used to calculate the probability weight to assign to each class. (Exhibit 6.4, Column 3.)

5. The class probabilities were cumulated and interpreted as fractile estimates. (Exhibit 6.4, Column 4.)

The value of ρ that gave a good fit differed from 1.0000 only in the third decimal place, so to facilitate calculations, ρ was rounded to two decimal places in all except Graph 6.1.

The Pareto could not be made to fit as well as either the Yule or the Lognormal distributions. Graph 6.1 illustrates the nature of the difficulty. When the Pareto is made to fit the data in the extreme right tail, it is an extremely poor fit for the middle and lower range of values of the data. (Pareto Curve B in 6.1.) When it is fitted at two widely separated points (as described below), it does not behave well in the middle range of values. This latter fit was achieved by

1. Choosing two widely separated points, u_1 and u_2 on the reported field size scale. For Graph 6.1, $u_1 = 5$ and $u_2 = 750$. The fractile estimates are such that u_1 is approximately at the .065 fractile estimate and u_2 is approximately at the .920 fractile estimate.

2. Noting that the cumulative right tail probability for a Pareto distribution function is

$$P(\tilde{u} > u \mid u_0, \rho) = \left(\frac{u}{u_0}\right)^{-\rho},$$

the following substitutions were made:

$$P(\tilde{u} > 5 \mid \hat{u}_0, \hat{\rho}) = \left(\frac{5}{u_0}\right)^{-\hat{\rho}} = (1 - .065),$$

$$P(\tilde{u} > 750 \mid \hat{u}_0, \hat{\rho}) = \left(\frac{760}{u_0}\right)^{-\hat{\rho}} = (1 - .920),$$

where $\hat{u}_0$ and $\hat{\rho}$ denote estimates of u_0 and of ρ.

3. Taking logs on both sides of the equations above gives

$$-\hat{\rho}(\log 5 - \log \hat{u}_0) = \log .935,$$
$$-\hat{\rho}(\log 750 - \log \hat{u}_0) = \log .080.$$

4. Solving these two linear equations for $\hat{u}_0$ and for $\hat{\rho}$ gives

$$\hat{u}_0 = .491 \quad \text{and} \quad \hat{\rho} = 4.36.$$

5. These values of the parameters were used to fit Pareto curve A.

In most instances the curve fit is good enough to obviate the need for more sophisticated analysis. In the writer's opinion, the graphical methods cited above are quite adequate for determining to a first approximation whether or not the functional forms of the Yule and Lognormal distributions can be reasonably used as conditional data generating process models of reported field sizes.[17] The Lognormal functional form seems to fit better in at least eleven of the sixteen graphs and hence has been given more attention in the succeeding pages. Although there may be some questions as to the adequacy of a Lognormal fit in a graph such as 6.1, Alberta's Established Gas Reserves, there is little doubt that the fit in 6.13, Total Ultimate Reserves in South Louisiana Fields, is excellent. The slight upward curvature away from the Lognormal line for small values of s on several of the graphs (e.g., Graph 6.4, Ultimate Primary Reserves in Basin III) can be explained by Arps and Roberts' comment:

> Fields of small size may not be reported because in many cases pipe may not be set on wells drilled on economically marginal fields, hence they are not recorded as producing fields.

Or, some smaller fields may just be omitted from the report:

> Nearly 98% of all new-field wildcats drilled are failures in that they are abandoned as dry or they discover reserves too small, on the average, to be profitable.[18]

In fact, one would suspect a downward curvature if many small fields were included in the sample. The Yule distribution can account nicely for this curvature. (See Graphs 6.2 and 6.9.)

Another observation that can be made about the data is that the fractile plots often show sharp discontinuities; e.g., Graph 6.15, Total Ultimate Primary Reserves in Oklahoma Fields, at the .71 fractile estimate. Two facts which account for this are, first, the reported data has usually been rounded to tens of thousands or even millions of barrels, and, second, field sizes reported represent a finite sample of reserve values measured on a continuous scale. The rounding tends to throw a particular field size either up or down in reported value depending on the rounding rule, so there is a discontinuity introduced by rounding. A

---

[17]See J. Y. Thebault, *op. cit.*

[18]*National Oil Scouts and Landmen's Yearbook — Review of 1957*, Vol. XXVIII (Austin, Texas: National Scouts and Landmen's Association, 1958), p. 1106.

major discontinuity such as that cited above simply means that fields of a size between the lower and upper values of the discontinuity did not happen to occur in the particular sample plotted. Such a field size might well show up in a larger sample at some future date.

Exhibit 6.1.

Group	Graph	Title	Source
A	6.1	Alberta's Established Gas Reserves as of 1959.	*The Financial Post*, Vol. XV (Toronto: McLean-Hunter Pub. Co., Ltd., 1959), pp. 91–93.
	6.2	Ultimate Primary Reserves in Coastal Basin I	
B	6.3	Ultimate Primary Reserves in Coastal Basin II	Confidential
	6.4	Ultimate Primary Reserves in Coastal Basin III	
	6.5	Ultimate Primary Reserves in Coastal Basin IV	
	6.6	Estimated Remaining Proven Reserves in All Louisiana Fields of 10^6 Bbls. Ultimate or More as of January, 1946	
	6.7	Estimated Remaining Proven Reserves in South Louisiana Fields of 10^6 Bbls. Ultimate or More as of January, 1946	*Oil and Gas Journal, Annual Number*, Vol. 44, No. 48 (January, 1946), pp. 209–210.
C	6.8	Estimated Remaining Proven Reserves in North Louisiana Fields of 10^6 Bbls. Ultimate or More as of January, 1946	
	6.9	Estimated Remaining Proven Reserves in Oklahoma Fields of 10^6 Bbls. Ultimate or More as of January, 1946	
	6.10	Total Ultimate Proven Reserves in South Louisiana Fields of 10^6 Bbls. or more as of January, 1946	
D	6.11	Total Ultimate Proven Reserves in North Louisiana Fields of 10^6 Bbls. or more as of January, 1946	*Oil and Gas Journal, Annual Number*, Vol. 44, No. 48 (January, 1946), pp. 209–210.
	6.12	Total Ultimate Proven Reserves in Oklahoma Fields of 10^6 Bbls. or More as of January, 1946	

6.13   Total Ultimate Primary Reserves in South Louisiana Onshore Fields with Production of at least 1000 Bbls. per Calendar Day in 1959

E   6.14   Total Ultimate Primary Reserves in North Louisiana Fields with Production of at least 1000 Bbls. per Calendar Day in 1959   *Oil and Gas Journal,* Annual Review Issue, Vol. 58, No. 4 (January 25, 1960), pp. 163–164.

6.15   Total Ultimate Primary Reserves in Oklahoma Fields with Production of at least 1000 Bbls. per Calendar Day in 1959

F   6.16   Estimated Primary Ultimate Oil Recovery from Cretaceous Fields in the Denver-Julesburg Basin as of 1958   *Economics of Drilling for Cretaceous Oil Production on the East Flank of the Denver-Julesburg Basin,* unpublished paper (April 3, 1958). J. J. Arps and T. G. Roberts.

Exhibit 6.2.

Group	Time of Reporting	Range of Field Size Reported	Definition of Reserves Used	Area Covered: Geographically Delineated? Politico-Geographic Delineation?
A	1959	Fields with estimated original gas in place of 10⁹ cubic feet or more.	"Established gas reserves": The original gas in place . . . Reservoir loss is calculated as 10% of the original gas in place except in particular cases where the following losses pertain: sand thickness of 10–15 feet, reservoir loss of 15%; sand thickness of 5–10 feet, reservoir loss of 25%.[a]	The Canadian Province of Alberta
B	Jan. 1957	Fields with ultimate primary reserves of 4×10^6 bbls. or more.	"Ultimate primary reserves": Reserves recoverable by known production methods excluding estimates of oil that can be produced by secondary recovery techniques.	A geological basin
C	Jan. 1946	Fields with estimated ultimate reserves of 10^6 bbls. or more.	"Remaining proven oil reserves": "The term 'proven reserves' is used in the narrow sense in all these estimates. The figures certainly do not include any 'potential reserves,' although there are many cases where it is almost certain that ultimately a great deal more oil will be found and produced than is given in the figures this year."[b] "Estimated remaining proven reserves" include only those oils that can reasonably be expected to be ultimately recovered by known production methods.[c]	The states of Louisiana and Oklahoma

Group	Time of Reporting	Range of Field Size Reported	Definition of Reserves Used	Area Covered: Geographically Delineated? Politico-Geographic Delineation?
			The total ultimate proven reserve figure for a field is the sum of (cumulative production to date) + (estimated remaining proven reserves).	
D	Jan. 1946	Fields with estimated ultimate reserves of 10^6 bbls. or more.	"Estimated remaining proven reserves": as defined for group C.	The states of Louisiana and Oklahoma.
E	Jan. 1960	Fields with production of at least 1000 bbls. per calendar day in 1959. "Those major fields with an ultimate recovery estimate of 100 million bbls. or more . . . are included here regardless of daily production today . . ."	"Total ultimate primary reserves": "Figures in these tables . . . refer to primary recovery only."[c]	The states of Louisiana and Oklahoma
F	1958		"Estimated primary ultimate oil recovery": "All fields producing from formations other than the lower cretaceous were excluded from the study . . . the analysis was further simplified by elimination of the gas-producing fields."[d]	East flank of the Denver-Julesburg Basin

[a] *The Financial Post*, Vol. XV (Toronto: McLean-Hunter Publishing Co., Ltd., 1959), p. 93.
[b] *Oil and Gas Journal*, Annual Number, Vol. 44, No. 48 (26 January 1946), pp. 178–179.
[c] *Ibid.*, Annual Review Issue, Vol. 58, No. 4 (25 January 1960), p. 163.
[d] J. Arps and T. G. Roberts, *op. cit.*, p. 10.

Exhibit 6.3.

TOTAL ULTIMATE PROVEN RESERVES IN NORTH LOUISIANA FIELDS OF 10^6 BARRELS
OR MORE AS OF JANUARY, 1946.

(Graph 6.11)

1 Field Size in (bbls. $\times 10^6$)	2 Fractile Estimate[a]
1	.0385
2	.0769
3	.1154
3	.1538
5	.1923
5	.2308
7	.2692
9	.3077
10	.3462
14	.3846
15	.4231
16	.4615
17	.5000
17	.5385
30	.5769
35	.6154
35	.6538
45	.6923
50	.7308
65	.7692
85	.8077
85	.8462
105	.8846
124	.9231
200	.9615

[a]There are 25 observations so that the kth largest observation is an estimate of the $(k/26)$th fractile.

Exhibit 6.4.

CALCULATIONS FOR THE YULE DISTRIBUTION FITTED TO THE DATA OF GRAPH 6.1, GIVEN
$\rho = 1.0000$

	1	2	3	4
s	Class Interval[a]	Midpoint	$\rho\beta(s, \rho + 1)$	$\rho\sum_{i=1}^{s} \beta\,(i, \rho + 1)$
1	20–80	50	.5000	.5000
2	80–140	110	.1667	.6667
3	140–200	170	.0833	.7500
4	200–260	230	.0500	.8000
5	260–320	290	.0333	.8333
6	320–380	350	.0238	.8571
7	380–440	410	.0178	.8749
8	440–500	470	.0138	.8887
9	500–560	530	.0111	.8998
10	560–620	590	.0091	.9089
11	620–680	650	.0076	.9165
12	680–740	710	.0064	.9229
13	740–800	770	.0055	.9284
14	800–860	830	.0048	.9332
15	860–920	890	.0042	.9374
16	920–980	950	.0037	.9411
17	980–1040	1010	.0033	.9444
18	1040–1100	1070	.0029	.9473
19	1100–1160	1130	.0026	.9499
20	1160–1220	1190	.0024	.9523
21	1220–1280	1250	.0022	.9545
22	1280–1340	1310	.0020	.9565
23	1340–1400	1370	.0018	.9583

[a]A field belongs to class "s" if its size is greater than the lower bound on s and less than or equal to the upper bound; e.g., a field of size 140 belongs to the class $s = 2$.

6.3. Stochastic Models of the Discovery Process

The validity of using a particular functional form in constructing a data generating process model of reported field sizes is strengthened if, in addition to showing that it provides a good fit to empirical histograms, a probabilistic rationale can be given for this fit. To this end the Yule and the Lognormal distribution functions can be derived from certain assumptions about the probabilistic nature of the discovery process. (A rationale for both should be given because the Yule functional form was found to fit better in five of sixteen graphs described in the preceding section.) These assumptions do *not* describe the actual exploration

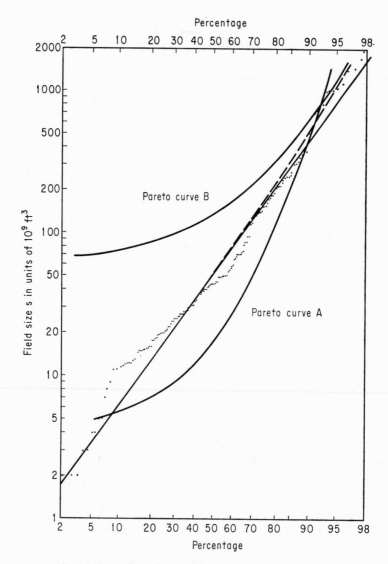

Graph 6.1. Alberta's established gas reserves as of 1959

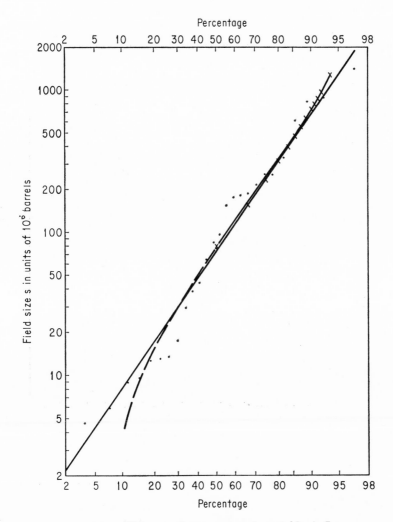

Graph 6.2. Ultimate primary reserves in costal basin I

process by which operators discover oil, but they do characterize two abstract stochastic processes which are mathematical models of how the long-run frequency distribution of reported field sizes builds up.

Although the assumptions of a probabilistic model must grossly simplify the real-world discovery process if the model is to be analytically manageable, we will show that most of the assumptions underlying the Lognormal models can be easily interpreted and that they are consistent in a common sense fashion with the real-world discovery process. At the

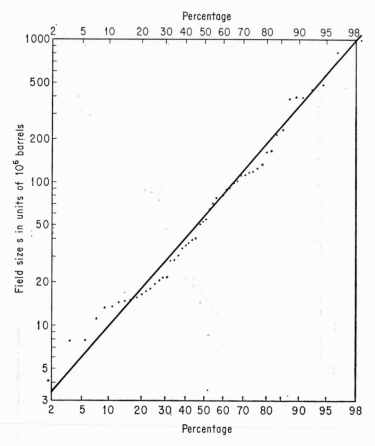

Graph 6.3. Ultimate primary reserves in costal basin II

same time we will point out some of the simplifications inherent in these assumptions.

The random process underlying a Lognormal model is essentially multiplicative rather than additive in nature, one in which the Law of Proportionate Effect holds sway:

> A variate subject to a process of change is said to obey the Law of Proportionate Effect if the change in the variate at any step of the process is a random proportion of the previous value of the variate.[19]

---

[19]J. Aitchison and J. A. C. Brown, *op. cit.* p. 22.

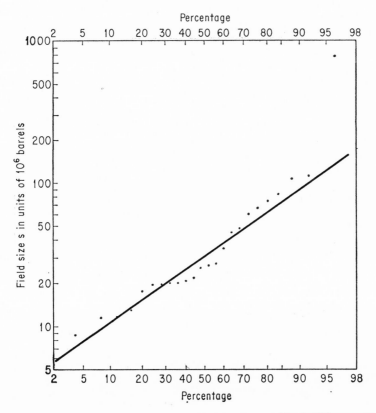

Graph 6.4. Ultimate primary reserves in costal basin III

In this section we will make the meaning of this statement more precise by example, showing that

1. a set of assumptions about the discovery process incorporating the Law of Proportionate Effect leads to a stochastic difference equation whose solution (in a sense to be defined later) is a Lognormal distribution function of the random variable, "reported field size,"

and demonstrating

2. that these assumptions are compatible with a model of the genesis of an individual field based on a connection between the Law of Proportionate Effect and a conception of the geochemical process by which mineral deposits are created.

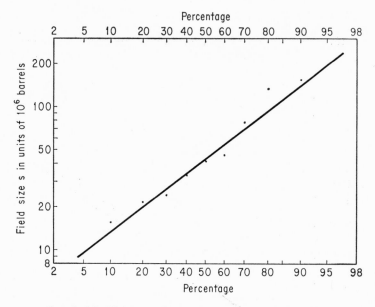

Graph 6.5. Ultimate primary reserves in costal basin IV

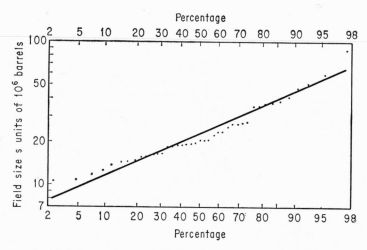

Graph 6.6. Estimated remaining proven reserves in all Louisiana fields of 10^6 bbls. ultimate or more as of January 1946

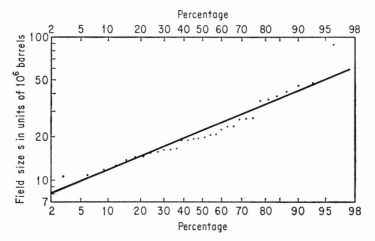

Graph 6.7. Estimated remaining proven reserves in south Louisiana fields of 10^6 bbls. ultimate or more as of January 1946

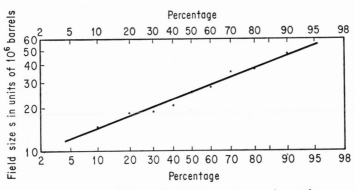

Graph 6.8. Estimated remaining proven reserves in northern Louisiana fields of 10^6 bbls. ultimate or more as of January 1946

The mathematics of the following approach is typical of that used by many authors.[20]

6.3.1. A Model of the Genesis of an Individual Field. If the Law of Proportionate Effect plays a major role in the geochemical process by which hydrocarbon deposits are formed, then a simple model of the

---

[20]Cf. *ibid.*, pp. 22–23.

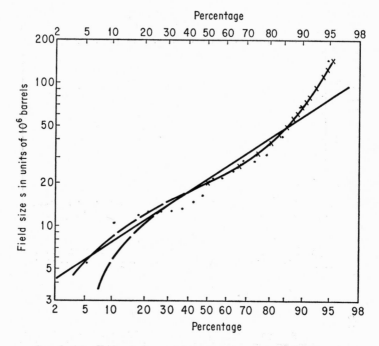

Graph 6.9. Estimated remaining proven reserves in Oklahoma fields of 10^6 or more as of January 1946

process can be built. The basic idea of this model is that as time passes, a deposit undergoes a series of chemical reactions, or "shocks," which cause it to behave as if it were growing in size from one time period to another.

Let the history of a particular field be divided into $n + 1$ discrete nonoverlapping time periods. Define the random variables

$\tilde{s}_n$ = field size during time period n,

$\tilde{\delta}_n$ = per cent increase in field size from time period $n - 1$ to time period n.

Make three assumptions.

Assumption 1. The Law of Proportionate Effect. The increase in field size from time period $n - 1$ to time period n is a random proportion of the field's size at time $n - 1$; i.e.,

$$\tilde{s}_n - \tilde{s}_{n-1} = \tilde{\delta}_n \tilde{s}_{n-1}. \tag{6.1}$$

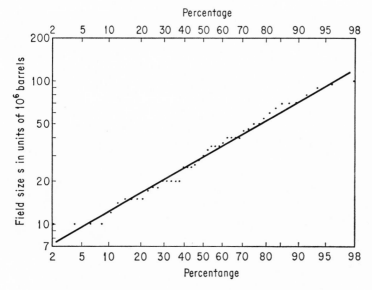

Graph 6.10. Total ultimate proven reserves in south Louisiana fields of 10^6 bbls. or more as of January 1946

Assumption 2: The set of random variables $\{\tilde{\delta}_n\}$ are mutually independent, identically distributed, and $\tilde{\delta}_n > 0$.

Assumption 3: Define $\tilde{\epsilon}_n = (1 + \tilde{\delta}_n)$, and $E(\log \tilde{\epsilon}_n) = \mu$ and $\mathrm{Var}(\log \tilde{\epsilon}_n) = \sigma^2$. Both μ and σ^2 exist.

From Assumption 1,

$$\tilde{s}_n = (1 + \tilde{\delta}_n)\tilde{s}_{n-1}$$

$$= \tilde{s}_0 \prod_{j=1}^{n} \tilde{\epsilon}_j,$$

or

$$\log \tilde{s}_n = \log \tilde{s}_0 + \sum_{j=1}^{n} \log \tilde{\epsilon}_j.$$

Now a random variable $\tilde{y}$ is said to be Lognormally distributed if

$$P(\tilde{y} < y) = F_L(y \mid \mu, 1/\sigma^2) = \frac{1}{\sigma\sqrt{2\pi}} \int_0^y \exp[\tfrac{1}{2}(\log x - \mu/\sigma)^2] \frac{dx}{x}.$$

$$(6.2)$$

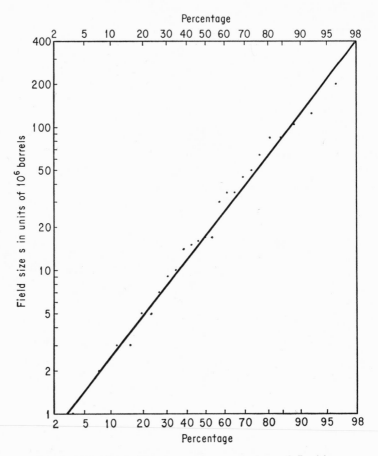

Graph 6.11. Total ultimate proven reserves in north Louisiana fields of 10^6 bbls. or more as of January 1946

As $n \to \infty$, $\bar{s}_n$ can be seen to be asymptotically Lognormally distributed by using Assumptions 2 and 3 together with the following form of the Central Limit Theorem.[17]

Theorem. If $\{\bar{\epsilon}_j\}$ is a sequence of independent, positive variates having the same probability distribution and such that

$$E(\log \bar{\epsilon}_j) = \mu \quad \text{and} \quad \text{Var} (\log \bar{\epsilon}_j) = \sigma^2$$

[17]J. Aitchison and J. A. C. Brown, *op. cit.*, p. 13.

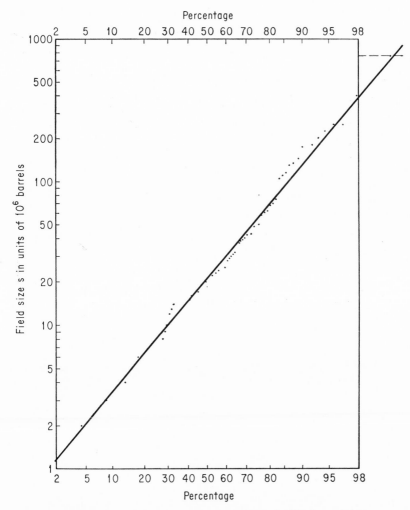

Graph 6.12. Total ultimate proven reserves in Oklahoma fields of 10^6 bbls. or more as of January 1946

both exist for $1 \leq j \leq n$, then the product

$$\prod_{j=1}^{n} \bar{\epsilon}_j$$

is asymptotically Lognormally distributed as

$$F_L\left(\cdot \mid \mu, \frac{1}{\sigma^2} \right)$$

when $n \to \infty$.

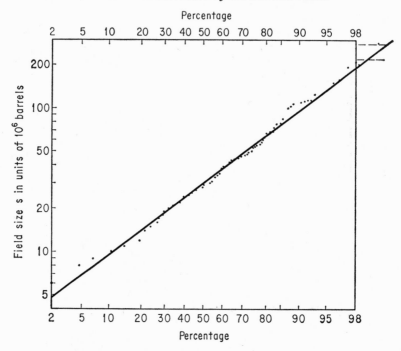

Graph 6.13. Total ultimate primary reserves in south Louisiana onshore fields with production of at least 1000 bbls. per calendar day in 1959

6.3.2. Two Models of the Empirical Aggregate of Oil and Gas Fields in a Sedimentary Basin.

In contrast to the purely physical model just presented, we will now construct two models of the exploration history of a generic basin in the single most important dimension of the output of the discovery process:[22] reported field size. In this dimension the basin's history can be portrayed by a sequence of empirical histograms of reported field sizes. Since this sequence is strongly influenced by the kinds of exploration programs undertaken in the basin, we will stress some aspects of the discovery process not accented in Chapter 2:

1. At some prehistoric time nature caused petroleum to be created in deposits of varying sizes throughout the sedimentary basins of the world.

---

[22]The discovery process is the process of conducting reconnaissance and advanced exploration surveys, drilling wells, and reporting an estimate of the amount of oil or gas discovered.

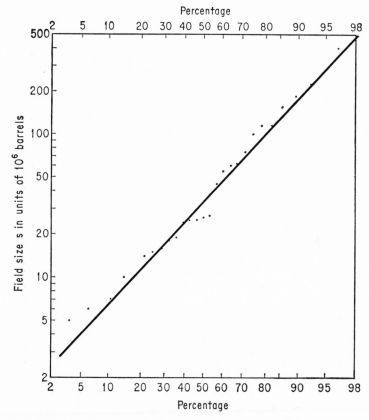

Graph 6.14. Total ultimate primary reserves in north Louisiana fields with production of at least 1000 bbls. per calendar day in 1959

2. Eons later, oilmen enter a basin, explore it, and drill wells which discover oil and gas deposits.

3. After each discovery an estimate of the amount of oil or gas discovered is made. This estimate is highly subject to error, especially before substantial production experience with the discovery accrues.

4. As the discovery process continues, an aggregate of fields discovered in the basin builds up.

5. As time passes, new fields are discovered and production experience with older fields accumulates. On the basis of this experience geologists and reservoir engineers may decide to alter their original

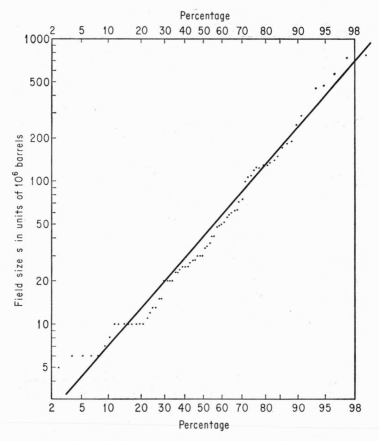

Graph 6.15. Total ultimate primary reserves in Oklahoma fields with production of at least 1000 bbls. per calendar day in 1959

estimates of the size of an older field. This is especially true if new wells have been drilled in or near a field which substantially change the geologists' original conception of the field.

Even as viewed in the single dimension of reported field size, the discovery process is a dynamic one, for substantial feedback of new information modifies the empirical histogram of reported data as time passes. By comparison with nature's true underlying distribution of petroleum deposits in the earth's crust, this histogram is highly contaminated with human error — it does not stem from a purely physical process.

The manager of Carter Oil Company's economics department stresses the practical importance of viewing the reporting of reserve estimates as

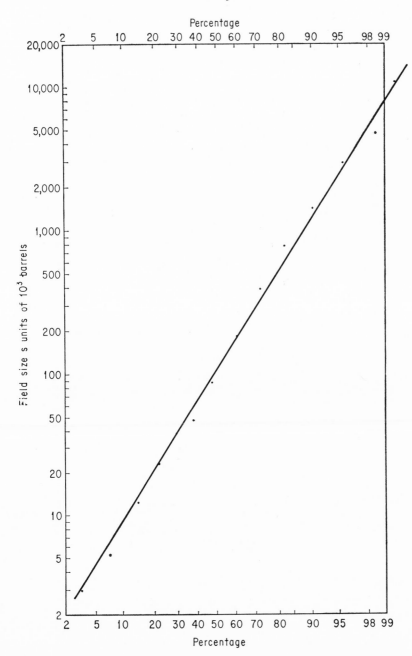

Graph 6.16. Estimated primary ultimate oil recovery from cretaceous fields in the Denver-Julesburg basin as of 1958

a dynamic feedback process in an article which describes how his company deals with reporting bias of their reserve estimating group:

> Every company searching for crude-oil reserves is constantly faced with the problem of evaluating its exploration program. The efficiency of a program can best be measured by relating exploration expenditures to the barrels of oil found. Usually the dollars can be determined or estimated, but the barrels of oil discovered by these expenditures are difficult to establish. The industry does not immediately know the size of its discoveries; there is a definite time lag before the adequate valuation of reserves can be made. Thus the true results of current exploration are not known. Unfortunately, oil men must make decisions involving large financial risks before they know all of the facts. The techniques for adjusting reserves described in this article are aimed at improving the evaluation of exploration programs much earlier.

> The most widely accepted published estimates of oil found by current wildcats are the initial estimates of discoveries by the API. These data have limitations. Initially, the estimates are conservative but more important, it is not possible to follow changes in a given year's discoveries or to trace their growth. Each year subsequent changes in the estimates of a particular year's reserves are lumped with discoveries of other years as they are extended and revised. The industry needs a system which will:

> 1. Isolate reserve estimates, grouping them by year of discovery.

> 2. Allocate each reserve change back to the year of discovery.

> 3. Adjust current estimates for future revisions.

> Such a system was developed in the mid-1950's for use with Carter's industry reserve statistics; it has been in use for over ten years and has given a realistic measure of the results of each year's exploration effort. This system follows the reservoirs discovered each year and provides for statistically adjusting current estimates for future revisions; the result is a probable final estimate for each year's discoveries. . . .

> Experience has shown that reserve changes are usually upward. For the first two or three years after a reservoir is discovered,

there will be both upward and downward revisions but the trend is usually upward.

The amount of growth is a function of knowledge and size of the virgin reservoir. The greater the knowledge of a new reservoir, the more accurate will be the initial estimate. Large fields normally have greater increases percentagewise than small fields. The philosophy of the estimating group affects also the rate of revision. If a conservative policy is followed in booking unproven reserves, the future changes in reserves obviously will be higher than for a more optimistic estimating group. Regardless of the factors affecting it, growth is normal although the amount varies from area to area and with various estimating groups.[23]

The first step in Carter's method is to determine the per cent of change in reserve estimates from year to year as a function of the number of years the estimate is removed from the year of discovery. Let

$x_{ij} \equiv$ reported size of ith field j years after discovery,

$$1 \leq i \leq N, \qquad 1 \leq j \leq M,$$

$\bar{x}_j \equiv \dfrac{1}{N} \displaystyle\sum_{i=1}^{N} x_{ij},$ the mean reported size of fields j years old.

Then

$$y_{j+1} = \left(\frac{\bar{x}_{j+1} - \bar{x}_j}{\bar{x}_j} \right)$$

is plotted against j as in Exhibit 6.5 below.

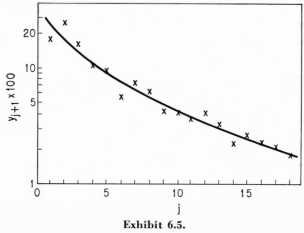

Exhibit 6.5.

[23]J. R. Arrington, "Size of Crude Reserves is Key to Evaluating Exploration Programs," *The Oil and Gas Journal*, Vol. 58, No. 9 (February 29, 1960), pp. 130–132.

A smooth curve is fitted to the plotted points. It is used to anticipate future revisions of reserve estimates, and to estimate expected true size. For example, using Exhibit 6.5, a field reported as having one million barrels ten years after discovery would be adjusted upwards by 4 per cent, so that the estimate of expected true size would be 1.04 million barrels.

The two Lognormal models, which we will call the *limit model* and the *reporting model*, treat human error, or more precisely reporting bias quite differently. The assumptions of the limit model put little structure on the probability distribution of the random variable, reported field size, but restrict the discovery process to one in which information feedback plays a minor role. A limit argument is used to prove the Lognormality of reported field sizes. The assumptions of the reporting model place much more stress on the structure of the probability distribution of reported field size but avoid the lack of realism in ignoring the effect of information feedback. No limit argument is necessary to construct this model.

To differentiate the two models further before examining their assumptions in detail, the reader can interpret them in terms of Exhibit 2.1. The limit model is derived by considering the long-run *cumulative* effect on the empirical histogram of reported field sizes of a very large number of repetitions of the reconnaissance exploration-advanced, exploration-wildcat drilling loops of the exhibit. The reporting model is derived by showing how a Lognormal distribution of true field sizes, together with certain assumptions about reporting bias, implies that the random variable reported field size is Lognormally distributed, not only in the long run, but also at any given point in time.

Verbal Description of the Reporting Model. The reporting model assumes that the distribution of true field sizes is Lognormal and that the reported size of a field discovered in the basin is the product of its true size and a proportion of true size which represents the reporting bias inherent in the reporting process. This proportion is also assumed to be Lognormally distributed. In broad outline the model is structured as follows:

1. In an interval of time t to $t + 1$, a field is discovered with probability proportional to the ratio of the areal extent of undiscovered fields to the area of the basin, and also proportional to the proficiency of the explorationists at time t.

2. If a field is discovered, this field's true size is generated according to the Lognormal distribution of true field sizes.

3. The reported size of this newly discovered field is determined by generating a value of the proportion of true size that will be reported at t according to the distribution of this proportion at t, and then multiplying the field's true size by this proportion.

4. The reported size at t of each field that has been discovered before t is found by following step 3 for each such field.

In carrying out this procedure, it is assumed that all fields are mutually independent with respect to their true size and the amount of bias affecting each and that at any given t, the *marginal* distribution of the proportion of true size that is reported is identical for all discovered fields. However, it can be that for any *given* field, the reported size at t is highly correlated with that at $t - 1$, or even with all $t - i, i = 1, 2, \ldots, t$. This possibility is allowed in the formal statement of the model's underlying assumptions.

Verbal Description of the Limit Model. The limit model assumes only that the mean and variance of the distribution of true field sizes both exist. It does not require specification of the functional form of this distribution. The reported size of a field at t is assumed to be the product of the field's reported size at $t - 1$ and a random proportion of this size. Each field's reported size is assumed to be independent of the reported size of every other field. The random proportion is distributed with finite mean and variance and such that the proportions for a given field at $t = 1, 2, \ldots$ are mutually independent, i.e., independent proportional increments. A basic feature of this model is that it describes only the distribution of the reported size of fields that have been discovered by $t = 1$, the time at which the model begins to function. It does not allow for the introduction of new fields into the group of fields which have been discovered by $t = 1$ but only describes the behavior of this particular group.

1. Each field in the group discovered by $t = 1$ is assumed to have a reported size at $t = 1$.

2. A value of the proportion of each field's reported size at $t = 1$ that will be reported at $t = 2$ is generated for each field according to the distribution of this proportion at $t = 2$. While the distribution of proportions is assumed to be the same for each field at a given time interval t, the distribution may change over time.

3. The reported size of each field at $t = 2$ is determined by multiplying its reported size at $t = 1$, by the proportion generated in step 2.

4. Steps 2 and 3 are repeated a very large number of times.

Some insight into the nature of the models can be gained by examining the stochastic difference equations which characterize them. These equations are presented below.

Definitions. Define the generic random variables

$\tilde{r}_t$ = reported field size at time t, $t = 0, 1, 2, \ldots, T$;

$\tilde{s}$ = true field size;

$\tilde{\epsilon}_t$ = the proportion of $\tilde{r}_t$ which is reported at time $t + 1$, i.e.,

$$\tilde{\epsilon}_t = \frac{\tilde{r}_{t+1}}{\tilde{r}_t};$$

$\tilde{\nu}_t$ = the proportion of $\tilde{s}$ which is reported at time t, i.e.,

$$\tilde{\nu}_t = \frac{\tilde{r}_t}{\tilde{r}}$$

In addition, define

$\pi_t = P(\tilde{r}_{t+1} \neq \tilde{r}_t)$

κ_t = probability of discovering a field at t,

and define, for a given number X,

$F_t^{(r)}(X) = P(\tilde{r}_t < X), \quad t = 1, 2, \ldots,$

$F^{(s)}(X) = P(\tilde{s} < X) = F_0^{(r)}(X),$

$$\delta_X(a) = \begin{cases} 1 & \text{if} \quad a \leq X \\ 0 & \text{if} \quad a > X. \end{cases}$$

Equations of the Models. If the discovery process is assumed to take place at discrete points in time $t = 0, 1, 2, \ldots$, the basic equation[24] of the limit model is

$$F_{t+1}^r(X) = \int_0^\infty \left\{ \pi_t P\left(\tilde{\epsilon}_t < \frac{X}{z} \right) + \delta_X(z)(1 - \pi_t) \right\} dF_t^{(r)}(z) \qquad (6.3)$$

---

[24]For a similar equation used to describe the size distribution (by volume) of particles subjected to a series of crushing operations, see B. Epstein, "The Mathematical Description of Certain Breakage Mechanisms Leading to the Logarithmico-normal Distribution," *Journal of the Franklin Institute*, Vol. 224, p. 471.

and that of the reporting model is

$$F_t^{(r)}(X) = \left(\sum_{i=1}^{t} \frac{\kappa_i}{t}\right) \int_0^\infty P\left(\bar{\nu}_t < \frac{X}{z}\right) dF^{(s)}(z) + 1 - \left(\sum_{i=1}^{t} \frac{\kappa_i}{t}\right). \quad (6.4)$$

For the moment, interpret (6.3) in terms of relative frequencies rather than probabilities. Then $F_{t+1}^{(r)}(X)$ is the relative frequency of fields of reported size less than X at time $t + 1$. Interpretation of the equations is simplified if each is written as a sum of two integrals. For example, (6.3) is expressible as

$$F_{t+1}^{(r)}(X) = \pi_t \int_0^\infty P\left(\bar{\epsilon}_t < \frac{X}{z}\right) dF_t^{(r)}(z) + (1 - \pi_t) \int_0^X dF_t^{(r)}(z). \quad (6.3')$$

By definition, π_t is the probability that a field which has been discovered by time t will change in reported size from t to $t + 1$. Thus the first integral in (6.3') is the proportion of fields discovered by t whose reported size changes from t to $t + 1$ so that they have reported sizes less than X at $t + 1$. Some of these fields (those whose reported sizes are greater than X at t) will be newcomers to the proportion of fields less than X, and others (those whose sizes lie between 0 and X at t) will change in reported size but not change the proportion of fields less than X, as they were already less than X in reported size and remain so at $t + 1$. The second integral is the proportion of fields whose reported sizes are less than X at t which do not change in reported size by $t + 1$.

Equation (6.4) of the reporting model has an interpretation which is quite different from that of (6.3). Imagine rank wildcats being drilled at $t = 1, 2, \dots$. The wildcat drilled at t discovers a new field of true size $s > 0$ with probability κ_t. Then

$$\sum_{i=1}^{t} \kappa_i$$

is the expected number of fields of true size $s > 0$ found up to and including t, and

$$\left(\sum_{i=1}^{t} \frac{\kappa_i}{t}\right) \int_0^\infty P\left(\bar{\nu}_t < \frac{X}{s}\right) dF^{(s)}(s)$$

is the proportion of these fields which have reported sizes less than X at t. Furthermore

$$1 - \left(\sum_{i=1}^{t} \frac{\kappa_i}{t}\right)$$

is the proportion of times that a field of size 0 is discovered in drilling t rank wildcats, i.e., a dry hole.

The functional form of the relative frequency distribution which results from a process described by (6.3) or by (6.4) is highly dependent on the assumptions made about the behavior of the sequences $\{\tilde{\varepsilon}_t, t = 0, 1, 2, \ldots \}$ and $\{\tilde{\nu}_t, t = 0, 1, 2, \ldots \}$, respectively. A more formal discussion of such assumptions is offered below.

The Reporting Model. Define the random variables

$$\tilde{s}_j = \text{true size of the } j\text{th field discovered in the basin,}$$

$$\tilde{r}_{tj} = \text{reported size of the } j\text{th field at time } t,$$

$$\tilde{\nu}_{tj} = \tilde{r}_{tj}/\tilde{s}_j = \text{the proportion of } \tilde{s}_j \text{ reported at time } t.$$

Let $\{\tilde{s}_j, j = 1, 2, \ldots, t\}$ be a sequence of mutually independent random variables with cumulative distribution function $F^{(s)}$. Let the double sequence $\{\tilde{\nu}_{tj}, t = 1, 2, \ldots, T, j = 1, 2, \ldots, t\}$ be such that for given t, $\{\tilde{\nu}_{tj}, j = 1, 2, \ldots, t\}$ is a sequence of mutually independent random variables each with marginal cumulative distribution function $F_t^{(\nu)}$, while for a given j, $\{\tilde{\nu}_{tj}, t = 1, 2, \ldots, T\}$ is a sequence of dependent random variables.

The sequence $\{\tilde{\nu}_{tj}, t = 1, 2, \ldots, T, j = 1, 2, \ldots, t\}$ can be best visualized as a triangular array of random variables:

$t \diagdown j$	1	2	3	4	...	t	...	T
1	$\tilde{\nu}_{11}$							
2	$\tilde{\nu}_{21},$	$\tilde{\nu}_{22}$						
3	$\tilde{\nu}_{31},$	$\tilde{\nu}_{32},$	$\tilde{\nu}_{33}$					
.	.	.	.	.				
t	$\tilde{\nu}_{t1},$	$\tilde{\nu}_{t2},$	$\tilde{\nu}_{t3},$	.		$\tilde{\nu}_{tt}$		
.	.	.	.	.	.	.		
T	$\tilde{\nu}_{T1},$	$\tilde{\nu}_{T2},$	$\tilde{\nu}_{T3},$	.		.		$\tilde{\nu}_{TT}$

in which the variables in the rows are mutually independent and are marginally identically distributed with a cumulative distribution function $F_t^{(\nu)}$ depending only on the row index, and those in the columns are dependent.

Suppose that the probability that a field is discovered at time t is κ_t, $0 < \kappa_t \le 1$, and let the random variable

$$\tilde{\delta}_t = \begin{cases} 1 \text{ if a field is discovered at time } t \\ 0 \text{ if there is no discovery at time } t. \end{cases}$$

One plausible way of defining κ_t in terms of the real world discovery process is as follows. The probability κ_t of discovering a field at time t is directly proportional to the proficiency k_t of the explorationists at t and to the ratio of areal extent A_t of fields undiscovered by t to the area extent A of the basin:

$$P(\tilde{\delta}_t = 1) = \left(\frac{k_t A_t}{A}\right) = \kappa_t, \quad 0 < k_t \le \left(\frac{A}{A_t}\right).$$

For the sake of ease in presentation, the convention is adopted that if $\tilde{\delta}_t = 0$, then the true size of the field discovered at time t is 0.

It is shown below that Assumptions 1 through 3 imply that the distribution of $\tilde{r}_{tj}, j = 1, 2, \ldots, t$ is a combination of a non-normalized Lognormal density function and a spike at the origin of probability weight

$$1 - p_{tj}, \text{ where } p_{tj} \equiv P\left(\sum_{i=1}^{t} \tilde{\delta}_i \ge j\right).$$

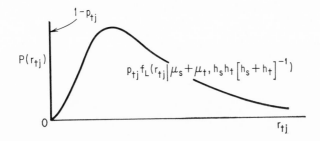

Assumption 1. The size distribution of the set of all fields in the basin is Lognormal. That is, the generic random variable $\tilde{s}$ is distributed according to

$$f_L(s \mid \mu_s, h_s) = \left(\frac{h_s}{2\pi}\right)^{\frac{1}{2}} e^{-1/2 h_s \, (\log s - \mu_s)^2} \frac{1}{s}, \quad s > 0.$$

Assumption 2. $\{\tilde{\nu}_{tj}, t = 1, 2, \ldots, T; \ j = 1, 2, \ldots, t\}$ is a double sequence of random variables such that given t, the sequence $\{\tilde{\nu}_{tj}, j = 1, 2, \ldots, t\}$ is a sequence of mutually independent random variables distributed according to

$$f_L(\nu \mid \mu_t, h_t) = \left(\frac{h_t}{2\pi}\right)^{\frac{1}{2}} e^{-1/2 h_t (\log \nu - \mu_t)^2} \frac{1}{\nu}, \quad \nu > 0.$$

and given j, the sequence $\{\tilde{\nu}_{tj}, t = 1, 2, \ldots, T\}$ is a sequence of mutually dependent random variables. Furthermore, the elements of this latter sequence are independent of $\tilde{s}_j$, for all j.

Assumption 3.

$$0 < \kappa_t \leq 1, \quad \text{all} \quad t.$$

In order to establish the desired result, two simple lemmas must be proved.

Lemma 1. Let D_t denote the set of all $\tilde{s}_j > 0$, $j = 1, 2, \ldots, t$. Then $\{\tilde{s}_j : \tilde{s}_j \, \epsilon \, D_t\}$ is a sequence of mutually independent identically distributed random variables distributed according to $f_L(\cdot \mid \mu_s, h_s)$.

Proof. Follows immediately from Assumption 1 and mutual independence of $\{\tilde{s}_j, j = 1, 2, \ldots, t\}$.

Lemma 2. The sequence $\{\tilde{r}_{tj} : \tilde{s}_j \, \epsilon \, D_t\}$ is a sequence of mutually independent random variables, marginally identically distributed according to $f_L(\tilde{r}_{tj} \mid \mu_s + \mu_t, \, h_s h_t [h_s + h_t]^{-1})$.

Proof. By definition

$$\tilde{r}_{tj} = \tilde{v}_{tj}\tilde{s}_j. \tag{6.5}$$

hence

$$\log \tilde{r}_{tj} = \log \tilde{v}_{tj} + \log \tilde{s}_j.$$

For all j such that $s_j \, \epsilon \, D_t$, let

$$\tilde{z} = \log \tilde{r}_{tj}, \quad \tilde{x} = \log \tilde{v}_{tj}, \quad \tilde{y} = \log \tilde{s}_j,$$

so that (6.5) implies

$$\tilde{z} = \tilde{x} + \tilde{y}.$$

Since

$$f_L(s_j \mid \mu_s, h_s) = f_N(\log s_j \mid \mu_s, h_s)\frac{1}{s_j}, \tag{6.6}$$

$$f_L(v_{tj} \mid \mu_t, h_t) = f_N(\log v_{tj} \mid \mu_t, h_t)\frac{1}{v_{tj}}, \tag{6.7}$$

and since $\tilde{v}_{tj}$ and $\tilde{s}_j$ are independent by Assumption 2, it is clear that $\tilde{z}$ is the convolution of a sum of two independent normally distributed random variables $\tilde{x}$ and $\tilde{y}$. By a well-known result,

$$\tilde{z} \sim f_N(z \mid \mu_s + \mu_t, \, h_s h_t [h_s + h_t]^{-1}),$$

or since $\tilde{z} = \log \tilde{r}_{tj}$,

$$\tilde{r}_{tj} \sim f_L(r_{tj} \mid \mu_s + \mu_t, \, h_s h_t [h_s + h_t]^{-1}),$$

as was to be proved.

That the distribution of $\tilde{r}_{tj}, j = 1, 2, \ldots, t$ is a combination of a non-normalized Lognormal density function $p_{tj}f_L(r_{tj} \mid \mu_s + \mu_t, \, h_s h_t [h_s + h_t]^{-1})$

and a spike at the origin of probability weight $1 - p_{tj}$ follows directly from Assumption 3 and Lemma 2.

Assumptions 1 through 3 are all that are needed to assure this result; however, they must be supplemented by more specific assumptions about the joint distribution of the $\tilde{r}_{tj}$'s, $t = j, j + 1, \ldots, T$, and the joint distribution of the $\tilde{\delta}_t$'s, $t = 1, 2, \ldots, T$, if the model is to be used as a data generating process model. As an example, make Assumptions 4 and 5:

Assumption 4. $\{\tilde{\delta}_t, t = 1, 2, \ldots, T\}$ is a sequence of mutually independent random variables.

Define the $T - j + 1$ component vectors

$$
\underline{\nu}_j = \begin{pmatrix} \nu_{jj} \\ \vdots \\ \nu_{tj} \\ \vdots \\ \nu_{Tj} \end{pmatrix}, \qquad
(\underline{\nu}_j)_I = \begin{pmatrix} \nu_{jj}^{-1} \\ \vdots \\ \nu_{tj}^{-1} \\ \vdots \\ \nu_{Tj}^{-1} \end{pmatrix}, \qquad
\underline{\mu}_j = \begin{pmatrix} \mu_j \\ \vdots \\ \mu_t \\ \vdots \\ \mu_T \end{pmatrix}
$$

and define the positive definite symmetric matrix

$$
\underline{\underline{h}}_j = \begin{bmatrix} h_{jj,jj} & \cdot & \cdot & \cdot & \cdot & \cdot & h_{jj,Tj} \\ & \cdot & & & & \cdot & \\ \cdot & & h_{ij,tj} & & & & \cdot \\ & \cdot & & & & \cdot & \\ h_{Tj,jj} & \cdot & \cdot & \cdot & \cdot & \cdot & h_{Tj,Tj} \end{bmatrix}
$$

Assumption 5.

$$
\underline{\tilde{\nu}}_j \sim f_L^{(T-j+1)}(\underline{\nu} \mid \underline{\mu}_j, \underline{\underline{h}}_j)
$$
$$
= (2\pi)^{-1/2(T-j+1)} \, e^{-1/2(\log \underline{\nu}_j - \underline{\mu}_j)^t \underline{\underline{h}}_j (\log \underline{\nu}_j - \underline{\mu}_j)} (\underline{\nu}_j)_I \mid \underline{\underline{h}}_j \mid^{1/2}.
$$

Now a sample realization $\{r_{tj}, j = 1, 2, \ldots, t\}$ can be generated as shown in Table 6.1:

1. At time t, $\tilde{\delta}_t$ is set equal to 1 with probability κ_t; i.e., $P(\tilde{\delta}_t = 1) = \kappa_t$ (Column 2).

2. If $\tilde{\delta}_t = 1$, a value s_t of $\tilde{s}_t$ is generated according to $F^{(s)}$. If $\tilde{\delta}_t = 0$, s_t is set equal to 0. (Column 3).

3. A sequence of values $\{\nu_{tj}, j = 1, 2, \ldots, t\}$ is generated. Each ν_{tj} is generated according to the conditional distribution of $\tilde{\nu}_{tj}$ given $\tilde{\nu}_{ti} = \nu_{tj}$ for $\ell = 1, 2, \ldots, t - 1$. (Column 4).

4. Each element s_j of $\{s_j, j = 1, 2, \ldots, t\}$ is multiplied by ν_{tj} to give r_{tj}. (Column 5).

TABLE 6.1.

t	δ_t	$\{s_j\}$	$\{\nu_{tj}\}$	$\{r_{tj}\}$
1	1	$\{10\}$	$\{1.2\}$	$\{12\}$
2	1	$\{10, 6\}$	$\{.8, 2.0\}$	$\{8, 12\}$
3	0	$\{10, 6, 0\}$	$\{.9, 1.5, 3.0\}$	$\{9, 8, 0\}$
.	.	.	.	.
.	.	.	.	.
.	.	.	.	.
t	1	$\{10, 6, 0, \ldots, 4\}$	$\{.2, 1.0, 2.0, \ldots, 1.5\}$	$\{2, 6, 0, \ldots, 6\}$

The sample realization $\{2, 6, 0, \ldots, 6\}$ can be plotted and interpreted as an empirical histogram of reported field sizes at time t. It is the functional form of this histogram that is of interest, and it is shown below that Assumptions 1 through 4 imply that as $t \to \infty$ *this form approaches a combination of a non-normalized Lognormal density function and a spike at the origin of probability weight*

$$1 - \left(\sum_{i=1}^{t} \frac{\kappa_i}{t} \right).$$

Proof. That the functional form of the histogram of sample realizations $\{r_{tj}, j = 1, 2, \ldots, t\}$ approaches a combination of a non-normalized Lognormal density function of measure

$$\left(\sum_{i=1}^{t} \frac{\kappa_i}{t} \right)$$

and a spike at the origin of measure

$$1 - \left(\sum_{i=1}^{t} \frac{\kappa_i}{t} \right)$$

follows directly from Lemma 2 and Assumptions 3 and 4. For the histogram of the sample realization $\{r_{tj}: s_j \epsilon D_t\}$ is asymptotically Lognormal as $t \to \infty$ by Lemma 2 and Assumption 4; by Assumption 3, the proportion of r_{tj}'s for which $r_{tj} > 0$, approaches

$$1 - \left(\sum_{i=1}^{t} \frac{\kappa_i}{t} \right)$$

as $t \to \infty$.

Since the parameters μ_t and h_t are arbitrary functions (subject only to $-\infty < \mu_t < \infty$ and $0 < h_t < \infty$), they can be specified so as to make the marginal distribution function $F_t^{(s)}$ converge to $F^{(s)}$ as rapidly as desired as t increases; alternatively, they can be chosen so that $F_t^{(s)}$ diverges from $F^{(s)}$ as t increases. Thus the choice of a sequence of functions $\{(\mu_t, h_t), t = 1, 2, \ldots, T\}$ corresponds to choice of a feedback process which dictates how $\{\tilde{r}_{tj}, j = 1, 2, \ldots, t\}$ is to behave as information about the basin accumulates over time.

The Limit Model. Whereas the reporting model is built by assuming that the distribution of reporting bias $F_t^{(\nu)}$ and the distribution of true field sizes $F^{(s)}$ are both Lognormal, the limit model requires no assumption as to the functional form of $F_t^{(\nu)}$ and of $F^{(s)}$. This advantage, however, is achieved by a sacrifice of plausibility, and an increase in the difficulty of making a common sense interpretation of one of the model's key assumptions (Assumption 3′ given below).

Together with (6.3),

$$F_{t+1}^{(r)}(X) = \int_0^\infty \left\{\pi_t P\left(\tilde{\epsilon}_t < \frac{X}{z}\right) + \delta_X(z)(1 - \pi_t)\right\} dF_t^{(r)}(z), \qquad (6.3)$$

the following Assumptions lead to the result that $F_{t+1}^{(r)}(X)$ is asymptotically Lognormal as $t \to \infty$:

Assumption 1′.

$\pi_t > 0$ for an infinite number of t's.

Assumption 2′. The generic random variable $\tilde{r}_0 = \tilde{s}$, so that $F_0^{(r)} = F^{(s)}$; furthermore,

$$E(\tilde{s}) < \infty, \qquad \text{Var}(\tilde{s}) < \infty.$$

Assumption 3′. $\{\tilde{\epsilon}_t, t = 1, 2, \ldots\}$ is a sequence of mutually independent random variables such that $\tilde{\epsilon}_t > 0$,

$$E(\log \tilde{\epsilon}_t) = \mu_t < \infty,$$

$$\text{Var}(\log \tilde{\epsilon}_t) = \sigma_t^2 < \infty,$$

and

$$E(\,|\,(\log \tilde{\epsilon}_t) - \mu_t\,|^3) = \mu_t^3 < \infty$$

for all $t > 0$. In addition,

$$\lim_{t \to \infty} \frac{\left(\sum_{j=1}^t w_j^3\right)^{1/3}}{\left(\sum_{i=1}^t \sigma_i^2\right)^{1/2}} = 0.$$

Proof: Define the cumulative distribution function

$$H_t\!\left(\frac{X}{r_t}\right) = \left\{\pi_t P\!\left(\bar{\epsilon}_t < \frac{X}{r_t}\right) + \delta_X(r_t)(1 - \pi_t)\right\}.$$

That $H_t(\cdot)$ is in fact a distribution function is verified by observing that the expression in curly brackets is a mixture of cumulative distribution functions.

Then

$$F_{t+1}^{(r)}(X) = \int_0^\infty H_t\!\left(\frac{X}{z}\right) dF_t^{(r)}(z).$$

Now if we define random variables $\tilde{r}_{t+1}$, $\tilde{r}_t$, and $\tilde{y}$ such that for all $X > 0$,

$$P(\tilde{r}_{t+1} < X) = F_{t+1}^{(r)}(X),$$

$$P(\tilde{r}_t < X) = F_t(X),$$

and

$$P(\tilde{y} < X) = H_t(X),$$

then a theorem due to H. J. Curtis [25] implies that

$$\tilde{r}_{t+1} = \tilde{y}\tilde{r}_t.$$

Theorem. If $\tilde{y}$ and $\tilde{r}_t$ are independent random variables with respective distribution functions $H_t(X)$ and $F_t(X)$, then the distribution $T(X)$ of their product is given by the formula

$$T(X) = \int_{0+0}^\infty H\!\left(\frac{X}{v} + 0\right) dF_t(v) + \int_{-\infty}^{0-0} H\!\left(\frac{X}{v} - 0\right) dF_t(v)$$
$$+ \begin{cases} F_t(0) & \text{if } X \geq 0 \\ F_t(-0) & \text{if } X < 0, \end{cases}$$

for all values of X.

The central limit theorem due to Liapounoff [26] then implies that $F_{t+1}^{(r)}(X)$ is asymptotically Lognormal as $t \to \infty$.

---

[25] H. J. Curtis, "On the Distribution of a Quotient of Two Chance Variables," *Annals of Mathematical Statistics*, Vol. 12 (1941), p. 421.

[26] See H. Cramer, *Mathematical Methods of Statistics* (Princeton: Princeton University Press, 1958), pp. 415–416.

CHAPTER 7

Distribution Theory of the Univariate Lognormal Distribution and an Application

In Chapter 6, it was argued that a Lognormal *conditional* sampling distribution of the random variable "reported field size" is appropriate. In Chapter 7, it is shown that the univariate Lognormal density function possesses properties which render it analytically tractable, hence highly useful, in certain contexts; e.g., in the analysis of drilling problems and in the construction of unconditional data generating process models of reported field sizes in a basin.

Section 7.1 develops aspects of the Bayesian distribution theory of the univariate Lognormal density function. Section 7.2 exploits the data of graphs 6.1 to 6.16 to show why a Lognormal (prior) distribution is a reasonable functional form to use for the distribution of the mean of reported field sizes in a basin whose parameter μ is not known with certainty. Section 7.3 shows how the Lognormal distribution can be used in the analysis of a drilling decision when management has adopted the expected utility criterion as a guide to action.

7.1. Bayes Distribution Theory of the Univariate Lognormal Distribution

This section develops some properties of the univariate Lognormal density function as is done in *Applied Statistical Decision Theory*[1] for a

[1]H. Raiffa and R. O. Schlaifer, *Applied Statistical Decision Theory* (Boston: Division of Research, Harvard Business School, 1961).

wide variety of distributions. The development is done in three stages:

1. The Lognormal density function is defined, and its first two complete moments and incomplete moments of all order are listed, in Sections 7.1.1 and 7.1.2;

2. An independent Lognormal process with noninformative stopping and with known precision is defined and its properties discussed in Section 7.1.3;

3. The prior, posterior, and preposterior analysis of an independent Lognormal process with known precision but unknown mean is examined in Sections 7.1.4 and 7.1.5.

All references in this chapter marked with an asterisk will be understood to refer to *Applied Statistical Decision Theory;* e.g., (6-21)* is formula (6-21) in the aforementioned book.

Conspectus of Independent Lognormal Process Properties. The process is defined as a generator of x's with density

$$(2\pi)^{-1/2} \left\{ \exp[-\tfrac{1}{2}h(\log x - \mu)^2] \right\} h^{1/2} \frac{1}{x}; \quad -\infty < \mu < \infty,$$

$$0 < x < \infty,$$

$$h > 0.$$

An expression such as $\log x$ without a subscript to indicate the logarithmic base will be understood to be the base e.

When h is known and the parameter μ is unknown (the only case considered here), the process has the following properties. Let

$$n \equiv \text{number of } \tilde{x}\text{'s observed,}$$

$$g^n \equiv \Pi \, x_i,$$

$$\mu_L \equiv \exp\left[\mu + \frac{1}{2h}\right].$$

Likelihood of Sample: proportional to

$$\exp[-\tfrac{1}{2}hn(\log g - \mu)^2],$$

Conjugate prior density[2] (Lognormal):

$$f_L\left(\mu_L \mid m' + \frac{1}{2h}, hn'\right) \propto \left\{\exp\left[-\tfrac{1}{2}hn'\left(\log \mu_L - m' - \frac{1}{2h}\right)^2\right]\right\}\frac{1}{\mu_L},$$

$$h > 0,$$
$$0 < \mu_L < \infty,$$
$$n' > 0,$$
$$-\infty < m' < \infty.$$

Posterior density:

$$f_L\left(\mu_L \mid m'' + \frac{1}{2h}, hn''\right)$$

where

$$m'' = \frac{n'm' + n \log g}{n' + n}, \qquad n'' = n' + n.$$

7.1.1. The Standardized Lognormal Density Function. This function is defined by

$$f_{L^*}(u) \equiv \frac{1}{\sqrt{2\pi}} \left\{\exp[-\tfrac{1}{2}(\log u)^2]\right\} \frac{1}{u}, \qquad 0 < u < \infty. \tag{7.1}$$

Its first two moments are shown in Section 7.1.2 to be

$$\mu_1 = \sqrt{e}, \qquad \mu_1(u) = \sqrt{e}\, F_{N^*}((\log u) - 1), \tag{7.2a}$$

$$\mu_2 = e[e - 1]. \tag{7.2b}$$

From equation (7.1) we observe that

$$f_{L^*}(u) = \frac{1}{u} f_{N^*}(\log u). \tag{7.3}$$

Thus we can use tables of $f_{N^*}(\log u)$ to determine values taken on by $f_{L^*}(u)$.

---

[2]See H. Raiffa and R. O. Schlaifer, *op. cit.*, subsections 2.1.2, 3.2.1, and 3.2.2.

Let $z \in Z$ be a (sufficient) sample statistic and $\ell(z \mid \theta)$ be the likelihood of z given the parameter $\theta \in \circledH$. If ρ and k are functions of z such that for each $z \in Z$ and $\theta \in \circledH$, $\ell(z \mid \theta) = k(z \mid \theta)\rho(z)$, then $k(z \mid \theta)$ is called a *kernel* of z given θ. Informally, a kernel of z is that portion of the likelihood which depends on θ.

In place of considering $k(\cdot \mid \theta)$ as a function with parameter θ on the sample space Z, we can consider it as a function $k(z \mid \cdot)$ with parameter z on the state space $\circledH$. Such a function when normalized and shown to be non-negative for all $\theta \in \circledH$ is called a *natural conjugate* with parameter z of the kernel function k.

A *prior conjugate density* $D'(\cdot)$ on $\tilde{\theta}$ is a density function on the state space proportional to $k(z' \mid \cdot)$ for some $z' \in Z$.

If the prior density $D'(\cdot)$ of $\tilde{\theta}$ is proportional to $k(z' \mid \cdot)$ for some $z' \in Z$, if $y(z') = y$ is a sufficient statistic and if $k(y \mid \theta)$ is a kernel of the likelihood of z' given θ, then the *posterior density of* $\tilde{\theta}$ given y is defined as $D''(\theta \mid y)$ and is proportional to $D'(\theta)k(y \mid \theta)$.

*7.1.2.　**The General or Nonstandardized Lognormal Density Function.**　*This function is defined by

$$f_L(z \mid \mu, H) \equiv \frac{1}{\sqrt{2\pi}} \{\exp[-\tfrac{1}{2}H(\log z - \mu)^2]\} \frac{\sqrt{H}}{z}; \qquad \begin{aligned} 0 &< z < \infty, \\ 0 &< H < \infty, \\ -\infty &< \mu < \infty. \end{aligned}$$

$$(7.4)$$

It is related to the standardized density (7.3) by

$$F_L(z \mid \mu, H) = F_{N^*}([\log z - \mu]\sqrt{H}). \tag{7.5}$$

The first two complete central moments of f_L are

$$\mu_1 = \exp\left[\mu + \frac{1}{2H}\right] \tag{7.6}$$

and

$$\mu_2 = \left\{\exp\left[2\mu + \frac{1}{H}\right]\right\}(e^{1/H} - 1). \tag{7.7}$$

The incomplete first moment can be expressed as

$$\mu_1(a) = \left\{\exp\left[\mu + \frac{1}{2H}\right]\right\} F_{N^*}(v(a),) \tag{7.8a}$$

where

$$v(a) = [\log a - \mu]\sqrt{H} - \frac{1}{\sqrt{H}}.$$

The incomplete kth moment about the origin can be expressed as

$$\mu_k(a) = \left\{\exp\left[k\mu + \frac{k^2}{2H}\right]\right\} F_{N^*}(w(a)), \tag{7.8b}$$

where

$$w(a) = [\log a - \mu]\sqrt{H} - \frac{k}{\sqrt{H}}.$$

Proofs.　That both f_{L^*} and f_L as shown in (7.1) and (7.4) are proper density functions can be seen by observing that f_{L^*} results from the integrand transform

$$y = \log u$$

of the standardized Normal density (7.3) and that f_L results from the integrand transform

$$\log u = [\log z - \mu]\sqrt{H}.$$

We will prove formulas (7.2a), (7.2b), (7.6), (7.7), and (7.8a) by showing that each is a special case of the expression for the incomplete kth moment of f_L as given by (7.8b).

The formula (7.8b) for the incomplete kth moment of f_L is proved as follows. Define

$$\mu_k(a) = \int_0^a \frac{z^k}{\sqrt{2\pi}} \{\exp[-\tfrac{1}{2}H(\log z - \mu)^2]\} \frac{\sqrt{H}}{z} dz.$$

Make the integrand transform

$$v = [\log z - \mu] \sqrt{H},$$

set

$$v(a) = [\log a - \mu] \sqrt{H},$$

and rewrite $\mu_k(a)$ in terms of v:

$$\mu_k(a) = \int_{-\infty}^{v(a)} \frac{1}{\sqrt{2\pi}} \{\exp[k(vH^{-1/2} + \mu)]\} \{\exp[-\tfrac{1}{2}v^2]\} dv$$

$$= e^{k\mu} \int_{-\infty}^{v(a)} \frac{1}{\sqrt{2\pi}} \{\exp[(-\tfrac{1}{2}v^2 + kvH^{-1/2})]\} dv.$$

Completing the square in the exponent gives

$$\mu_k(a) = \exp[k\mu + (k^2/2H)] \int_{-\infty}^{v(a)} \frac{1}{\sqrt{2\pi}} \{\exp[-\tfrac{1}{2}(v - kH^{-1/2})^2]\} dv.$$

Now setting

$$w = \left(v - \frac{k}{\sqrt{H}}\right) = [\log z - \mu]\sqrt{H} - \frac{k}{\sqrt{H}},$$

and

$$w(a) = [\log a - \mu]\sqrt{H} - \frac{k}{\sqrt{H}},$$

it follows that

$$\mu_k(a) = \left\{\exp\left[k\mu + \frac{k^2}{2H}\right]\right\} F_{N^*}(w(a))$$

as was to be proved.

Formulas (7.6) and (7.7) follow directly from (7.8b) by letting $a \to \infty$ and setting $k = 1$ and $k = 2$ respectively. Formula (7.8a) follows from (7.8b) by setting $k = 1$. The formula (7.7) for the second central moment

μ_2' follows from (7.8b) by letting $a \to \infty$, setting $k = 2$ in (7.8b), and then subtracting the square of (7.6) from the result:

$$\mu_2' = \left\{ \exp\left[2\mu + \frac{2}{H} \right] \right\} - \left\{ \exp\left[2\mu + \frac{1}{H} \right] \right\}$$

$$= \left\{ \exp\left[2\mu + \frac{1}{H} \right] \right\} \left\{ \left(\exp\left[\frac{1}{H} \right] \right) - 1 \right\}.$$

Finally, formulas (7.2a) and (7.2b) follow from the above results by noting that the moments of the standardized Lognormal density function are identical to (7.6), (7.7).

For later convenience, we will restate (7.5) in random variable terminology.

Theorem 1. If $\tilde{x}$ is a Lognormal random variable with cumulative distribution function $F_L(a \mid \mu, H)$, then log $\tilde{x}$ is a Normal random variable with cumulative distribution function $F_N(\log a \mid \mu, H)$.

Proof. Since
$$P(\tilde{x} < e^a) = P(\log \tilde{x} < a),$$
it follows that
$$F_L(e^a \mid \mu, H) = F_N(a \mid \mu, H).$$

7.1.3. Independent Lognormal Process, Precision Known.

Definition of an Independent Lognormal Process. An independent Lognormal process can be defined as a process generating independent random variables $\tilde{x}_1, \ldots, \tilde{x}_i, \ldots, \tilde{x}_n$ with identical densities

$$f_L(x \mid \mu, h) \equiv (2\pi)^{-1/2} \left\{ \exp[-\tfrac{1}{2} h(\log x - \mu)^2] \right\} \frac{h^{1/2}}{x}; \quad \begin{array}{c} 0 < x < \infty, \\ -\infty < \mu < \infty, \\ h > 0. \end{array}$$

$$(7.9)$$

This is the Lognormal density as defined in (7.4), and therefore the process mean and variance can be obtained from (7.6) and (7.7):

$$E(\tilde{x} \mid \mu, h) = \exp\left[\mu + \left(\frac{1}{2h} \right) \right], \tag{7.10}$$

$$V(\tilde{x} \mid \mu, h) = \left\{ \exp\left[2\mu + \frac{1}{h} \right] \right\} \left\{ \left(\exp\left[\frac{1}{h} \right] \right) - 1 \right\}. \tag{7.11}$$

Likelihood of a Sample When h is Known. The likelihood that an independent Lognormal process *will generate* n successive values $x_1, \ldots, x_i, \ldots, x_n$ is the product of their individual likelihoods as given by (7.9):

$$(2\pi)^{-\frac{1}{2}n} \{\exp[-\tfrac{1}{2}h\Sigma(\log x_i - \mu)^2]\} \, h^{\frac{1}{2}n} \, \Pi \left(\frac{dx_i}{x_i}\right) \qquad (7.12)$$

If the stopping process is noninformative in the sense of Section 2.2* then (7.12) is also the *likelihood* of observations $x_1, \ldots, x_i, \ldots, x_n$. Now define the statistic

$$g \equiv (\Pi \, x_i)^{1/n}. \qquad (7.13)$$

We can then write (7.12) as

$$(2\pi)^{-\frac{1}{2}n} \exp[-\tfrac{1}{2}h\Sigma(\log x_i - \log g)^2]$$
$$\{\exp[-\tfrac{1}{2}hn(\log g - \mu)^2]\} \, h^{\frac{1}{2}n}g^{-n} \, \Pi \, dx_i. \qquad (7.14)$$

When the process precision h is known and only the mean $e^{\mu + (1/2h)}$ is unknown, the only factor in (7.14) which varies with the unknown parameter μ is:

$$\exp[-\tfrac{1}{2}hn(\log g - \mu)^2]. \qquad (7.15)$$

Thus (7.15) is the kernel of the likelihood and the statistic (g, n) is sufficient when h is known and the stopping process is noninformative.

7.1.4. Prior and Posterior Analysis Distribution of $\tilde{\mu}_L$.

When the precision h of an independent Lognormal process is known but the mean is a random variable

$$\tilde{\mu}_L = \exp\left[\tilde{\mu} + \frac{1}{2h}\right], \qquad (7.16)$$

the natural conjugate of $\tilde{\mu}_L$ is the Lognormal distribution defined by (7.4). This follows from the fact that the kernel (7.15) may be rewritten as a function of μ_L: substituting $\log \mu_L - 1/2h$ for μ in (7.15) shows that the kernel of the likelihood in terms of μ_L is

$$\exp\left[-\tfrac{1}{2}hn\left(\log g - \log \mu_L + \frac{1}{2h}\right)^2\right]. \qquad (7.17)$$

Letting $m = \log g$ we have

$$\tilde{\mu}_L \sim f_L\left(\mu_L \mid m + \frac{1}{2h}, H\right) \propto \left\{\exp\left[-\tfrac{1}{2}H\left(\log \mu_L - m - \frac{1}{2h}\right)^2\right]\right\} \frac{1}{\mu_L}. \qquad (7.18)$$

As in the Normal case we can think of H as measuring the "information" on μ_L. To express this measure in units of the process precision h, we define for the distribution of $\tilde{\mu}_L$,

$$n = \frac{H}{h}; \qquad (7.19)$$

that is, we say that the information H is equivalent to n observations on the process, and we write the density of $\tilde{\mu}_L$ in the form

$$f_L\left(\mu_L \mid m + \frac{1}{2h}, hn\right) \propto \left\{\exp\left[-\tfrac{1}{2}hn\left(\log \mu_L - m - \frac{1}{2h}\right)^2\right]\right\}\frac{1}{\mu_L}. \qquad (7.20)$$

Providing we assign a distribution of this kind with parameter (m', n') to $\tilde{\mu}_L$ and if a sample from the process then yields a sufficient statistic (g, n), the posterior distribution of $\tilde{\mu}_L$ will be Lognormal with parameters

$$m'' = \frac{n'm' + n \log g}{n' + n}, \qquad hn'' = h(n' + n). \qquad (7.21)$$

Proof. To show this, multiply the prior density (7.18) by the kernel of the likelihood (7.12):

$$\left\{\exp\left[-\tfrac{1}{2}hn'\left(\log \mu_L - m' - \frac{1}{2h}\right)^2 - \tfrac{1}{2}hn(\log g - \mu)^2\right]\right\}\frac{1}{\mu_L}.$$

Noting that $\log \mu_L - 1/2h = \mu$ from (7.12), and adding and dropping constants, we can write the product above as

$$\left\{\exp\left[-\tfrac{1}{2}h(n' + n)\left[\log \mu_L - 2 \log \mu_L\left(\frac{n'm' + n \log g + \dfrac{n' + n}{2h}}{n' + n}\right)\right]^2\right]\right\}\frac{1}{\mu_L}.$$

Aside from constants this is a Lognormal density like (7.4) but with parameters specified in (7.21).

Cumulative probabilities under the distribution (7.18) can be obtained from tables of the unit Normal function by use of the relation

$$F_L\left(\mu_L \mid m + \frac{1}{2h}, hn\right) = F_{N^*}\left(\left[\log \mu_L - \left(m + \frac{1}{2h}\right)\right]\sqrt{hn}\right). \qquad (7.22)$$

The mean, partial expectation, and variance of the Lognormal distribution (7.18) of $\bar{\mu}_L$ are, by (7.6), (7.7), and (7.8),

$$E\left(\bar{\mu}_L \mid m + \frac{1}{2h}, hn\right) = \exp\left[m + \frac{1}{2h}\left(1 + \frac{1}{n}\right)\right] \qquad (7.23)$$

$$E_0^{\mu_L}\left(\bar{\mu}_L \mid m + \frac{1}{2h}, hn\right) = \left\{\exp\left[m + \frac{1}{2h}\left(1 + \frac{1}{n}\right)\right]\right\}F_{N^*}(k) \quad (7.24)$$

where

$$k = \left[\log\mu_L - \left(m + \frac{1}{2h}\right)\right]\sqrt{hn} - \frac{1}{\sqrt{hn}},$$

$$V\left(\bar{\mu}_L \mid m + \frac{1}{2h}, hn\right) = \left\{\exp\left[2m + \frac{1}{h}\left(1 + \frac{1}{n}\right)\right]\right\}[e^{1/hn} - 1]. \quad (7.25)$$

From (7.5) and (7.8) it follows that the linear-loss integrals are given by

$$L_\ell(\mu_L) \equiv \int_0^{\mu_L} (\mu_L - z)f_L\left(z \mid m + \frac{1}{2h}, hn\right)dz$$

$$= \mu_L F_{N^*}(y) - \left\{\exp\left[m + \frac{1}{2h}\left(1 + \frac{1}{n}\right)\right]\right\}F_{N^*}(k), \quad (7.26)$$

and

$$L_R(\mu_L) \equiv \int_{\mu_L}^{\infty} (z - \mu_L)f_L\left(z \mid m + \frac{1}{2h}, hn\right)dz$$

$$= \left\{\exp\left[m + \frac{1}{2h}\left(1 + \frac{1}{n}\right)\right]\right\}[1 - F_{N^*}(k)] - \mu_L[1 - F_{N^*}(y)] \qquad (7.27)$$

where

$$y = \left[\log\mu_L - \left(m + \frac{1}{2h}\right)\right]\sqrt{hn},$$

$$k = y - \frac{1}{\sqrt{hn}}.$$

States with very little information. As the parameter n of (7.20) approaches 0 while μ_L is held constant, both the mean and variance of the distribution become infinite and the ratio of the densities of any two points $\mu_L^{(1)}$ and $\mu_L^{(2)}$ such that $0 < \mu_L^{(1)} \leq \mu_L^{(2)} < \infty$ approaches the quantity $\mu_L^{(2)}/\mu_L^{(1)}$.

Proof. The behavior of the mean and variance follow from (7.23) and

(7.25). That the ratio of the densities of any two points $\mu_L^{(1)}$ and $\mu_L^{(2)}$ approaches $\mu_L^{(2)}/\mu_L^{(1)}$ is proved by observing that this ratio is

$$\left\{\exp\left\{-\tfrac{1}{2}hn\left[\left(\log \mu_L^{(1)} - m - \frac{1}{2h}\right)^2 - \left(\log \mu_L^{(2)} - m - \frac{1}{2h}\right)^2\right]\right\}\right\}\frac{\mu_L^{(2)}}{\mu_L^{(1)}},$$

and that as $n \to 0$ this quantity approaches $\mu_L^{(2)}/\mu_L^{(1)}$.

7.1.5. Preposterior Analysis with Fixed n.

Conditional Distribution of $(\tilde{g} \mid \mu, hn)$. If a sample of fixed size n is to be taken from an independent Lognormal process, the conditional distribution of $(g \mid \mu, hn)$ is Lognormal with density

$$D(g \mid \mu, hn) = f_L(g \mid \mu, hn). \tag{7.28}$$

Proof. To prove (7.28), first recall that an independent Lognormal process is defined as a process generating independent random variables $\tilde{x}_1, \ldots, \tilde{x}_2, \ldots, \tilde{x}_n$ with identical densities as shown in (7.9). Now the statistic

$$\tilde{g} = (\Pi \, \tilde{x}_i)^{1/n}$$

so that

$$\log \tilde{g} = \frac{1}{n} \Sigma \log \tilde{x}_i.$$

Let $\tilde{y}_i = \log \tilde{x}_i$. Then by (7.5), $\tilde{y}_1, \ldots, \tilde{y}_i, \ldots, \tilde{y}_n$ are random variables generated by an independent Normal process as defined in (11-1)*. Therefore, the argument used to prove (11-38)* suffices to prove (7.28).

It follows from (7.6) and (7.7) that

$$E(\tilde{g} \mid \mu, hn) = \exp\left[\mu + \frac{1}{2hn}\right], \tag{7.29}$$

$$V(\tilde{g} \mid \mu, hn) = \left\{\exp\left[2\mu + \frac{1}{hn}\right]\right\}(e^{1/hn} - 1). \tag{7.30}$$

Unconditional Distribution of the Statistic $\tilde{g}$. If the process mean $\exp[\tilde{\mu} + 1/2h]$ is treated as a random variable having a Lognormal distribution with parameter $(m' + 1/2h, n')$ and with known precision h, then the unconditional distribution of the statistic $\tilde{g}$ is Lognormal with density

$$D(g \mid m', n'; \; n) = f_L(g \mid m', hn_u) \tag{7.32a}$$

where

$$n_u = \frac{n'n}{n' + n}, \qquad \frac{1}{n_u} = \frac{1}{n'} + \frac{1}{n}. \tag{7.32b}$$

The mean and variance of the marginal distribution of $\tilde{g}$ are

$$E(\tilde{g} \mid m', n'; \; n) = \exp[m' + 1/2hn_u] \qquad (7.33a)$$

and

$$V(\tilde{g} \mid m', n'; \; n) = \left\{\exp\left[2m' + \frac{1}{hn_u}\right]\right\}\left\{\left(\exp\left[\frac{1}{hn_u}\right]\right) - 1\right\}. \qquad (7.33b)$$

Proof. To prove (7.32a) not that by Theorem 1, if $\tilde{g} \mid \mu$ is Lognormal with parameter (μ, n), then $\log \tilde{g} \mid \mu$ is Normal with parameter (μ, n).

We may obtain the distribution of $\tilde{\mu}$ by observing that by (7.16)

$$\tilde{\mu} + \frac{1}{2h} = \log \tilde{\mu}_L.$$

It follows from Theorem 1 that if $\tilde{\mu}_L$ is Lognormal with parameter $(m' + 1/2h, n')$, then $\tilde{\mu} + 1/2h$ is Normal with parameter $(m' + 1/2h, n')$. Hence $\tilde{\mu}$ is Normal with parameter (m', n').

Furthermore, (11-29)*, together with (7.3), implies that the unconditional distribution of the statistic $\log \tilde{g}$ is

$$D(\log g \mid m', n'; n) = \frac{1}{g} f_N (\log g \mid m', hn_u)$$

where

$$n_u = \frac{n'n}{n' + n}, \qquad \frac{1}{n_u} = \frac{1}{n'} + \frac{1}{n}.$$

Using the converse of Theorem 1 (which is easily proved), we obtain

$$D(g \mid m', n'; \; n) = f_L(g \mid m', hn_u)$$

as was to be proved.

Formulas (7.33a) and (7.33b) follow directly from (7.6) and (7.7).

Distribution of $\tilde{\mu}_L''$. If h is known, if the prior distribution of $\tilde{\mu}_L$ is Lognormal with parameter (m', n'), and if a sample then yields a sufficient statistic (g, n), formula (7.21) shows that the parameter (m'', n'') will have the value

$$m'' = \frac{n'm' + n \log g}{n' + n}, \qquad n'' = n' + n, \qquad (7.34)$$

and (7.23) shows that the mean $\tilde{\mu}_L''$ of the posterior distribution of $\tilde{\mu}_L$ will have the value

$$\tilde{\mu}_L'' = \exp\left[m'' + \frac{1}{2h}\left(1 + \frac{1}{n''}\right)\right]. \qquad (7.35)$$

When the $\tilde{m}''$ to be obtained by sampling with fixed n is still unknown and $\tilde{\mu}_L''$ is therefore a random variable, the distribution of $\tilde{\mu}_L''$ is determined by the unconditional distribution (7.32a) of $\tilde{g}$; the density of $\tilde{\mu}_L''$ is

$$D\left(\tilde{\mu}_L'' \mid m' + \frac{1}{2h}, n', n \right) = f_L\left(\tilde{\mu}_L'' \mid m' + \frac{1}{2h}\left(1 + \frac{1}{n''}\right), hn^* \right)$$

(7.36a)

where

$$n^* = \frac{n' + n}{n}n', \qquad \frac{1}{n^*} = \frac{1}{n'} - \frac{1}{n''}.$$

(7.36b)

Its mean and variance are

$$E\left(\tilde{\mu}_L'' \mid m' + \frac{1}{2h}, n'; n \right) = \exp\left[m' + \frac{1}{2h}\left(1 + \frac{1}{n'}\right) \right],$$

(7.37a)

and

$$V\left(\tilde{\mu}_L'' \mid m' + \frac{1}{2h}, n'; n \right) = \left\{ \exp\left[2m' + \frac{1}{h}\left(1 + \frac{1}{n'}\right) \right] \right\} [e^{1/hn^*} - 1].$$

(7.37b)

Since this distribution is of the same Lognormal form as the distribution (7.20) of $\tilde{\mu}_L$ itself, formulas for cumulative probabilities, partial expectations, and linear-loss integrals can be obtained from formulas* (7.22) through (7.25).

Proof. To prove (7.36a), observe that

$$\log \tilde{\mu}_L'' = \tilde{m}'' + \frac{1}{2h}\left(1 + \frac{1}{n''}\right)$$

$$= \frac{n'm'}{n''} + \left(\frac{n}{n''}\right) \log \tilde{g} + \frac{1}{2h}\left(1 + \frac{1}{n''}\right).$$

(7.38)

Since $\log \tilde{g}$ is Normal with parameter (m', n_u) by (7.32a), and since $\log \tilde{\mu}_L''$ is a linear transformation of $\log \tilde{g}$, it follows that $\log \tilde{\mu}_L''$ must also be Normal. The parameter of the distribution of $\log \tilde{g}$ is (m', n_u) so we have

$$E(\log \tilde{\mu}_L'') = \frac{n'm'}{n''} + \frac{n}{n''} E(\log \tilde{g}) + \frac{1}{2h}\left(1 + \frac{1}{n''}\right)$$

$$= m' + \frac{1}{2h}\left(1 + \frac{1}{n''}\right)$$

and

$$V(\log \tilde{\mu}_L'') = \left(\frac{n}{n''}\right)^2 V(\log \tilde{g}) = \frac{n}{hn''n'} = \frac{1}{hn^*}.$$

Thus log $\tilde{\mu}_L''$ is Normal with parameter

$$\left(m' + \frac{1}{2h}\left(1 + \frac{1}{n''} \right), n^* \right).$$

From Theorem 1, it follows that $\tilde{\mu}_L''$ is Lognormal with parameter

$$\left(m' + \frac{1}{2h}\left(1 + \frac{1}{n''} \right), n^* \right).$$

Formula (7.37a) is proven by observing that

$$E\left(\tilde{\mu}_L'' \mid m' + \frac{1}{2h}, n'; n \right) = \exp\left[m' + \frac{1}{2h}\left(1 + \frac{1}{n''} \right) + \frac{1}{2hn^*} \right]$$

$$= \exp\left[m' + \frac{1}{2h}\left(1 + \frac{1}{n'} \right) \right]$$

by (7.23) and (7.36b). Formula (7.37b) follows directly from (7.25).

7.2. Distribution of the Mean of Reported Field Sizes

In Chapter 6 it was suggested that the generation of reported field sizes within a given basin can be interpreted in terms of a well-defined stochastic process called a conditional data generating process model. That is, conditional upon being given the value θ of the generic parameter which characterizes the basin, and given a precise formulation of the data generating process model, one could simulate the discovery process in the basin. It was further remarked that each basin can be regarded as drawn from a population of basins. This observation led to the notion of an unconditional data generating process model, one in which the parameter θ is assumed to be a random variable.

The ideas above may be usefully exploited in discussing the distribution of the mean of reported field sizes in an unexplored basin. To illustrate, we will assume on the basis of the empirical evidence of Chapter 6 that the conditional sampling distribution of reported field sizes in a given basin is independent Lognormal. More precisely, let there be ℓ highly exploited basins. Without loss of generality we may assume that the discovery process commences at the same point in time for each of the ℓ basins. This point is arbitrarily scaled to 0. Then at time $t > 0$ a sample realization $\{r_{ij}^{(i)}, j = 1, 2, \ldots, t\}$ of reported field sizes in the ith basin will obtain for $1 \leq i \leq \ell$. This sample realization is generated by a Lognormal process with parameter $(\mu^{(i)}, H^{(i)})$ characteristic of the ith basin. The realizations from all ℓ basins may be conveniently displayed as follows:

Basin Number	Sample Realization at Time t	True Basin Parameter
1	$r_{t1}^{(1)}, r_{t2}^{(1)}, \ldots, r_{tj}^{(1)}, \ldots, r_{tt}^{(1)}$	$(\mu^{(1)}, H^{(1)})$
2	$r_{t1}^{(2)}, r_{t2}^{(2)}, \ldots, r_{tj}^{(2)}, \ldots, r_{tt}^{(2)}$	$(\mu^{(2)}, H^{(2)})$
.	. . . .	.
.	. . . .	.
.	. . . .	.
i	$r_{t1}^{(i)}, r_{t2}^{(i)}, \ldots, r_{tj}^{(i)}, \ldots, r_{tt}^{(i)}$	$(\mu^{(i)}, H^{(i)})$
.	. . . .	.
.	. . . .	.
.	. . . .	.
ℓ	$r_{t1}^{(\ell)}, r_{t2}^{(\ell)}, \ldots, r_{tj}^{(\ell)}, \ldots, r_{tt}^{(\ell)}$	$(\mu^{(\ell)}, H^{(\ell)})$

We may use the sample realizations above to make estimates $(\hat{\mu}^{(i)}, \hat{H}^{(i)})$, $i = 1, 2, \ldots, \ell$, of the parameter of each of the ℓ basins. Columns 2 and 3 of Exhibit 7.1 display such estimates derived from the data of Graphs 6.1 to 6.16. As was pointed out in Chapter 6, we would expect these estimates to vary from basin to basin, and just as for the r_{tj}'s within a basin, an empirical histogram of the $(\hat{\mu}^{(i)}, \hat{H}^{(i)})$'s may be drawn which will give insight into the nature of their variability. This histogram may be used in turn to aid in assessment of the variability of the unknown mean $\exp\left\{\mu^{(\ell+1)} + \dfrac{1}{2H^{(\ell+1)}}\right\}$ of reported field sizes in an $(\ell + 1)$st unexplored basin.

As a prelude to this assessment, the functional form of the histogram of $(\hat{\mu}^{(i)}, \hat{H}^{(i)})$'s should be examined to see whether the assumption that $\hat{\mu}^{(\ell+1)}$ is Lognormal conditional on knowing $H^{(\ell+1)}$ is a reasonable one. For if the true conditional sampling distribution of reported field sizes within the $(\ell + 1)$st basin is Lognormal, then the most convenient functional form for the distribution of $\hat{\mu}_L^{(\ell+1)}$ conditional on knowing $H^{(\ell+1)} = h$ is Lognormal, as this allows us to utilize theory like that of Section 7.1 in assessing a distribution for the unknown

$$\mu_L^{(\ell+1)} \equiv \exp\left\{\mu^{(\ell+1)} + \frac{1}{2H^{(\ell+1)}}\right\} \equiv \exp\left\{\mu^{(\ell+1)} + \frac{1}{2h}\right\}.$$

If it is reasonable to assume that given $\tilde{r}_{tj}^{(i)} > 0$,

1. $\qquad \tilde{r}_{tj}^{(i)} \mid \mu^{(i)} \sim f_L(r_{tj}^{(i)} \mid \mu^{(i)}, h), \quad i = 1, 2, \ldots, \ell + 1,$

$$j = 1, 2, \ldots, t, \qquad (7.39)$$

$$t = 1, 2, \ldots, T,$$

and the $\tilde{r}_{tj}^{(i)}$'s are mutually independent given t and j,

Exhibit 7.1

GRAPHICAL ESTIMATES OF $\mu^{(i)}$ AND $[H^{(i)}]^{-1/2}$

Graph	Estimate of $\mu^{(i)}$: $\hat{\mu}^{(i)}$	Estimate of $[H^{(i)}]^{-1/2}$: $[\hat{H}^{(i)}]^{-1/2}$	POINTS ON GRAPHS USED TO DETERMINE ESTIMATES IN EXHIBIT 7.2[a]			
			Median Estimate	16th Fractile Estimate: $f_{16}^{(i)}$	50th Fractile Estimate: $f_{50}^{(i)}$	84th Fractile Estimate: $f_{84}^{(i)}$
6.1	17.76675	1.64800	52.5	10.0	52.5	270.0
6.2	18.13300	1.62531	75.0	12.5	75.0	420.0
6.3	17.87595	1.36509	58.0	15.0	58.0	230.0
6.4	17.24950	.81853	31.0	13.5	31.0	70.0
6.5	17.56266	.91039	42.5	17.0	42.5	105.0
6.6	16.95100	.93807	23.0	13.6	23.0	37.5
6.7	16.91110	.49046	22.1	13.5	22.1	36.0
6.8	17.05419	.44278	25.5	13.5	25.5	40.0
6.9	16.81422	.77853	21.3	9.8	21.3	46.5
6.10	17.19990	.67541	29.5	15.0	29.5	58.5
6.11	16.67770	1.51057	17.5	3.9	17.5	80.0
6.12	16.88356	1.41290	21.5	5.1	21.5	86.0
6.13	17.21671	.89725	30.0	12.3	30.0	74.0
6.14	17.33301	1.28290	33.7	9.3	33.7	121.0
6.15	17.52908	1.37123	41.0	10.5	41.0	163.0
6.16	11.56172	1.88205	.105	.016	.105	.690

[a]The formula

$$\log \frac{1}{2}(f_{50}^{(i)}/f_{16}^{(i)} + f_{84}^{(i)}/f_{50}^{(i)})$$

is used to estimate $[H^{(i)}]^{-1/2}$; cf. J. Aitchison and J. A. C. Brown, *op. cit.*, pp. 32–33.

2. $$\tilde{\mu}^{(\ell+1)} \mid m' \sim f_N(\mu^{(\ell+1)} \mid m', hn'), \quad 1 \le i \le \ell + 1, \qquad (7.40)$$

and the $\tilde{\mu}^{(i)}$'s are mutually independent given m',

3. $$\tilde{m}' \sim f_N(m' \mid M', hN'), \qquad (7.41)$$

then (7.39), (7.40), and (7.41) imply that

$$\tilde{\mu}_L^{(\ell+1)} \sim f_L\left(\mu_L^{(\ell+1)} \mid M' + \frac{1}{2h}, hN_u\right), \qquad (7.42)$$

where

$$N_u \equiv \frac{N'n'}{N' + n'},$$

provided that we consider only fields of reported size greater than zero.

Proof. The marginal distribution of $\tilde{\mu}^{(\ell+1)}$ is found as follows:

$$
\begin{aligned}
D(\mu^{(\ell+1)} \mid M', N', n') &= \int_{-\infty}^{\infty} f_N(\mu^{(\ell+1)} \mid m', hn')f_N(m' \mid M', hN')dm' \\
&= f_N\left(\mu^{(\ell+1)} \mid M', h\left[\frac{1}{N'} + \frac{1}{n'}\right]^{-1}\right) \qquad (7.43) \\
&= f_N(\mu^{(\ell+1)} \mid M', hN_u).
\end{aligned}
$$

By (7.17)

$$\log \tilde{\mu}_L^{(\ell+1)} = \tilde{\mu}^{(\ell+1)} + \frac{1}{2h}$$

so that

$$\log \tilde{\mu}_L^{(\ell+1)} \sim f_N\left(\log \tilde{\mu}_L \mid M' + \frac{1}{2h}, hN_u\right).$$

By Theorem 1,

$$\tilde{\mu}_L^{(\ell+1)} \sim f_L\left(\mu_L^{(\ell+1)} \mid M' + \frac{1}{2h}, hN_u\right).$$

Expression (7.39) gives the conditional sampling distribution of reported field sizes given the basin's parameter; (7.40) is the prior distribution of the parameter $\tilde{\mu}^{(\ell+1)}$ which is a member of a population of $\tilde{\mu}$'s; and (7.41) is the prior distribution of the parameter $\tilde{m}'$ of this population.

As an initial test of the plausibility of assuming (7.40) and (7.41) the mean of the data displayed in each of Graphs 6.1 through 6.16 was estimated as shown in Exhibit 7.2 and seven means from Exhibit 7.2 were ordered according to size and plotted as fractile estimates on Lognormal probability paper after the fashion of Graphs 6.1 to 6.16. Among the nine different petroliferous areas represented in the graphs of Chapter 6, the data of Graphs 6.2, 6.3, 6.4, 6.5, 6.13, 6.14, and 6.15

are based on sufficiently homogeneous definitions of "reserves" to warrant their use. The result is shown in Graph 7.1. While the plots can be

Exhibit 7.2

ESTIMATES OF MEAN AND MODE USING GRAPHICAL ESTIMATES OF μ AND H

| Graph | Estimate of Mean[a] | | Estimate of Mode[a] | |
	$\hat{\mu}_i + \dfrac{1}{2\hat{H}^{(i)}}$	$\exp\left\{\hat{\mu} + \dfrac{1}{2\hat{H}^{(i)}}\right\}$	$\hat{\mu} - \dfrac{1}{\hat{H}^{(i)}}$	$\exp\left\{\hat{\mu} - \dfrac{1}{\hat{H}^{(i)}}\right\}$
6.1	19.11286	199.81	15.05085	3.4394
6.2	19.45382	280.98	15.49137	5.3436
6.3	18.80768	147.26	16.01248	8.9980
6.4	17.58450	43.336	16.57951	15.863
6.5	17.97706	64.173	16.73385	18.511
6.6	17.39098	35.712	16.07102	9.3886
6.7	17.03138	24.925	16.67055	17.3748
6.8	17.25222	31.084	16.85814	20.959
6.9	17.17727	28.841	16.26811	11.618
6.10	17.42798	37.058	16.74372	18.694
6.11	17.81861	54.767	14.39588	1.7868
6.12	17.88170	58.334	14.88727	2.9206
6.13	18.02177	67.288	16.41165	13.412
6.14	18.15592	76.737	15.68718	6.4993
6.15	18.46922	104.97	15.64881	6.2550
6.16	13.33278	.61712	8.01961	.2835

[a]In millions of barrels for Graphs 6.2 to 6.16. In 10^9 MCF for Graph 6.1.

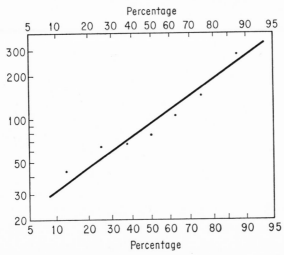

Graph 7.1. Estimated means of Graphs 6.2, 6.3, 6.4, 6.5, 6.13, 6.14, 6.15 in millions of barrels of oil

roughly fitted with a straight line, seven observations are not sufficient to determine with any degree of exactitude the true functional form of the histogram of means. Interpretation is made even more difficult when one notes that the ith mean is a function of both $\mu^{(i)}$ and $H^{(i)}$ and that the range of variation of estimates of $\frac{1}{2}H^{(i)}$ is just as large as that of estimates of $\mu^{(i)}$ for the above-mentioned seven observations; as can be seen in Exhibit 7.1, the $\hat{\mu}^{(i)}$'s vary from 17.22 to 18.13, while the $\frac{1}{2}\hat{H}^{(i)}$'s vary from .095 to 1.32. It is reasonable to assume that $H^{(\ell+1)}$ is known *only as a rough first approximation.* One that immediately suggests itself is to assume that

$$H^{(\ell+1)} = \frac{1}{\ell}\sum_{i=1}^{\ell} \hat{H}^{(i)},$$

which in this case yields $H^{(\ell+1)} = .85654$.

Once this assumption is made, however, it is possible to test the validity of (7.40) directly by plotting the $\hat{\mu}^{(i)}$'s on Normal probability

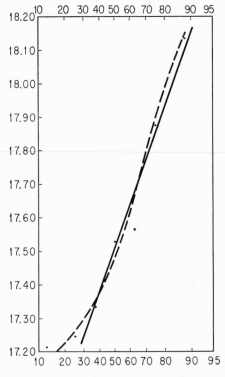

Graph 7.2. Estimates of $\mu^{(\ell)}$

paper in the same fashion as the means were plotted. Graph 7.2 displays the results. The plotted points can be roughly fitted with a straight line, aside from the smallest valued observation which imparts a noticeable curvature to the lower portion of a line of best visual fit.

Provided that we are willing to assume (7.40) and (7.41), that $H^{(\ell+1)} = .85654$, that we have no prior information on either $\hat{\mu}^{(\ell+1)}$ or m' other than that contained in the seven estimates $\hat{\mu}^{(1)}, \hat{\mu}^{(2)}, \ldots, \hat{\mu}^{(7)}$, and that we are willing to accept these estimates as certainty equivalents for the $\tilde{\mu}^{(i)}$'s of the basins they represent, the marginal distribution of $\tilde{\mu}_L^{(\ell+1)}$ will be Lognormal as in (7.42) with parameter $(M' + 1/2h, hN_u)$ where

$$H^{(\ell+1)} = h = .85654, \quad N' = 1, \quad n' = 7, \quad M' = \sum_{i=1}^{M} \hat{\mu}^{(i)} = 17.55713,$$

or with parameter (18.14096, .61190).

The posterior-preposterior theory of a Lognormal process with prior-priors as suggested by (7.40) and (7.41) is rather complicated and will not be done in this monograph, although the generalization from what has been done in Section 7.1 is straightforward.[3]

We may, however, carry out one more useful step in analysis by showing that the marginal distribution of reported field sizes greater than 0 in the $(\ell + 1)$st basin is Lognormal:

$$\tilde{r}^{(\ell+1)} \mid \tilde{r}^{(\ell+1)} > 0 \sim f_L\left(r^{(\ell+1)} \mid M', h\left[\frac{N_u}{N_u + 1}\right]\right) \tag{7.44}$$

where

$$N_u = \frac{n'N'}{N' + n'}.$$

Proof. Using (7.39) and (7.43), and assuming $H^{(\ell+1)} = h$, we obtain

$$D(r_{\ell j}^{(\ell+1)} \mid M', N', n) = \int_{-\infty}^{\infty} f_L(r_{\ell j}^{(\ell+1)} \mid \mu^{(\ell+1)}, h) f_N(\mu^{(\ell+1)} \mid M', hN_u) d\mu^{(\ell+1)}$$

$$= f_L\left(r_{\ell j}^{(\ell+1)} \mid M', h\left[\frac{N_u}{N_u + 1}\right]\right).$$

Thus the marginal distribution of $\tilde{r}_{\ell j}^{(\ell+1)} \mid \tilde{r}_{\ell j}^{(\ell+1)} > 0$ under the assumptions of the preceding paragraphs is Lognormal with parameter (17.55713, .45675).

---

[3]Some unpublished work of this type has been done for the Normal process by Gordon Antelman, Assistant Professor at the University of Chicago.

In spite of roughness in the approximations that lead to assumptions resulting in (7.44), there is little loss in generality in using a Lognormal prior, for it certainly is rich enough to capture all of the most reasonable of oilmen's prior judgements about the distribution of reported field sizes.

7.3. A Drilling Decision Problem

As a logical completion to the discussion of Chapters 6 and 7, it will be shown how the Lognormal distribution is used in the analysis of a drilling decision when management has adopted the expected utility criterion as a guide to action. A hypothetical drilling problem will be solved, using the utility-in-money curve of an actual oil and gas operator. The analysis will be done in nine parts:

7.3.1 Statement of the Problem

7.3.2 Formal Structure of the Problem

7.3.3 Utility Assignments

7.3.4 The Breakeven Point

7.3.5 Probability Assignments

7.3.6 Determination of the Parameter of a Lognormal Distribution from a Decision Maker's Statements

7.3.7 Expecting Out and Folding Back

7.3.8 Evaluation of the Logarithmic Utility Integral

7.3.9 Three Modified Approaches to Probability Assessments

Initially it will be assumed that the operator's probability assessment is made directly on the number of barrels of oil in the prospect under consideration and that this assessment is a blend of all available information about the amount of oil present. This approach is arbitrarily called Method I, and it is presented in Section 7.3.5. In Section 7.3.9 it will be shown how the operator may use different methods for making probability assessments:

Method II   He uses his knowledge of the ith basin to put a prior distribution on the unknown parameter $\tilde{\mu}^{(i)}$ which characterizes the basin by making probability statements about the distribution of the mean number of barrels in the basin.

Or he may decide to add yet another level of judgement:

Method III   He states his probability beliefs about the distribution
of the parameter $\tilde{m}'$ of the distribution of $\tilde{\mu}^{(i)}$.

The third method is particularly appropriate in analyzing a prospect in a
virtually unexplored basin. All three methods are illustrated in detail,
and a fourth method of a quite different nature is briefly outlined.

The reader should note that the first three approaches to probability
assessment just mentioned parallel the three levels of analysis of the size
distribution of oil and gas fields in this and the preceding chapter: The
conditional sampling distribution of field sizes was examined in Chapter
6, followed by a discussion of the distribution of the basinal parameters
$(\mu^{(i)}, H^{(i)})$, $i = 1, 2, \ldots, \ell$, in 7.2; then came a discussion of the parameter
(M', hN') of the distribution of the parameter $\tilde{m}'$ of the distribution of
$\tilde{\mu}^{(\ell+1)}$ conditional on knowing $H^{(\ell+1)}$.

The multilevel approach to probability assessments presented here
can serve a truly useful function in allowing the operator to break up a
difficult problem in judgement into two or three parts so that he may
concentrate on one part at a time in place of considering all parts at once.

7.3.1. A Drilling Decision Problem. The exploration manager of
Girt Oil Company[4] wishes to decide whether or not to drill one of its
prospects. The prospect has been shot, and in his opinion the probability
of hitting oil is .3.

Dry hole costs are estimated at $135,000. Completion costs will be an
additional $75,000. Net to working interest will be $2.19 per barrel,
according to the exploration manager.

Girt is planning to drill the well with a partner, and the terms of their
agreement are that Girt will bear 25 per cent of the well cost to the casing
point,[5] and receive 50 per cent of cash inflow from production. Thus,
Girt's share of drilling expenses will be about $(\frac{1}{4} \times \$135,000) = \$33,750$.
If the well is completed, 50 per cent or $(\frac{1}{2} \times \$75,000) = \$37,500$ of completion costs must be paid by Girt.

The exploration manager feels that the most likely number of barrels
of reserves that will be discovered *if* the well hits oil is 800,000. He estimates the chances of finding more than a million barrels at 2 out of 10.

---

[4]Fictitious company but realistic cost figures, i.e., cost figures adapted from a real
drilling venture.

[5]The point at which the decision to complete or not to complete the well must
be made.

This judgement is a blend of his analysis of historical results in the vicinity of the prospect together with the information he has on this particular prospect.

The utility-in-money curve of Girt's president is reproduced in Exhibit 7.4 on page 178 and discussed in detail in Section 7.3.3. The president owns 95 per cent of Girt Oil Company stock.

Should Girt Drill the Well?

We shall show that Girt should drill the well and that it should be completed if more than 34,090 barrels of reserves[6] are discovered; if less than this amount are discovered, the well should be abandoned.

7.3.2. Formal Structure of the Problem. The drilling problem can be pictorially represented by a flow diagram in which the operator is imagined to be playing a game against nature which allows him a two-

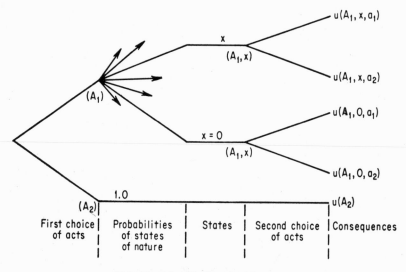

Exhibit 7.3. Drilling decision tree

***

[6]In order to simplify the presentation we assume that a drill stem test will tell exactly how many barrels of reserves are in the prospect. However, this assumption can be dropped and the method of analysis of 7.2 can easily be expanded to take account of any uncertainty due to the inability of a drill stem test to tell us the exact amount of reserves in the prospect.

stage choice. The moves in the game are laid out in sequence from left to right in Exhibit 7.3. Before the flow of the game can be explained, its terminology must be defined:

A_1 = the act "drill the well."

A_2 = the act "do not drill the well."

a_1 = the act "complete the well."

a_2 = the act "abandon the well."

$\tilde{x}$ = the random variable "number of barrels of recoverable reserves in the prospect," $\tilde{x} \geq 0$.

$u(A_1, x, a_1)$ = the utility of drilling the well, discovering an amount x of recoverable reserves, then completing the well.

$u(A_1, x, a_2)$ = the utility of drilling the well, discovering an amount x of recoverable reserves, and then abandoning the well.

$u(A_2)$ = the utility of not drilling the well.

x_b = the number of barrels of recoverable reserves at which $u(A_1, x_b, a_2) = u(A_1, x_b, a_1)$, i.e., the breakeven.

$P(\text{dry})$ = the probability of a dry hole if the well is drilled, i.e., $P(\tilde{x} = 0) = P(\text{dry})$.

We will assume that $\tilde{x}$ is distributed as follows:

$$\tilde{x} \mid \tilde{x} > 0 \sim f_L(x \mid \mu, H) \tag{7.45a}$$

where the parameter (μ, H) is to be determined from the operator's probability statements about $\tilde{x}$, and

$$P(\tilde{x} = 0) = P(\text{dry}). \tag{7.45b}$$

The sequence of moves in the game is:

1. The operator selects A_1 or A_2.

2. If he selects A_1, his choice is followed by nature selecting an x according to (7.45).

3. After nature selects x, the operator chooses one of the two acts, a_1 or a_2.

4. If the operator chooses a_1, the consequence is $u(A_1, x, a_1)$.
   If the operator chooses a_2, the consequence is $u(A_1, x, a_2)$.

5. If the operator selects A_2, he has no opportunity to determine x, his asset position is unchanged, and the consequence is $u(A_2)$.

7.3.3. Utility Assignments. The utility-in-money curve depicted in Exhibit 7.4 will be used in the subsequent analysis. This curve is that of a real oil and gas operator (William Beard of Beard Oil Company), and it has been adapted from *Decisions under Uncertainty*,[7] with permission of

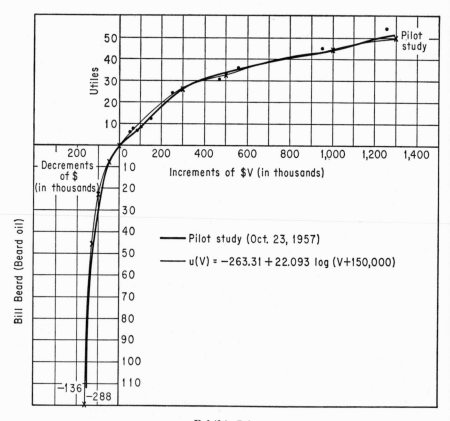

Exhibit 7.4.

---

[7]C. J. Grayson, Jr., *op. cit.*, pp. 291–313.

the author. On pages 291 to 313, Professor Grayson explains how he obtained utility functions like that of Exhibit 7.4. Each of the utility-in-money curves that he obtained were fitted by eye to plotted points such as those of Exhibit 7.4.

In attempting to formalize the analysis of decision problems where utility-in-money curves are not linear, as indeed they are not in Exhibit 7.4, the question arises, "Is there any function that is easy to manipulate analytically which fits an empirical utility-in-money curve such as shown in Exhibit 7.4?" Several functions immediately suggest themselves: Quadratic, cubic, and logarithmic functions are three. It happens that a logarithmic function fits the curve of Exhibit 7.4 very well; that is, the utility $u(v)$ of $\$v$ to William Beard as of October, 1957, is closely approximated by the function

$$u(v) = -263.31 + 22.093 \log_e (v + 150{,}000). \qquad (7.46)$$

To see how (7.46) was obtained, suppose that we choose to fit a function of the form

$$u(v) = k_1 + k_2 \log_e (v + k_3), \qquad k_1, k_2, k_3 \text{ constant}, \qquad (7.47)$$

to the pilot study curve of Exhibit 7.4. We first observe that $\log_e(v + k_3)$ approaches $-\infty$ as $v + k_3$ approaches 0. Now the utility of any amount less than $-\$150{,}000$ appears to approach $-\infty$ in Exhibit 7.4 so that to insure $v + k_3 \geq 0$ we must set $k_3 = \$150{,}000$. This leaves parameters k_1 and k_2 to be determined. We may arbitrarily select any two points on Bill Beard's utility curve and in view of our freedom of choice of k_1 and k_2 insure that $u(v) = k_1 + k_2 \log_e (v + k_3)$ goes through these two points. The points selected were $u(0) = 0$ and $u(10^6) = 45$. The simultaneous equations

$$0 = k_1 + k_2 \log_e 150{,}000$$

$$45 = k_1 + k_2 \log_e 1{,}150{,}000$$

were then solved to give $k_1 = 22.093$ and $k_2 = 263.31$. The fit is astoundingly good.

Neither quadratic nor cubic functions will fit Bill Beard's curve as well as (7.46). A quadratic will fit on the left-hand portion of the curve, but will begin to bend down much too soon in the right-hand portion of the curve to render it as good a fit as (7.46). The cubic has an inflexion point which renders it unsuitable for Bill Beard's curve by comparison with (7.46).[8]

Given (7.46) we must make a translation from x into dollars before numerical utility assignments can be made:

(1) If Girt does not drill the well, it invests 0 dollars for 0 dollars return, so

$$u(A_2) = -263.31 + 22.093 \log_e (0 + 150{,}000) = 0 \text{ utiles.}$$

(2) If Girt drills the well, and it is abandoned, it will have invested $33,750 in drilling costs for 0 barrels of reserves, so

$$u(A_1, 0, a_2) = -263.31 + 22.093 \log_e (-33{,}750 + 150{,}000)$$
$$= -5.63 \text{ utiles.}$$

(3) If Girt drills, x barrels of recoverable reserves are discovered, and the well is completed, Girt will receive 50 per cent of $2.19 net to working interest per barrel for a cash outlay of $33,750 for drilling expenses and of $37,500 for completion expenses, so the net cash flow is

$$\$1.10x - (\$33{,}750 + \$37{,}500) = \$1.10x - \$71{,}250.$$

Thus

$$u(A_1, x, a_1) = -263.31 + 22.093 \log_e (1.10x + 78{,}750)$$

is the utility of drilling the well, observing x, and completing.

---

[8]Lest the reader believe that a logarithmic function is suited to all money-in-utility curves, he should refer to the utility curve of Robert Halliday on page 308 of *Decisions under Uncertainty*. A cubic will provide a much better fit to this curve than a function like (7.46).

When $\tilde{v}$ is Lognormally distributed and the utility-in-money curve $u(v)$ is accurately approximated by a polynomial

$$\sum_{i=1}^{n} a_i v^i$$

for all v in the domain of $u(v)$, computation is very simple. For then integrals such as

$$I(k) \equiv \int_0^k u(v) f_L(v \mid \mu, h) dv$$
$$\doteq \sum_{i=1}^{n} a_i \int_0^k v^i f_L(v \mid \mu, h) dv$$

may be directly evaluated using (7.8b) and Normal probability tables; i.e.,

$$I(k) = \sum_{i=1}^{n} a_i e^{i\mu + (i^2/2h)} F_N^*(v_i(a))$$

where

$$v_i(a) \equiv [\log a - \mu]\sqrt{h} - \frac{i}{\sqrt{h}}.$$

7.3.4.   The Breakeven Point x_b. There is a breakeven number of barrels of reserves x_b such that

$$u(A_1, x, a_1) \underset{>}{\overset{<}{\gtrless}} u(A_1, x, a_2) \quad \text{if} \quad x \underset{>}{\overset{<}{\gtrless}} x_b.$$

Since it has just been shown that if the well is completed, $\$1.10x -$ $\$71,250$ accrues to Girt conditional on discovering x barrels of reserves and that the cost of abandoning the well is $-\$33,750$, the breakeven number x_b must be such that

$$-\$33,750 = \$1.10x_b - \$71,250$$

or

$$x_b = 34,090 \text{ barrels.} \tag{7.48}$$

7.3.5.   Probability Assignments. Needed for the analysis are $P(\text{dry})$, $P(\text{hit})$, and the probability distribution function $f(x \mid \mu, H)$ of $\tilde{x} \mid \tilde{x} > 0$. The exploration manager has estimated that $P(\text{hit}) = .3$, so that $P(\text{dry}) = 1 - P(\text{hit}) = .7$. Conditional on hitting (on $\tilde{x} > 0$) he estimates the most likely value of $\tilde{x}$ as 800,000 barrels and judges $P(\tilde{x} > 1,000,000) = .2$.

The parameter (μ, H) of the distribution of $\tilde{x} \mid \tilde{x} > 0$ must be determined from the judgement made above about the distribution of $\tilde{x} \mid \tilde{x} > 0$, and the procedure for doing this is outlined in Section 7.3.6 where the (μ, H) corresponding to the exploration manager's assessment is shown to be (13.597, 204.08).

7.3.6.   Determination of the Parameter (μ, H) ***of a Lognormal Distribution from a Decision Maker's Statements.*** Suppose that a random variable $\tilde{x}$ is Lognormally distributed:

$$H > 0,$$
$$\tilde{x} \sim f_L(x \mid \mu, H), \quad 0 < x < \infty,$$
$$-\infty < \mu < \infty,$$

and suppose that (μ, H) is to be selected in concordance with the decision maker's statements about the mode of the distribution of $\tilde{x}$, and about a right tail probability. Define

$x_m =$ the mode of the distribution of $\tilde{x}$,

$\sigma^2 = \dfrac{1}{H}$,

$x^*, p =$ numbers such that $p = G_L(x^* \mid \mu, H)$,

$\tilde{u} =$ a standardized, Normally distributed random variable (mean 0 and standard deviation 1).

The one restriction that must be placed on the decision maker's assessments is that he select an $x^* > x_m$. The reason for this restriction will be presented later.

Given x_m, x^*, and p by the decision maker, μ and H are calculated in the following manner:

1. From tables of the cumulative standardized Normal distribution, $P_N(\tilde{u} > u^* \mid 0, 1)$, look up the u^* for which

$$P_N(\tilde{u} > u^* \mid 0, 1) = p \tag{7.49}$$

2. Calculate $\sigma = (1/H)^{1/2}$ from

$$\sigma = \frac{-u^* + \sqrt{u^{*2} - 4 \log_e (x_m/x^*)}}{2}. \tag{7.50}$$

3. Having calculated σ, calculate μ from the formula

$$\mu = (\log_e x_m) + \sigma^2 \tag{7.51}$$

An Example

In the drilling problem of 7.3.1, Girt Oil Company's exploration manager assessed the mode of the distribution of $\tilde{x}$ at 800,000 barrels, and the probability that $\tilde{x} > 1,000,000$ barrels at .2, conditional upon hitting. These assessments correspond to

$x_m = 800,000$ barrels,

$x^* = 1,000,000$ barrels, and

$p = .2$.

1. From tables of the cumulative standardized Normal distribution, the u^* for which

$$P_N(\tilde{u} > u^* \mid 0, 1) = .2$$

is found to be .842.

2. Substituting $u^* = .842$, $x_m = 800,000$, and $x^* = 1,000,000$ into the equation

$$\sigma = \frac{-u^* + \sqrt{u^{*2} - 4 \log (x_m/x^*)}}{2} \tag{7.50}$$

and solving for σ gives

$$\sigma = .070, \quad \text{or} \quad H = \frac{1}{\sigma^2} = 204.082.$$

3. From equation (7.51)

$$\mu = (\log x_m) + \sigma^2 = (13.592 + .005) = 13.597.$$

A proof that the procedure above leads to the correct values of the parameters μ and H is given below.

Proof.

1. By differentiating $f_L(x \mid \mu, H)$ with respect to x we see that

$$x_m = e^{\mu - \frac{1}{H}} = e^{\mu - \sigma^2}, \tag{7.52}$$

from which

$$\log x_m = \mu - \sigma^2,$$

or

$$(\log x_m) + \sigma^2 = \mu. \tag{7.51}$$

2. If the decision maker gives the probability that $\tilde{x}$ is greater than a particular x^*, then by (7.5)

$$P_L(\tilde{x} > x^* \mid \mu, H) = P_N(\log \tilde{x} > \log x^* \mid \mu, H)$$

$$= P_N(\tilde{u} > u^* \mid 0, 1) = p,$$

where

$$u^* = (\log x^* - \mu)\sqrt{H} = \frac{(\log x^* - \mu)}{\sigma}. \tag{7.53}$$

3. Substituting from (7.51) above,

$$u^* = \frac{\log x^* - \log x_m - \sigma^2}{\sigma},$$

or

$$0 = \sigma^2 + \sigma u^* + \log\left(\frac{x_m}{x^*}\right),$$

or

$$\sigma = \frac{-u^* \pm \sqrt{u^{*2} - 4\log(x_m/x^*)}}{2}. \tag{7.54}$$

This is the formula for calculating σ once u^* is looked up in the tables for a given p. The larger of the two values of σ that can be calculated with the above formula is the desired σ.

4. In order to establish that the calculating procedure will always give the correct value for σ, it must be proven that there is only one distinct, real, positive root to the equation

$$\sigma^2 + \sigma u^* + \log\left(\frac{x_m}{x^*}\right) = 0 \qquad (7.55)$$

under the condition $x^* > x_m$, for σ is constrained (by the definition of the Lognormal density function) to be greater than zero. The proof is as follows: Let

$$g(\sigma) = \sigma^2 + \sigma u^* + \log\left(\frac{x_m}{x^*}\right). \qquad (7.56)$$

Since $x_m < x^*$, $\log(x_m/x^*) < 0$, so that $g(0) < 0$. Also, $g(\infty) = \infty$. Inasmuch as $g(\sigma)$ is a quadratic it is clear from the graph below that $g(\sigma) = 0$ can have only one positive real root:

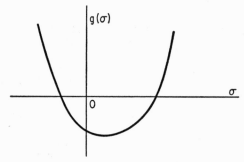

7.3.7. Expecting Out and Folding Back. Since we have adopted the expected utility criterion, we wish to choose the sequence of acts which will maximize expected utility. In order to determine the expected utility of the best two-stage act, we may expect out and fold back according to the procedure explained in Chapter 10 of *Decisions under Uncertainty*. Referring to Exhibit 7.3, this requires the following steps:

1. At each (A, x) node choose that act which maximizes $u(A, x, a)$. The utility of being at an (A, x) node will be written as $\max_a u(A, x, a) \equiv u^*(A, x)$.

2. Expect out the utilities $u^*(A, \tilde{x})$ with respect to $\tilde{x}$. This is the expected utility of being at an (A) node and it will be written as $E_x \max_a (A, \tilde{x}, a) \equiv u^*(A)$.

3. Choose that A for which $u^*(A)$ is greatest; i.e., $\max_A E_x \max_a u(A, \tilde{x}, a) = u^*$.

Calculation of u*(A₁). To find $u^*(A_1)$ we note that if act A_1 is taken, then act a_1 is the better act if $\tilde{x} > x_b$, and act a_2 is the better act if $\tilde{x} < x_b$. Thus $u^*(A_1)$ may be written as

$$u^*(A_1) = E_x \max_a u(A_1, \tilde{x}, a)$$

$$= P(\text{hit}) \int_0^{x_b} u(A_1, z, a_2) f_L(z \mid \mu, H) \, dz$$

$$+ P(\text{hit}) \int_{x_b}^{\infty} u(A_1, z, a_1) f_L(z \mid \mu, H) \, dz$$

$$+ [1 - P(\text{hit})] u(A_1, 0, a_2)$$

$$= u(A_1, 0, a_2)[1 - P(\text{hit}) G_L(x_b \mid \mu, H)]$$

$$+ P(\text{hit}) \int_{x_b}^{\infty} u(A_1, z, a_1) f_L(z \mid \mu, H) \, dz. \tag{7.58}$$

From 7.3.3, 7.3.4, and 7.3.5, we have

$$u(A_1, 0, a_2) = -5.63,$$

$$u(A_1, x, a_1) = -263.31 + 22.093 \log_e (1.10x + 78{,}750),$$

$$(\mu, H) = (13.597, 204.08),$$

$$P(\text{hit}) = .3,$$

and

$$x_b = 34{,}090.$$

Substituting in (7.58) gives

$$u^*(A_1) = -82.933 +$$

$$6.6279 \int_{34{,}090}^{\infty} \log_e (1.10z + 78{,}750) f_L (z \mid 13.597{,}204.08) dz. \tag{7.59}$$

The integral in (7.59) cannot be evaluated in terms of a closed expression, but in 7.3.7 it is shown to be equal to 90.042 by numerical integration. The relative error in this integration is less than 1 per cent. Thus

$$u^*(A_1) = -82.933 + 90.042 \doteq 7.11 \text{ utiles}, \tag{7.60}$$

with an error in calculation of less than .75 utiles, as will be shown.
Calculation of u*. We show that A_1 is the better initial act by noting

that from the above calculation and from 7.3.3, the following flow diagram obtains:

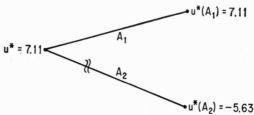

Conditional on taking act A_1, a_1 is preferred to a_2 if $\tilde{x} > x_b = 34{,}090$, as shown in 7.3.4. Therefore, our conclusion is that *Girt should drill the well and then should complete it if more than 34,090 barrels are discovered. If less than 34,090 barrels are discovered, it should abandon the well.*

7.3.8. Evaluation of the Logarithmic Utility Integral. We define

$$I = \int_{x_b}^{\infty} [\log (z + a)] f_L(z \mid \mu, H) \, dz, \qquad a, x_b > 0,$$

and show how to evaluate it numerically in this subsection.

The integral I is similar to the integral in (7.59) except for constants; so after showing how to integrate I numerically, we will numerically integrate the integral in (7.59). The integration of I will proceed in two main steps:

1. The domain of integration x_b to ∞ is divided into two parts by selecting a $k_0 \ni x_b < k_0 < \infty$. The left tail of I, defined as

$$I_1 = \int_{x_b}^{k_0} \log (z + a) f_L(z \mid \mu, H) dz, \qquad (7.61)$$

is numerically integrated by Simpson's Rule so that the error in the result is less than a desired (small) amount e_1.

2. The right tail of I, defined as

$$I_2 = \int_{k_0}^{\infty} \log (z + a) f_L(z \mid \mu, H) \, dz, \qquad (7.62)$$

is approximated by the function

$$\int_{w}^{\infty} (\mu + H^{-1/2}u) f_{N^*}(u) \, du \qquad (7.63)$$

where

$$w = [\log k_0 - \mu]\sqrt{H},$$

and k_0 is chosen so that the error in this approximation is less than a desired (small) amount e_2.

To show that the procedure above will allow us to make the total error in our approximation to I smaller than an arbitrarily small pre-specified number e, we must prove two lemmas.

Lemma 1. Let $a, x_b > 0$, $k_0 > x_b$, and define $w = [\log k_0 - \mu]\sqrt{H}$ and $u = [\log z - \mu]\sqrt{H}$. Then for any $e_2 > 0$ there exists a k_0 such that

$$\Delta(k_0) \equiv \left| \int_{k_0}^{\infty} \log (z + a) f_L(z \mid \mu, H) dz \right.$$

$$\left. - \int_{w}^{\infty} (\mu + H^{-1/2}u) f_{N^*}(u) du \right| < e_2.$$

Proof. Define

$$\delta(k_0) = \left| \int_{k_0}^{\infty} \log (z + a) f_L(z \mid \mu, H) dz \right.$$

$$\left. - \int_{k_0}^{\infty} \log z \, f_L(z \mid \mu, H) dz \right| \cdot$$

Clearly $\lim_{k_0 \to \infty} \delta(k_0) = 0$. Now by making the integrand transform $u = [\log z - \mu]\sqrt{H}$ in the second integral in $\delta(k_0)$, we may write

$$\delta(k_0) = \left| \int_{k_0}^{\infty} \log (z + a) f_L(z \mid \mu, H) dz \right.$$

$$\left. - \int_{w}^{\infty} (\mu + H^{-1/2}u) f_{N^*}(u) du \right|.$$

On comparing terms we see that $\delta(k_0) = \Delta(k_0)$.
Thus

$$\lim_{k_0 \to \infty} \delta(k_0) = \lim_{k_0 \to \infty} \Delta(k_0) = 0,$$

so that by choosing k_0 large enough, we may make $\Delta(k_0)$ less than an arbitrarily small $e_2 > 0$.

Lemma 2. If k_0 is chosen such that $\Delta(k_0) < e_2$, where e_2 is a pre-specified (small) number, and $k_0 > x_b$, then

$$g(k_0) \equiv \left| \int_{x_b}^{\infty} \log (z + a) f_L(z \mid \mu, H) dz \right.$$

$$- \left[\int_{x_b}^{k_0} \log (z + a) f_L(z \mid \mu, H) dz \right.$$

$$\left. \left. + \int_{k_0}^{\infty} (\mu + H^{-1/2}u) f_{N^*}(u) du \right] \right| < e_2.$$

Proof. Divide the domain of integration x_b to ∞ of I into two parts: x_b to k_0 and k_0 to ∞. Then $g(k_0) = \Delta(k_0)$ and, by Lemma 1, $g(k_0) < e_2$.

In addition to Lemma 2, we need only remark that the error in numerical integration of I_1 by Simpson's Rule may be made arbitrarily small[9] to conclude that the total error in approximating $I = I_1 + I_2$ via steps 1 and 2 may be made less than an arbitrarily small number $e = e_1 + e_2$.

In order to have a way of conveniently computing a bound on the error $\Delta(k_0)$ *given* a particular k_0, we prove Lemma 3.

Lemma 3. Given that $w = [\log k_0 - \mu]\sqrt{H}$,

$$\Delta(k_0) < |\log (\{\exp[\mu + H^{-1/2}w]\} + a) - (\mu + H^{-1/2}w) | \, G_{N^*}(w).$$

Proof. If we make the integrand transform

$$u = [\log z - \mu]\sqrt{H},$$

and remember that

$$w = [\log k_0 - \mu]\sqrt{H},$$

we may write

$$\Delta(k_0) = \left| \int_w^\infty \{\log (\{\exp[\mu + H^{-1/2}u]\} + a) - (\mu + H^{-1/2}u)\} f_{N^*}(u)du \right|.$$

Since

$$\{\log (\{\exp[\mu + H^{-1/2}u]\} + a) - (\mu + H^{-1/2}u)\}$$

decreases monotonically as u increases,

$$\Delta(k_0) < \left| \int_w^\infty \{\log (\{\exp[\mu + H^{-1/2}w]\} + a) - (\mu + H^{-1/2}w)\} f_{N^*}(u)du \right|,$$

or,

$$\Delta(k_0) < \left| \log (\{\exp[\mu + H^{-1/2}w]\} + a) - (\mu + H^{-1/2}w) \right| G_{N^*}(w).$$

Now aside from the constant -82.933, the integral in (7.59) is

$$6.6279 \int_{34,090}^\infty [\log (1.10z + 78,750)] f_L(z \mid 13.597, 204.08)dz,$$

or

$$(.63171)G_L(34,090 \mid 13.597,204.08)$$

$$+ 6.6279 \int_{34,090}^\infty [\log (z + 71,591)] f_L(z \mid 13.597,204.08)dz. \quad (7.59')$$

---

[9] See J. B. Scarborough, *Numerical Mathematical Analysis*, 4th ed. (Baltimore: The Johns Hopkins University Press, 1958), p. 178.

The integral in (7.59') is identical to I, aside from the multiplicative constant 6.6279, when

$$x_b = 34{,}090, \qquad \mu = 13.597,$$

$$a = 71{,}591, \qquad H = 204.08.$$

If we choose $w = 2$ so that the relative error in integration of I_2 using the approximation (7.63) is less than 2 per cent (as will be shown shortly), we must set

$$k_0 = e^{\mu + H^{-\frac{1}{2}w}} = e^{13.737} = 924{,}470.$$

Thus if we split the integral in (7.59') into two parts,

$$I'_1 = \int_{34{,}090}^{924{,}470} [\log (z + 71{,}591)] f_L(z \mid 13.597{,}204.08) dz \quad (7.64a)$$

and

$$I'_2 = \int_{924{,}470}^{\infty} [\log (z + 71{,}591)] f_L(z \mid 13.597{,}204{,}08) dz, \qquad (7.64b)$$

we may evaluate I'_1 and I'_2 as suggested in the preceding pages.

Evaluation of I'_1. To evaluate I'_1 by Simpson's Rule,[10] the interval of integration 34,090 to 924,470 is divided into twenty equal intervals of width $\omega = 44{,}519$. Then letting

$$y_0 = [\log (34{,}090 + 71{,}591)] f_L(34{,}090 \mid 13.597{,}204.08),$$

$$y_1 = [\log (78{,}609 + 71{,}591)] f_L(78{,}609 \mid 13.597{,}204.08),$$

$$\cdot$$
$$\cdot$$
$$\cdot$$

$$y_{20} = [\log (924{,}470 + 71{,}591)] f_L(924{,}470 \mid 13.597{,}204.08),$$

Simpson's Rule is

$$I'_1 = \frac{\omega}{3} \sum_{j=0}^{20} c_j y_j$$

where

$$c_0 = c_{20} = 1, \qquad c_1 = 4,$$

and

$$c_{2i} = 2, \qquad c_{2i+1} = 4$$

---

[10]See J. B. Scarborough, *op. cit.*, pp. 132–133.

for $i = 1, 2, \ldots, 9$. A table of values of $c_j y_j$ for $j = 0, 1, \ldots, 20$ is presented in Exhibit 7.5.

Exhibit 7.5

VALUES OF y_j AND $c_j y_j$

z	j	$\log (z + 71{,}591)$	$f_L(z \mid 13.597{,}208.08)^a$	$y_j \times 10^{-6}$	c_j	$c_j y_j \times 10^{-6}$
34,090	0	—	.00000 $\times 10^{-6}$	0	1	—.
78,609	1	—	0 10^{-6}	0	4	—
123,128	2	—	0 10^{-6}	0	2	—
167,647	3	—	0 10^{-6}	0	4	—
212,166	4	—	0 10^{-6}	0	2	—
256,685	5	—	0 10^{-6}	0	4	—
301,204	6	—	0 10^{-6}	0	2	—
345,723	7	—	0 10^{-6}	0	4	—
390,242	8	—	0 10^{-6}	0	2	—
434,761	9	—	0 10^{-6}	0	4	—
479,280	10	—	0 10^{-6}	0	2	—
527,799	11	—	0 10^{-6}	0	4	—
568,318	12	13.369	.00004 10^{-6}	.00053	2	.00106
612,837	13	13.436	.00518 10^{-6}	.06959	4	.27836
657,356	14	13.500	.15542 10^{-6}	2.09817	2	4.19634
601,875	15	13.559	1.26332 10^{-6}	17.12936	4	68.51744
746,394	16	13.615	4.36762 10^{-6}	59.46515	2	118.93020
790,913	17	13.665	7.01893 10^{-6}	95.91368	4	383.65472
835,432	18	13.718	5.85318 10^{-6}	80.29392	2	160.58784
879,951	19	13.767	2.54718 10^{-6}	35.06703	4	140.26812
924,470	20	13.811	.83429 10^{-6}	11.52238	1	11.52238
968,989	21	13.855	2.40895 10^{-6}	33.37600		

Total: 887.956×10^{-6}

^{a}The ordinate $f_L(z \mid 13.597{,}208.08)$ is found from unit normalized Normal probability tables by using (7.3); i.e.,

$$f_L(z \mid 13.597{,}208.08) = \frac{1}{z} f_{N^*}([\log z - 13.597] \sqrt{204.08}) \sqrt{204.08}.$$

Using this rule, we have

$$\sum_{j=0}^{20} c_j y_j = (887.956 \times 10^{-6}) \doteq .88796 \times 10^{-3},$$

so that

$$I_1' = \frac{44{,}519}{3}(.88796 \times 10^{-3}) \doteq 13.177.$$

The error in the calculations[11] above is less than

$$-\frac{\omega}{90}[y_{-1} + y_{21} - 4(y_0 + y_{20}) + 7(y_1 + y_{19})$$
$$- 8(y_2 + y_4 + \ldots + y_{18}) + 8(y_3 + y_5 + \ldots + y_{17})]$$

$$= -\left(\frac{44,519}{90} \times 10^{-6}\right)[0 + 33.376 - 4(0 + 11.522) + 7(0 + 35.067)$$
$$- 8(0 + \ldots + 0 + .00053 + 2.0982 + 17.129 + 95.914)$$
$$+ 8(0 + \ldots + 0 + .06959 + 17.129 + 95.914)]$$

$$\doteq 107.105 \times 10^{-3} = .10710.$$

The relative error is thus less than

$$\frac{.10710}{13.1770} = .008$$

or less than 1 per cent. Although more accuracy could be obtained without increasing the number of calculations by increasing the number of significant figures retained in the calculations of Exhibit 7.5, in view of the lack of sensitivity of the final result to an error in the region of 1 per cent, greater accuracy is not warranted.

Evaluation of I_2'. To evaluate

$$I_2' = \int_{924,470}^{\infty} \log (z + 71,591) f_L(z \mid 13.597, 204.08) dz \qquad (7.64b)$$

using the approximation (7.63), we remember that we chose $w = 2$, so that I_2' is approximated by

$$\int_2^{\infty} (\mu + H^{-1/2}u) f_{N^*}(u) du = \mu G_{N^*}(2) + H^{-1/2} f_{N^*}(2). \qquad (7.65)$$

Substituting for μ and H from (7.64b), looking up $G_{N^*}(2)$ in cumulative standardized Normal probability tables, and $f_{N^*}(2)$ in tables of standardized Normal probability ordinates, we obtain

$$I_2' \doteq (13.597)(.02275) + (.0700)(.05399) = .3131.$$

---

[11]See J. B. Scarborough, *op. cit.*, p. 178.

Using the result of Lemma 3, we compute the error in this approximation to be less than

$$e_2 = (.2463)(.02275) = .0056$$

for a relative error less than

$$\frac{.0056}{.3131} = .0179$$

or less than 2 per cent.

Finally, we have

$$I_1' + I_2' \doteq 13.177 + .3131 \doteq 13.490.$$

From (7.59) and $I \doteq 13.490$, we may now compute

$$u^*(A_1) \doteq -82.933 + (.63171)G_L(34,090 \mid 13.597,204.08)$$
$$+ (6.6279)(13.490)$$
$$= -82.933 + 90.042 \doteq 7.11 \text{ utiles,}$$

as was to be shown.

From the error calculations above, we may compute the error in the approximation $u^*(A_1) \doteq 7.11$ to be less than

$$(.0056 + .1071)(6.6279) = .75.$$

This error is clearly too small to affect the nature of the optimal decision.

7.3.9. Three Modified Methods of Making Probability Assessments. At the beginning of Section 7.3 it was mentioned that the operator might choose to express his probability beliefs in a fashion different from that of Girt's exploration manager. In this subsection we will examine in detail two additional methods suggested earlier, point out some practical difficulties in their use, and then briefly outline a fourth method which at least conceptually will overcome these difficulties.

Methods II and III might be called *macroscopic* in that the marginal distribution of barrels of reserves $\bar{x}$ of a prospect are inferred from the operator's judgement about the *basinal* parameter $(\mu^{(i)}, H^{(i)})$ rather than from his judgement about the environs of the prospect itself. When very little is known about the prospect, the macroscopic approach is appropriate. This would be the case if, before examining a particular prospect in detail, the operator wished to set a prior distribution on the size of reserves of a generic prospect in the basin in order to determine whether or not he should begin a program in the basin. The model on which Method II is based is built to accommodate *objective* sample evidence about the outcome x_j of jth discovery in a basin; i.e., x_j can be folded into the operator's prior distribution on the unknown parameter $\tilde{\mu}$ as described in Section 7.1 to give a posterior distribution on $\tilde{\mu}$, which in turn affects the distribution of $\tilde{x}_{j+1}$. The model underlying Method III is even more flexible, for, in addition, this model allows objective sample evidence about the μ's of other basins to be processed systematically after the fashion of the prior-posterior analysis of 7.1.

If, however, the operator has a great deal of specific knowledge about a particular prospect, say the ℓth, then he would be ignoring vital information if he based the marginal distribution of $\tilde{x}_\ell$ solely on his probability beliefs about $\tilde{\mu}$. In other words, a *microscopic* point of view becomes necessary, and either the approach of Girth's exploration manager should be adopted or a fourth method should be used which takes advantage of this specific information. A model which reflects this viewpoint is conceptually different from the data generating process models presented earlier. Method IV is based on a model which assumes that the basin is segmented into areas each of which is characterized by its own parameter. In general the correlation between parameters of areas which are geographically contiguous will be high, and this is taken into account in the model.

Method II.

Method II is based on a model akin to the model of the discovery process discussed in Section 7.1. Since the model considers only a single basin, we will drop basin identifying subscripts, and make the following definitions:

x = the outcome of a new field discovery in the basin in barrels of reserves, $x > 0$,

μ = a basinal parameter.

The model rests on two assumptions:

1. $\tilde{x} \mid \mu \sim f_L(x \mid \mu, h)$;   (7.66)

2. $\tilde{\mu}_L \sim f_L\left(\mu_L \mid m' + \dfrac{1}{2h}, hn'\right)$;   (7.67)

as before, h is presumed known and $\tilde{\mu}_L \equiv \exp\left\{\tilde{\mu} + \dfrac{1}{2h}\right\}$. Assumptions 1 and 2 imply that the marginal distribution of $\tilde{x}_j$ is

$$\tilde{x}_j \sim f_L\left(x_j \mid m', \frac{hn'}{n'+1}\right).$$ (7.68)

(The proof follows directly from the proof of (7.32a.)

The empirical evidence of Chapter 6 renders Assumption 1 plausible. The plausibility of 2 is established in 7.2. One of the most desirable features of this model is that it allows objective evidence in the form of a sample realization $x_1, \ldots, x_j, \ldots, x_n$ of n discoveries to be systematically processed according to the theory of 7.1; i.e., the operator's prior on $\bar{\mu}_L$ may be inferred from the operator's statements about

1. the mode

$$\zeta \equiv \exp\left[m' + \frac{1}{2h}\left(1 - \frac{2}{n'}\right)\right] \tag{7.69}$$

of the distribution of the mean $\bar{\mu}_L$ of the distribution of field sizes in the basin,

2. the probability α that $\bar{\mu}_L$ is greater than a specified amount $\mu_L^* > \zeta$.

Given ζ, α, μ_L^*, and defining u^* such that

$$G_L\left(\mu_L^* \mid m' + \frac{1}{2h}, hn'\right) = G_{N^*}(u^*), \tag{7.70}$$

we solve for

$$n' = \frac{2}{h}[-u^* + \{u^{*2} + 4\log(\mu_L^*/\zeta)\}^{1/2}]^{-1}, \tag{7.71}$$

and then substitute n' into (7.72) to solve for m':

$$m' = \log \zeta - \frac{1}{h}\left(\frac{1}{2} - \frac{1}{n'}\right). \tag{7.72}$$

Proof. To show (7.72), simply take the log of both sides of (7.69). Equation (7.72) follows directly from the proof of (7.50): Setting $\sigma = (hn')^{-1/2}$, (7.71) may be seen to be identical to (7.56); and since the ζ, α, μ_L^*, and u^* of Method II are formally identical to the x_m, p, x^*, and μ^*, respectively, of Method I, the proof for Method I suffices to prove (7.71).

An Example

Prior Analysis. Suppose that an operator wishes to decide whether or not to begin a program in a particular basin about which he makes the following judgements:
1. the mode of the distribution of $\bar{\mu}_L$ is 10^6 barrels;
2. the probability that $\bar{\mu}_L$ exceeds 10^7 is .1000;
3. the precision h can be reasonably set at .8565.[12]

---

[12]The mean of the estimates $\hat{H}^{(i)}$ of $H^{(i)}$ for each of the seven basins whose $\bar{\mu}^{(i)}$'s are plotted in Graph 7.1 is .85654.

We then have

$$\zeta = 10^6, \qquad \log \zeta = 13.8155$$

$$\mu_L^* = 10^7, \qquad \log \mu_L^* = 16.1181$$

and from Normal tables the u^* such that

$$P(\tilde{u} > u^*) = .1000$$

is $u^* = 1.1817$. We use (7.71) to solve for $n' = 1.574$ and (7.72) to solve for $m' = 14.132$.

An analysis of a generic prospect in the basin can now proceed as in 7.3.1 to 7.3.8, using the parameter $(m', hn'[n' + 1]^{-1}) = (14.132,.504)$ for the marginal distribution of $\tilde{x}$, the barrels of reserves in a generic discovery.

Posterior Analysis. If, following the operator's judgements about $\tilde{\mu}_L$, two important new field discoveries are made in the basin, of size 50×10^6 and 20×10^6 barrels, respectively, then we use (7.13) and (7.20) to calculate the posterior parameter $(m'', hn''[n'' + 1]^{-1})$ of the distribution of $\tilde{x}$. Setting $n = 2$,

$$\log g = \frac{1}{2}[\log (50 \times 10^6) + \log (20 \times 10^6)] = 17.270,$$

(7.20) together with $n' = 1.574$ and $m' = 14.132$ gives

$$hn'' = h(n' + n) = .8565(3.574) = 3.061,$$

and

$$m'' = \frac{(1.574)(14.132) + 2(17.270)}{3.574} = 15.888,$$

so that $(m'', hn''[n'' + 1]^{-1}) = (15.888, 1.189)$.

Method III.

Method III differs from Method II in that explicit provision is made for folding information about the μ's of other basins into an operator's prior judgements about a given basin. Another level of structure is added to the model underlying Method II by assuming that there is an objective population of μ's from which the μ of each basin is drawn, and that the operator does not know with certainty either the parameter of the distribution of μ's or the particular μ of any given basin. Thus information about new field discoveries in, say, the jth basin will influence his judgement about the parameter of the distribution of μ's and hence about the μ of the ith basin, $i \neq j$. (However, this influence will be appreciable only when he has very little information about the μ of the particular basin in which he is interested.)

To be more specific, the following definitions are made.

$x^{(j)}$ = the outcome of a new field discovery in the jth basin,

   $j = 1, 2, \ldots, q,$

$\mu^{(j)}$ = a parameter of the jth basin,

   m' = a parameter of the distribution of $\mu^{(j)}$.

Assume that for $j = 1, 2, \ldots, q,$

1. $\tilde{x}^{(j)} \mid \mu^{(j)} \sim f_L(x^{(j)} \mid \mu^{(j)}, h),$ $\qquad\qquad$ (7.72)
   and the $\tilde{x}^{(j)}$'s are mutually independent given $\mu^{(j)}$'s;

2. $\tilde{\mu}^{(j)} \mid m' \sim f_N(\mu^{(j)} \mid m', hn')$ $\qquad\qquad$ (7.73)
   and the $\tilde{\mu}^{(j)}$'s are mutually independent given m';

3. $\tilde{m}' \sim f_N(m' \mid M', hN').$ $\qquad\qquad\qquad$ (7.74)

We will state without proof a list of pertinent results derived from assumptions like those above by Gordon Antelman.[13] The undefined symbols used below are as defined in Section 12.1.1*, entitled, *Definition of the Independent Multinormal Process.*

The prior distribution of the random vector

$$\underline{\tilde{\omega}} = (\tilde{\mu}^{(1)}, \ldots, \tilde{\mu}^{(j)}, \ldots, \tilde{\mu}^{(q)}, \tilde{m}')^t$$

is $q + 1$ variate Normal with mean

$$\underline{M}' \equiv M(1, 1, \ldots, 1)^t \qquad\qquad (7.75a)$$

and matrix precision

$$\underline{\underline{H}}' \equiv h \begin{bmatrix} n' & 0 & 0 & \cdots\cdots & -n' \\ 0 & n' & 0 & \cdots\cdots & -n' \\ \cdot & & \cdot & & \cdot \\ \cdot & & & \cdot & \cdot \\ \cdot & & & & \cdot \\ 0 & & & n' & -n' \\ -n' & -n' & \cdots & -n' & -n' & (N' + qn') \end{bmatrix}$$

---

[13]G. Antelman, "Notes on Prior — prior Theory" (unpublished). We deeply appreciate his cooperation in allowing the following results to be stated before they are formally published under his own name.

Define

$x_\ell^{(j)}$ = the ℓth sample observation on $\tilde{x}^{(j)}$ from a sample of size n_j,
  $j = 1, 2, \ldots, q$,

and the sufficient statistic

$$g_j = \left[\prod_{\ell=1}^{n_j} x_\ell^{(j)} \right]^{1/n_j}.$$

Then if a Multinormal distribution with parameter $(\underline{M}', \underline{H}')$ is assigned to $\tilde{\omega}$ and if a sample of size n_j of $\tilde{x}^{(j)}$ for $j = 1, 2, \ldots, q$ yields a sufficient statistic $(\log \underline{G}, \underline{n})$, where

$$\underline{\underline{n}} = \begin{bmatrix} n_1 & 0 & \cdots & & \cdots & 0 \\ & & & & & \cdot \\ 0 & n_2 & & & & \cdot \\ \cdot & & & & & \cdot \\ \cdot & & \cdot & & & \cdot \\ \cdot & & & \cdot & & \cdot \\ \cdot & & & & \cdot & 0 \\ 0 & \cdots & & 0 & & \cdot \; n_q \end{bmatrix} \qquad (7.76a)$$

and

$$\log \underline{G}^t = (\log g_1, \ldots, \log g_j, \ldots, \log g_q), \qquad (7.76b)$$

the posterior distribution of $\tilde{\omega}$ will be $q + 1$ variate Normal with parameters

$$\underline{M}''^t = (E''(\tilde{\mu}^{(1)}), \ldots, E''(\tilde{\mu}^{(j)}), \ldots, E''(\tilde{\mu}^{(q)}), E''(\tilde{m}')) \qquad (7.77a)$$

and

$$\underline{H}'' = h \begin{bmatrix} n' + n_1 & 0 & \cdots & & 0 & -n' \\ 0 & n' + n_2 & & & & -n' \\ & & \cdot & & & \\ \cdot & & & & & \cdot \\ \cdot & & \cdot & & & \cdot \\ \cdot & & & \cdot & & \cdot \\ & & & & \cdot & \\ \cdot & & & & n' + n_q & -n' \\ -n' & -n' & \cdots & \cdots & -n' & (Nn' + qn') \end{bmatrix} \qquad (7.77b)$$

given that

$$E''(\tilde{m}') = \frac{w_0 M' + w_1 \log g_1 + \ldots + w_q \log g_q}{w_0 + w_1 + \ldots + w_q}, \qquad (7.77c)$$

$$w_0 = \frac{N'}{n'}, \qquad w_j = \frac{n_j}{n' + n_j}, \qquad (7.77d)$$

and

$$E''(\tilde{\mu}^{(j)}) = w_j \log g_j + (1 - w_j) E''(\tilde{m}'), \qquad (7.77e)$$

for $j = 1, 2, \ldots, q$.

An Example

An operator is evaluating a prospect in a basin which is arbitrarily labelled "Basin 1." Basin 1 is virtually unexplored, and he feels very uncertain about the parameter $\tilde{\mu}^{(1)}$ of Basin 1 but is willing to assume that the scalar precision h is known with certainty to equal .8565.

He is willing to let objective evidence from Basin 2 and Basin 3[14] come to bear by virtue of their gross similarity to Basin 1. The information he has about the fields of Basins 2 and 3 is as follows:

Basin Number	Number of Fields	Geometric Mean of Field Size
2	12	$e^{15.000}$
3	4	$e^{17.000}$

He is unwilling to venture a guess as to the parameter (M', N') of the distribution of the parameter $\tilde{m}'$ of the population of μ's from which the unknown parameters $\tilde{\mu}^{(1)}$, $\tilde{\mu}^{(2)}$, and $\tilde{\mu}^{(3)}$ are drawn. However, conditional on knowing $\tilde{m}' = m'$, he feels that it is reasonable to set $n' = 2$.

Prior Analysis. If the operator is willing to let objective evidence from Basins 2 and 3 determine his (marginal) prior distribution for $\tilde{\mu}_1$, then we may use (7.77) to determine this distribution. We show that

$$\tilde{x}^{(1)} \sim f_L(x^{(1)} \mid 15.875, .577) \tag{7.78}$$

as follows. Set

$$n_1 = 0, \quad n_2 = 12, \quad n_3 = 4, \quad N' = 0,$$

$$n' = 2, \quad \log g_2 = 15.000, \quad \log g_3 = 17.000,$$

and use (7.77) to calculate

$$E''(\tilde{\mu}^{(1)}) = E''(\tilde{m}') = 15.875, \quad E''(\tilde{\mu}^{(2)}) = 15.120, \quad E''(\tilde{\mu}^{(3)}) = 16.620$$

Defining

$$\underline{\tilde{\omega}}^t = (\tilde{\mu}^{(1)}, \tilde{\mu}^{(2)}, \tilde{\mu}^{(3)}, \tilde{m}'),$$

we then have

$$\underline{\tilde{\omega}} \sim f_N^{[4]}(\omega \mid \underline{M}'', \underline{H}'') \tag{7.79}$$

where

$$\underline{M}''^t = (15.875, 15.120, 16.620, 15.875)$$

and

$$\underline{H}'' = .8565 \begin{bmatrix} 2.000 & 0 & 0 & -2.000 \\ 0 & 14.000 & 0 & -2.000 \\ 0 & 0 & 6.000 & -2.000 \\ -2.000 & -2.000 & -2.000 & 6.000 \end{bmatrix}.$$

[14]Only three basins are considered in this example to keep the calculations simple. There is no loss in generality from this simplification.

While (7.79) is the distribution of $\underline{\tilde{\omega}}$ posterior to the blending of information from Basins 1 and 2 into the operator's "informationless" prior distribution on $\underline{\tilde{\omega}}$, it can be considered a prior distribution for purposes of drilling the prospect. The marginal distribution of $\tilde{\mu}^{(1)}$ is

$$\tilde{\mu}^{(1)} \sim f_N(\mu^{(1)} \mid M', h[n' + n_1]) = f_N(\mu^{(1)} \mid 15.875, 1.713) \quad (7.80)$$

and as in (7.68), it follows that

$$\tilde{x}^{(1)} \sim f_L(x^{(1)} \mid M', hn'[n' + 1]^{-1})$$

$$= f_L(x^{(1)} \mid 15.875, .571). \quad (7.81)$$

Using (7.81), we can now carry through the analysis of the drilling decision as in 7.3.1 to 7.3.8.

Posterior Analysis. If a field of 10^7 barrels is discovered in Basin 1, the distribution of $\tilde{x}^{(1)}$ must be modified to account for this new piece of information. By virtue of (7.77), the distribution of $\tilde{x}^{(2)}$ and $\tilde{x}^{(3)}$ is also affected. We show that

$$\tilde{x}^{(1)} \sim f_L(x^{(1)} \mid 15.916, .6425)$$

and

$$\underline{\tilde{\omega}} \sim f_N^{[4]}(\underline{\omega} \mid \underline{M''}, \underline{\underline{H''}}),$$

where

$$\underline{M''}^t = (15.916 \quad 15.102 \quad 16.571 \quad 15.713)$$

and

$$\underline{\underline{H''}} = .8565 \begin{bmatrix} 3.000 & 0 & 0 & -2.000 \\ 0 & 14.000 & 0 & -2.000 \\ 0 & 0 & 6.000 & -2.000 \\ -2.000 & -2.000 & -2.000 & 6.000 \end{bmatrix}$$

as follows. Set

$$n_1 = 1, \quad n_2 = 12, \quad n_3 = 4, \quad N' = 0,$$

$$n' = 2, \quad \log g_1 = 16.118, \quad \log g_2 = 15.000,$$

$$\log g_3 = 17.000$$

and use (7.77) to calculate

$$E''(\tilde{m}') = 15.713, \quad E''(\tilde{\mu}^{(1)}) = 15.916,$$

$$E(\tilde{\mu}^{(2)}) = 15.102, \quad E''(\tilde{\mu}^{(3)}) = 16.571.$$

Then $\underline{M}''$ and $\underline{H}''$ will be as shown above, and it follows that

$$\tilde{\mu}^{(1)} \sim f_N(\mu^{(1)} \mid E''(\tilde{\mu}^{(1)}), h[n' + n_1]^{-1}) = f_N(\mu^{(1)} \mid 15.916, 2.570)$$

and

$$\tilde{x}^{(1)} \sim f_L(x^{(1)} \mid E''(\tilde{\mu}^{(1)}, h[n' + n_1][n' + n_1 + 1]^{-1}) = f_L(x^{(1)} \mid 15.916, .6425),$$

as was to be shown.

Method IV.

As stated earlier, if the operator has a great deal of information about the enrivons of a prospect and wishes to reflect this in his probability judgements, Methods II and III are not suitable, for they allow him to express his beliefs *only* about the basinal parameter. As an alternative to Method I, we have Method IV, which is based on a model of the following form: Suppose a basin is partitioned into K segments, and the following definitions are made.

$x_{i\ell} =$ the ℓth discovery outcome in the ith segment, or sub-basin, $1 \le i \le K, \ell = 1, 2, \ldots,$

$(\mu_i, h_i) =$ a parameter of the ith sub-basin.

We now make two assumptions:

1. The ith sub-basin is a univariate Lognormal data generating process characterized by a parameter (μ_i, h_i) and generating independent random variables $\tilde{x}_{i1}, \ldots, \tilde{x}_{i\ell}, \ldots,$ with identical densities

$$f_L(x_i \mid \mu_i, h_i),$$

and each of the K processes operates independently of all others.

2. The parameters $\{h_i, i = 1, 2, \ldots, K\}$ are known with certainty. However, the parameters $\{\mu_i, i = 1, 2, \ldots, K\}$ are not known with certainty but rather are regarded as a set of dependent random variables with a Multinormal distribution function; i.e., define

$$\underline{\underline{H}} = \begin{bmatrix} H_{11} \cdots H_{1i} \cdots H_{1K} \\ \\ \cdot \quad \cdot \\ \cdot \quad H_{ii} \quad \cdot \\ \cdot \quad \cdot \\ H_{K1} \cdots H_{Ki} \cdots H_{KK} \end{bmatrix}, \quad \begin{array}{l} -\underline{\infty} < \underline{\mu} < \underline{\infty}, \\ \\ -\underline{\infty} < \underline{m} < \underline{\infty}, \\ \\ \underline{\underline{H}} \text{ is } PDS, \end{array}$$

then

$$\tilde{\underline{\mu}} \sim f_N^{[K]}(\underline{\mu} \mid \underline{m}, \underline{\underline{H}}) = (2\pi)^{-K/2}\{\exp[-\tfrac{1}{2}(\underline{\mu} - \underline{m})'\underline{\underline{H}}(\underline{\mu} - \underline{m})]\} \mid \underline{\underline{H}} \mid^{1/2}$$

$$(12\text{-}1)^*$$

As pointed out in 12.7*, *Introduction to Interrelated Univariate Normal Processes,* because each sub-basin operates independently of all others, within any given period of time, a different number of x's may appear in each. In order to express the results which follow from Assumptions 1 and 2 concisely, suppose that we examine the output of the processes during a given span of time t to $t + t'$, $t' > 0$, and make the following definitions.

$n_i =$ the number of x_{it}'s observed in the ith sub-basin from t to $t + t'$, $1 \leq i \leq K$,

$$\log g_i = \frac{1}{n_i} \sum_{t=1}^{n_i} \log x_{it} \qquad (= 0 \quad \text{if} \quad n_i = 0),$$

$h = [\prod_{i=1}^{K} h_i]^{1/K},$ the mean precision of the K processes, $\qquad$ (12-50a)*

$\eta_{ii} = \dfrac{h_i}{h},$ the relative precision of the Kth process, $\qquad$ (12-50b)*

$n_{ii} = n_i\eta_{ii},$ the effective number of observations on the ith process from t to $t + t'$,

$$\underline{n} = \begin{bmatrix} n_{11} & & & 0 \\ & \ddots & & \\ & & n_{ii} & \\ & & & \ddots \\ 0 & & & n_{KK} \end{bmatrix},$$

$$\log \underline{G}^t = (\log g_1, \ldots, \log g_i, \ldots, \log g_K).$$

If we regard the x's which occur in each of the K basins from t to $t + t'$ as a sample, then two possibilities can occur which must be distinguished in analysis: $n_i > 0$ for all $1 \leq i \leq K$ or $n_i > 0$ for p i's, $0 < p < K$.

If all K sub-basins are sampled, it is shown in 12.8* that if $\tilde{\mu}$ is assigned a Normal prior distribution with parameter $(\underline{m}', h\underline{n}')$, where $\underline{n}' \equiv \underline{H}'/h$, and if the sample yields a sufficient statistic $(\log \underline{G}, \underline{n})$, the posterior distribution of $\tilde{\mu}$ will be Normal with parameters

$$\underline{m}'' = (\underline{n}' + \underline{n})^{-1}(\underline{n}'\underline{m}' + \underline{n} \log \underline{G}), \qquad (12\text{-}14a)^*$$

$$\underline{n}'' = \underline{n}' + \underline{n}. \qquad (12\text{-}14b)^*$$

The unconditional density of $\log \tilde{G}$ is

$$D(\log \underline{G} \mid \underline{m}', \underline{n}'; \underline{n}) = f_N^{[K]}(\log \underline{G} \mid \underline{m}', h\underline{n}_u) \qquad (12\text{-}17a)*$$

where

$$\underline{n}_u = \underline{n}'\underline{n}''^{-1}\underline{n}, \qquad \underline{n}_u^{-1} = \underline{n}'^{-1} + \underline{n}^{-1}. \qquad (12\text{-}17b)*$$

If only p processes, $p < K$, are sampled, we arrive at formally similar results. Assuming without loss of generality that observations are taken on the first p processes, partition

$$\underline{\mu} = \begin{pmatrix} \mu_1 \\ \mu_2 \end{pmatrix} \qquad \text{where} \quad \begin{array}{l} \mu \text{ is } K \times 1, \\ \mu_1 \text{ is } p \times 1, \end{array} \qquad (12\text{-}57)*$$

and partition the parameters of the prior distribution of $\tilde{\mu}$ accordingly:

$$\underline{m}' = \begin{pmatrix} m_1' \\ m_2' \end{pmatrix} \qquad \text{where} \quad \begin{array}{l} \underline{m}' \text{ is } K \times 1, \\ \underline{m}_1' \text{ is } p \times 1, \end{array}$$

$$\underline{n}' = \begin{bmatrix} \underline{n}_{11}' & \underline{n}_{12}' \\ \underline{n}_{21}' & \underline{n}_{22}' \end{bmatrix} \qquad \text{where} \quad \begin{array}{l} \underline{n}' \text{ is } K \times K, \\ \underline{n}_{11}' \text{ is } p \times p. \end{array}$$

Define

$$\log \underline{G}_1^t = (\log g_1, \ldots, \log g_1, \ldots, \log g_p),$$

$$\underline{n}_{11} = \begin{bmatrix} n_{11} & & & 0 \\ & \cdot & & \\ & & n_{ii} & \\ & & & \cdot \\ 0 & & & & \cdot \\ & & & & & n_{pp} \end{bmatrix}, \qquad (12\text{-}59b)*$$

so that we may write

$$\log \underline{G} = \begin{pmatrix} \log \underline{G}_1 \\ 0 \end{pmatrix}, \qquad \text{where} \quad \begin{array}{l} \log \underline{G} \text{ is } K \times 1, \\ \log \underline{G}_1 \text{ is } p \times 1, \end{array}$$

$$\underline{n} = \begin{bmatrix} \underline{n}_{11} & \underline{0} \\ \underline{0} & \underline{0} \end{bmatrix} \qquad \text{where} \quad \begin{array}{l} \underline{n} \text{ is } K \times K, \\ \underline{n}_{11} \text{ is } p \times p. \end{array}$$

$$(7.82a)$$

If h is known, if the $K \times 1$ random vector $\tilde{\mu}$ is assigned a Normal prior distribution with parameter $(\underline{m}', \underline{n}')$ and if samples from p of K processes yield the statistics defined in (7.82a), then the posterior distribution of $\tilde{\mu}$ is Normal and its parameters are given by (12-14)* without change:

$$\underline{n}'' = \underline{n}' + \underline{n} \qquad (12\text{-}61a)*$$

$$\underline{m}'' = \underline{n}''^{-1}(\underline{n}'\underline{m}' + \underline{n}\log \underline{G}). \qquad (12\text{-}61b)*$$

Also, the unconditional density of $\log \tilde{\underline{G}}_1$ is

$$D(\log \underline{G}_1 \mid \underline{m}', \underline{n}'; \underline{n}) = f_N^{[p]} (\underline{m}_1 \mid \underline{m}_1', h\underline{n}_u) \qquad (12\text{-}67\text{a})^*$$

where

$$\underline{n}_u = \underline{n}_m' \underline{n}_m''^{-1} \underline{n}_{11}, \quad \underline{n}_u^{-1} = \underline{n}_m'^{-1} + \underline{n}_{11}^{-1}, \quad \underline{n}_m'' = \underline{n}_m' + \underline{n}_{11}, \qquad (12\text{-}67\text{b})^*$$

and

$$\underline{n}_m' = \underline{n}_{11}' - \underline{n}_{12}' \underline{n}_{22}'^{-1} \underline{n}_{21}', \quad \underline{n}'_m^{-1} = (\underline{n}'^{-1})_{11}. \qquad (12\text{-}64\text{b})^*$$

The mean and variance of $\log \tilde{\underline{G}}$ are

$$E(\log \tilde{\underline{G}} \mid \underline{m}', \underline{n}'; \underline{n}) = \underline{m}' = E(\tilde{\mu} \mid \underline{m}', \underline{n}'), \qquad (7.82\text{b})$$

$$V(\log \tilde{\underline{G}} \mid \underline{m}', \underline{n}'; \underline{n}) = (h\underline{n}_u)^{-1} \qquad (7.82\text{b})$$

where $\underline{n}_u$ is defined as in $(12\text{-}17\text{b})^*$. The mean and variance of $\log \tilde{\underline{G}}_1$ are

$$E(\log \tilde{\underline{G}}_1 \mid \underline{m}', \underline{n}'; \underline{n}) = \underline{m}_1', \qquad (7.83\text{a})$$

$$V(\log \tilde{\underline{G}}_1 \mid \underline{m}', \underline{n}'; \underline{n}) = (h\underline{n}_u)^{-1}, \qquad (7.83\text{a})$$

where $\underline{n}_u$ is as defined in $(12\text{-}67\text{b})^*$. From (7.32d) we may deduce that if $\log \tilde{\underline{G}}_1$ is 1×1 and $n_{11} = [1]$, then $\tilde{x}_{11} \equiv \tilde{\underline{G}}_1$ given $\tilde{x}_{11} > 0$ is Lognormally distributed as follows:

$$\tilde{x}_{11} \mid \tilde{x}_{11} > 0 \sim f_L(x_{11} \mid \underline{m}_1', h\underline{n}_u). \qquad (7.84)$$

The expression $f_L(x_{11} \mid \underline{m}_1', h\underline{n}_u)$ is the marginal distribution of the size of the first discovery to be made in the first sub-basin between t and $t + t'$.

An Example

An operator wishes to decide whether or not to drill a wildcat in the Christine area,[15] a map of which is shown on the next page. He is shooting for the Wilcox formation at about 9,000 feet. Although this is an expensive well — $100,000 for a dry hole, $160,000 if a producer — it has a potential of several million barrels if the structure indicated on the seismic map is there and if the structure is oil-bearing.

The area falls to the west of a major producing trend which runs north-northeast. In the counties to the west of Major County, there are

---

[15]Map and data adopted from C. J. Grayson, *op. cit.*, pp. 205–206.

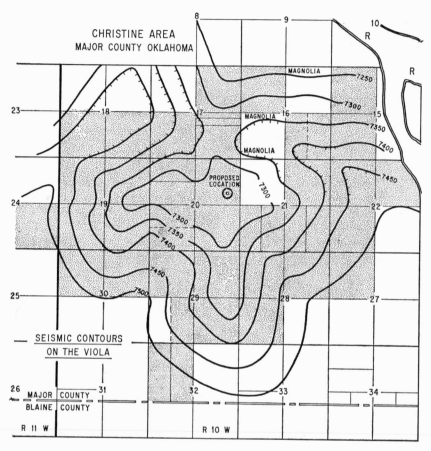

relatively few fields by comparison with the major trend. The operator feels that the prospect falls within an area bordered on the west by an unexploited area of uncertain potential and on the right by an area of known high productivity.[16]

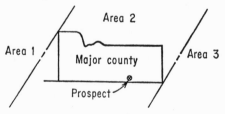

---

[16]This grossly simplified "zoning" is done to keep the calculations in the example simple. It is conceptually easy to handle, say, ten or twenty areas, but the numerical calculations become tedious, and subjective probability beliefs are more difficult to extract from an operator.

Analysis of his probability beliefs about each of the three areas leads to the following assignment of parameters:[17]

$$h_1 = .533, \quad h_2 = 1.066, \quad h_3 = 2.132,$$

so that

$$h = [\prod_{i=1}^{3} h_i]^{1/3} = 1.066.$$

Prior Analysis. If, in addition, the operator judges that

$$\underline{m}' = (15.000 \quad 16.000 \quad 17.000),$$

and

$$\underline{n}' = \begin{bmatrix} 1.500 & .500 & .300 \\ .500 & 1.000 & .400 \\ .300 & .400 & .500 \end{bmatrix},$$

then from (7.84) we may determine the marginal distribution of the outcome $\tilde{x}_2 \mid \tilde{x}_2 > 0$ of drilling the prospect:

$$\tilde{x}_2 \mid \tilde{x}_2 > 0 \sim f_L(x_2 \mid \underline{m}'_2, h\underline{n}_u) \tag{7.84}$$

where $\underline{m}'_2 = 16.000$, $h = 1.066$, and $\underline{n}_u = .3861$.

The parameter $\underline{n}_u$ is found by using (12-67b)* and rearranging terms in $\underline{n}$ and $\underline{n}'$:

$$\underline{n}_u^{-1} = \underline{n}_m'^{-1} + \underline{n}_{11}^{-1} = (\underline{n}'^{-1})_{11} + \underline{n}_{11}^{-1}. \tag{12-67b*}$$

Setting

$$\underline{n} = \begin{bmatrix} n_2\eta_{22} & 0 & 0 \\ 0 & 0 & 0 \\ 0 & 0 & 0 \end{bmatrix} = \begin{bmatrix} 1 & 0 & 0 \\ 0 & 0 & 0 \\ 0 & 0 & 0 \end{bmatrix},$$

and

$$\underline{n}' = \begin{bmatrix} 1.000 & .500 & .400 \\ .500 & 1.500 & .300 \\ .400 & .300 & .500 \end{bmatrix},$$

we find

$$(\underline{n}'^{-1})_{11} = 1.590, \quad \underline{n}_{11}^{-1} = 1,$$

so that

$$\underline{n}_u^{-1} = 1.590 + 1.000 = 2.590$$

or

$$\underline{n}_u = .3861.$$

---

[17]Methods for determining these parameters from the operator's probability statements will not be explained here. In *Portfolio Selection: Efficient Diversification of Investments*, Cowles Foundation Monograph 16 (New York: John Wiley & Sons, Inc., 1949), H. Markowitz shows how subjective judgements about pairwise covariances may be obtained in an economical fashion.

While the most likely number of barrels of oil that will occur *if* the well is successful is only

$$e^{16.000-\ (1/.4116)} = 3^{13.570} = 787{,}300 \text{ barrels,}$$

the expected number of barrels *if* the well is successful is from (7.6)

$$e^{16.000+1.215} = e^{17.215} = 29{,}949{,}000 \text{ barrels.}$$

An analysis like that of Sections 7.3.1 through 7.3.8 can now be carried through to determine whether the well should be drilled.

Posterior Analysis. If new field discoveries are made in any of the three areas before the well is drilled, the information they provide can be accommodated by using formulas (12–14)* to determine $\underline{m}''$ and $\underline{n}''$ and then substituting $(\underline{m}'', \underline{n}'')$ for $(\underline{m}', \underline{n}')$ in the example presented above.

PART III

In Chapters 6 and 7 we examined aspects of the discovery process in order to discover a class of distribution functions which are analytically tractable, rich enough to capture a wide range of probability beliefs about the size distribution of oil and gas fields, and which can be interpreted as an accurate model of this size distribution. The Lognormal distribution function was found to have these properties, so we gave examples of how it might be utilized in quantifying an operator's probability beliefs and how these in turn can be used in analyzing a drilling decision.

Chapters 8 and 9 of Part III deal with a quite different aspect of oil and gas exploration — the problem of how to select from the stream of inside prospects and outside deals which the operator must review each year. Part III is related to Part II in practice, for an operator must judge the potential number of barrels of oil or MCF of gas in a prospect before he can make a reasoned decision to accept or to reject it. However, Part III will not emphasize this relation.

Part III's primary objectives are, first, to formulate a series of mathematical models which capture the essence of operator's *sequential investment* problem, second, to analyze these models, and third, to explore some of the administrative implications of the models.

Chapter 8 pursues the first two of these objectives. Chapter 9 pursues the third. It is a report on an experiment done with two groups of volunteers to determine whether the formal (mathematical) decision rules derived in Chapter 8 are more effective than unaided judgement in attaining a preassigned goal, and if so, how much.

CHAPTER 8

A Sequential Investment Problem

The preceding two chapters were concerned with two special aspects of oil and gas exploration. This chapter deals with a problem more directly associated with over-all allocation of the firm's capital — a sequential investment problem.

The essence of the problem is this: Even if the operator has developed the best potential exploration program over areas and deals *presently* available to him for exploitation, he cannot be sure that he has allocated his capital in the most efficient manner possible, for as the fiscal year passes, he will be required to review and accept or reject a large number of inside prospects and outside deals which he has not yet seen. Both the *number* of future deals or prospects which will appear and the *value* of each deal or prospect when it does appear are unknown to him. If he commits all of his capital to those ventures before him now, he may have difficulty raising funds for the "real hot one" which may come along next month. If he holds back and does not invest the cash throw-off from his present holdings of oil and gas properties, the throw-off will be taxed at 52 per cent at the end of the year — a penalty which might be avoided by relaxing his acceptance criteria and accepting more deals earlier in the year. One independent operator presented his quandry by saying:

> After Labor Day people start worrying how they're going to spend their money. They begin a frantic search for good places to put it. This is when the per cent of dry holes starts to go up. After Christmas, the opposite occurs. Taxes are over — they're not looking very hard.

Good capital budgeting can help avoid "a frantic search for good places . . . " to put cash throw-off. However, the key to good capital budgeting vis-à-vis inside prospects and outside deals is an effective scheme for handling the uncertainty about them, and classical capital budgeting techniques offer little insight. In fact, Harry V. Roberts has said:

> The most serious deficiency in the present state of knowledge about capital budgeting is the absence of a satisfactory framework for incorporating uncertainty into the analysis.[1]

This deficiency in the theory of capital budgeting of course carries over to practical budgeting in the firm; neither Dr. Grayson nor the present writer found a single company which *explicitly* took into account future expectations in determining an acceptance level above which deals would be accepted and below which they would be rejected. "Explicitly" means a scheme that *formally* relates future expectations to decisions about deals that must be made now. Almost everyone in the oil business does this intuitively.

One of the main purposes of this chapter is to explore ways in which uncertainties about future deals can be systematically and explicitly taken into account.

Within the assumptions set forth in succeeding sections, the analysis leads to:

1. decision rules for deciding whether or not to accept or reject inside prospects or outside deals. These rules differ from economic decision rules presently in use in that they take into account in an explicit fashion the operator's future expectations about investment opportunities;

2. models which provide a basis for a systematic investigation of the impact of uncertainty and of the decision maker's future expectations on the firm's capital budgeting problems; e.g., the decision to hold cash instead of purchasing physical assets.

The models do *not:*

1. lead to a solution of the over-all capital budgeting problem; i.e., determine the total volume of funds that should be allocated to exploration activities as against other potential investment opportunities, or indicate the optimum financing mix for the firm; or

---

[1] H. V. Roberts, "Current Problems in the Economics of Capital Budgeting," *The Management of Corporate Capital*, edited by Ezra Solomon (Glencoe, Ill.: The Free Press, 1959), p. 202.

2. in any way replace the need for the operator to make careful, subjective assessments of the economic and geological worth of a particular deal or prospect, as well as of future expectations.

Chapter 8 consists of five sections. Section 8.1 is a taxonomy of the mathematical models motivated by the sequential investment problem. Section 8.2 shows how the results of analysis are used in terms of a numerical example based on Model I. A mathematical analysis of each of the six models posited in 8.1 is done in 8.3. Section 8.4 presents a computer program for calculating the optimal strategies for the models. Finally, 8.5 is a discussion of two generalizations of the sequential investment problem of this chapter.

8.1. Outline of Models

The sequential investment problem briefly outlined in the introduction to this chapter is a motivation for the six models analyzed in 8.3. A verbal outline of the structure of and assumptions underlying each model will help the reader intuit the meaning of the precise mathematical formulations of 8.3.

8.1.1. Structure. All of the models are structured in terms of six elements:

1. the planning period spanned by the model,

2. the tax effects at the end of the planning period,

3. the investment required in a deal,

4. the payoff[2] of a deal,

5. the number of deals offered during the planning period,

6. subjective probability assessments.

The planning period, tax effects, and subjective probability assessments are considered as given elements of the model. In particular, the fiscal year is a natural planning period because of tax effects,[3] although the models are in no way restricted to such an arbitrary span of planning. In the simplest model the number of deals and the investment required in a deal are considered as given for all deals, and only the payoff of a deal

---

[2]"Payoff" will be used as the generic label for the worth of a deal as measured in units of the criterion function chosen by the operator.

[3]C. J. Grayson, *op. cit.*, pp. 106–113, discusses the effect of federal tax regulations on the drilling decision.

(before it is seen) is a random variable. In the more complex models, "number of deals" and "investment in a deal" are random variables along with "payoff."

The general features of the models are summarized in Table 8.1 which lists for each model the assumptions made about payoff, investment, planning period, number of deals appearing in the planning period, taxes, capital available for investment, and (subjective) probability assessments of random variables in the model.

8.2. Discussion of Model I

The purpose of a mathematical analysis of sequential investment models is to arrive at a set of optimal sequential decision rules. A decision rule, or strategy for decision making, is a set of instructions which tells the decision maker what action to take conditional upon the occurrence of any event or events in the set of events under consideration. It must be unambiguous and cover every eventuality. It is an *optimal* decision rule if it is better than or at least as good as any other decision rule in helping the decision maker to achieve his desired goal. The decision rules derived from these models are called "sequential" because they specify what action to take in making a sequence of interrelated decisions over time.

To show how the results of Section 8.3 are used, we will present in all detail a simple example which is based on Model I. The decision rules for Models II, IIa, III, and IIIa are conceptually similar to that for Model I, so that the example should serve to clarify the nature of the decision rules for all models.

The optimal decision rule for investment when Model I is used is intuitively appealing. If we reinterpret the definitions and rules of 8.3.1, we may informally state the optimal decision rule in terms of

n = number of deals offered during the planning period,

θ_j = the payoff of the $(n - j + 1)$st deal, $j = n, n - 1, \ldots, 1$,

x = the generic symbol for number of units left for investment at the operator's $(n - j + 1)$st deal,

$V_{x,j}^*$ = the expected value of following an optimal strategy with x units of capital remaining for investment and j deals left to review,

as follows. Accept the $(n - j + 1)$st deal only if

$$V_{x-1,j-1}^* + \theta_j \geq V_{x,j-1}^*.$$

TABLE 8.1

Assumptions of Particular Models

Assumptions about	Assumptions Common to all Models	Assumptions	I	Ia	II	IIa	III	IIIa
Payoff	1. Before a deal is reviewed its payoff is a random variable.	1. *Full information:* After review, the payoff of a deal is known with certainty.	X	X	X	X	⋮	⋮
		2. *Probabilistic Information:* After a deal is reviewed its payoff is still a random variable, but the operator knows the conditional distribution of payoff given investment.	⋮	⋮	⋮	⋮	X	X
Investment	1. Payoffs from accepted deals cannot be reinvested during the planning period. 2. Operator can invest only those funds available for investment at start of planning period.	1. Each accepted deal requires one unit of investable funds.	X	X	⋮	⋮	⋮	⋮
		2. Before review the investment required in a deal is a random variable. After review the investment required is known with certainty.	⋮	⋮	X	X	X	X
Number of deals that will appear during planning period.		1. Number of deals is known with certainty.	X	⋮	X	⋮	X	⋮
		2. Number of deals is a random variable. Operator knows the mean recurrence time between deals.	⋮	X	⋮	X	⋮	X
Planning period	Planning period chosen by operator is fixed.							
Taxes	Tax at end of planning period is a fixed percentage of capital that remains uninvested.							

In other words, accept the $(n - j + 1)$st deal only if the sum of its payoff and the expected value of having only $x - 1$ to invest in the $j - 1$ remaining deals is greater than the expected value of having x to invest in the $j - 1$ remaining deals. Alternatively, we may write the inequality above as

$$\theta_j \geq V^*_{x,j-1} - V^*_{x-1,j-1},$$

which suggests that we may characterize the complete optimal strategy for a given (x, n) pair by a set of numbers, each of which gives the minimum acceptable payoff for a particular combination of capital and deals left to review,

$$\{\alpha^*_{i,j}, i = x, x - 1, \ldots, 1; j = n, n - 1, \ldots, 1\}$$

such that, given $i = x$, say, the $(n - j + 1)$st deal is accepted only if

$$\theta_j \geq \alpha^*_{x,j} = V^*_{x,j-1} - V^*_{x-1,j-1}.$$

We will now apply these notions to a simple numerical example based on Model I. Suppose the operator knows that he will see fifteen more deals during the remainder of the fiscal year $(n = 15)$, he has $50,000 of cash throw-off remaining to invest $(x = \$50,000)$, and each deal that he accepts will require an investment of $10,000. He assesses working probabilities over the payoff of each of these future deals as:

Amount of Payoff	Probability of Payoff
−$10,000	.2
$30,000	.3
$40,000	.3
$70,000	.1
$100,000	.1
	1.0

If he wishes to maximize the expected value of the sum of payoffs from accepted deals, where payoff is defined for this example as the difference between the market value of reserves the deal will yield to the operator and the investment required in it, then he accepts each deal which, upon review, promises a higher payoff than the cutoff amounts shown in Table 8.2.

Table 8.2 lists values of $V^*_{x,n-1} - V^*_{x-1,n-1}$ for $n = 15$ and $x = 5$, x being expressed in units of $10,000. Table 8.3 lists the values of $V^*_{x,n}$ from which entries in Table 8.2 were calculated. For ease in calculation the value of cash throw-off which remains uninvested at the end of the

TABLE 8.2. MINIMUM ACCEPTABLE PAYOFFS $\alpha^*_{i,j}$ OF FOLLOWING AN OPTIMAL STRATEGY IN ILLUSTRATIVE MODEL I GAME WHEN OPERATOR HAS i UNITS OF CAPITAL AND j DEALS TO REVIEW FOR $i = 5, 4, \ldots, 1$ AND $j = 15, 14, \ldots, 1$

$$(\alpha^*_{i,j} = V^*_{i,j-1} - V^*_{i-1,j-1})$$

i	1	2	3	4	5	6	7	8	9	10	11	12	13	14	15
5	0	0	0	0	0	1.434	2.557	3.046	3.317	3.569	3.778	3.914	4.013	4.104	4.216
4	0	0	0	0	1.792	2.837	3.269	3.587	3.822	3.987	4.123	4.283	4.465	4.665	4.877
3	0	0	0	2.240	3.158	3.603	3.905	4.140	4.382	4.647	4.921	5.197	5.465	5.723	5.967
2	0	0	2.800	3.620	4.118	4.521	4.938	5.347	5.706	6.021	6.297	6.540	6.754	6.943	7.110
1	0	3.800	4.800	5.540	6.132	6.606	6.984	7.288	7.559	7.803	8.023	8.220	8.398	8.559	8.703
0															

j

TABLE 8.3. EXPECTED VALUES $V^*_{i,j}$ OF OPTIMAL STRATEGIES FOR ILLUSTRATIVE MODEL I GAME GIVEN i UNITS OF CAPITAL TO INVEST AND j DEALS TO REVIEW FOR $i = 5, 4, \ldots, 1$ AND $j = 15, 14, \ldots, 1$

i	1	2	3	4	5	6	7	8	9	10	11	12	13	14	15
5	3.800	7.600	11.400	15.200	19.000	21.653	23.408	24.785	26.027	27.142	28.153	29.096	29.994	30.873	31.730
4	3.800	7.600	11.400	15.200	17.566	19.096	20.362	21.469	22.458	23.364	24.240	25.083	25.890	26.657	27.382
3	3.800	7.600	11.400	13.408	14.729	15.828	16.775	17.647	18.471	19.241	19.957	20.618	21.225	21.780	22.287
2	3.800	7.600	9.160	10.250	11.126	11.922	12.635	13.265	13.824	14.320	14.760	15.152	15.502	15.813	16.102
1	3.800	4.800	5.540	6.132	6.606	6.984	7.288	7.559	7.803	8.023	8.220	8.398	8.559	8.703	8.832
0															

j

fiscal year is assumed to be zero. (This is equivalent to a 100 per cent year-end tax on uninvested cash throw-off and constitutes only a minor modification of boundary conditions. The principle is quite the same as with a 52 per cent tax on uninvested cash throw-off.) Values of $V_{x,n-1}^* -$ $V_{x-1,n-1}^*$ are calculated to the nearest \$10. To use the table, the operator looks for the entry corresponding to the units of funds x and number of deals n he has left to review; e.g., for $x = 5$ and $n = 15$ the table entry is 4.216. This implies that $\alpha_{5,15}^* = \$42,160$. If the payoff of the next deal which the operator reviews is greater than or equal to \$42,160, then the operator should accept that deal. If the payoff is less than this, he should reject it. If the next deal is accepted, then the $\alpha_{4,14}^*$ for the succeeding deal is \$46,650. And so on.

Now imagine that the operator sees a sequence of deals like that shown in Table 8.4 below. The payoffs of these deals were generated by means of random numbers picked according to probabilities assessed by the operator. He sees these deals one by one, starting with Deal 1, and he must make a decision to accept or reject each deal before seeing the next.

TABLE 8.4

Deal	Payoff	Deals To Review[a]	Remaining Funds	Cutoff from Table 2	Decision
$i = $ 1	$-\$10,000$	15	\$50,000	\$42,200	Reject
2	40,000	14	50,000	41,100	Reject
3	30,000	13	50,000	40,200	Reject
4[b]	40,000	12	50,000	39,200	Accept
5	40,000	11	40,000	41,200	Reject
6	$-$ 10,000	10	40,000	39,800	Reject
7[b]	40,000	9	40,000	38,100	Accept
8	30,000	8	30,000	41,300	Reject
9	$-$ 10,000	7	30,000	39,100	Reject
10[b]	40,000	6	30,000	36,300	Accept
11	30,000	5	20,000	41,200	Reject
12	$-$ 10,000	4	20,000	36,200	Reject
13[b]	40,000	3	20,000	28,000	Accept
14	30,000	2	10,000	38,000	Reject
15[b]	70,000	1	10,000	0	Accept

[a]This column lists the number of deals to review *before* the ith deal is seen.
[b]Deal accepted.

Of the fifteen deals in this example, the operator would have accepted deals numbered 4, 7, 10, 13, and 15 for a total payoff of \$230,000 on an investment of \$50,000. All funds available for investment were invested.

The decision rules for Models II and III, although slightly more complicated, are used in the same fashion. Models Ia, IIa, and IIIa have decision rules which replace "number of deals remaining to review" with "time remaining to invest."

8.3. Formal Analysis of Sequential Investment Models

8.3.1. Formal Statement of Model I.[4] The sequential investment problem can be considered as a game with adversaries "operator" and "nature." To this end the following definitions are made.

n = Number of moves by nature in the game.

θ_j = The payoff chosen by nature at her $(n - j + 1)$st move, $j = n$, $n - 1, \ldots, 1$.

$a_j = 1$; the operator accepts θ_j.

$a_j = 0$; the operator rejects θ_j.

X = Units of capital possessed by the operator at the beginning of the game.

Let $\bar{\theta}_n, \bar{\theta}_{n-1}, \ldots, \bar{\theta}_1$ be n independent random variables with common measure P_θ and common cumulative distribution function F.

With the specifications above, the moves in the game can be listed as follows:

Move No. $N1$ Nature selects a θ_n according to P_θ.

Move No. 01 Operator either accepts or rejects θ_n.

Move No. $N2$ Nature selects a θ_{n-1} according to P_θ.

Move No. 02 Operator either accepts or rejects θ_{n-1}.

.

.

.

.

Move No. 0_n Operator either accepts or rejects θ_1.

The game terminates after n moves by the operator.

---

[4]Models I and II are similar to those derived by J. L. Fisher in "A Class of Stochastic Investment Problems,"*Operations Research,*Vol. 9, No. 1 (Jan.–Feb. 1961), pp. 53–65.

Payoff Function. Let $0 \leq k \leq 1$ denote the value of a unit of capital left uninvested after the game terminates. A particular realization of a sequence of θ_j's, $\{\theta_n, \theta_{n-1}, \ldots, \theta_j, \ldots, \theta_1\}$, results in the operator possessing capital and payoff in the following amounts:

$$\sum_{j=n}^{1} a_j\theta_j + k(X - \sum_{j=n}^{1} a_j), \quad \text{if} \quad \sum_{j=n}^{1} a_j \leq X,$$

or   (8.1)

$$0 \quad \quad \text{if} \quad \sum_{j=n}^{1} a_j > X.$$

The form of the payoff function implies that the operator cannot accept more than X θ_j's if he wishes to accumulate more than 0 units of payoff and capital by the end of the game. More formally, (8.1) implies that if

$$X - \sum_{j=n}^{\nu} a_j = 0 \quad\quad (8.2)$$

for some $\nu > 0$, then for all $m < \nu$, $a_m = 0$ if the operator wishes to possess more than 0 units of capital and payoff at the game's termination.

Flow Diagram. Defining x as the generic symbol for the amount of remaining capital, a typical sequence of moves in flow diagram format looks like this:

Move number:	n−j+1	n−j+1	n−j
Move by:	Nature	Operator	Nature

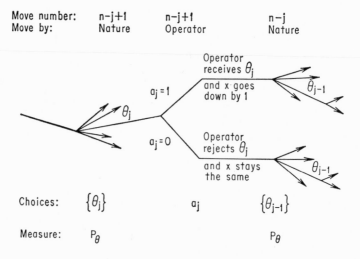

Choices:	$\{\theta_j\}$	a_j	$\{\theta_{j-1}\}$
Measure:	P_θ		P_θ

Operator's Strategy. The operator's strategy in playing the game can be characterized by a sequence of numbers $\{\alpha_{i,j}, i = X, X - 1, \ldots, 1;$

$j = n, n - 1, \ldots, 1\}$. Each $\alpha_{i,j}$ is a number such that if $x = i$ and the operator is at j (operator move number $n - j + 1$), he chooses

$$\text{act} \quad a_j = 1 \quad \text{if} \quad \theta_j \geq \alpha_{i,j},$$

or

$$\text{act} \quad a_j = 0 \quad \text{if} \quad \theta_j < \alpha_{i,j}.$$

Expected Value of the Game. The expected value of being at the node of nature's move number $n - j$ (j operator moves remaining), with capital x and following a strategy $\{\alpha_{i,\ell}, i = x, x - 1, \ldots, 1; \ell = j, j - 1, \ldots, 1\}$, will be denoted by $V_{x,j}$. The maximal value of $V_{x,j}$ will be distinguished by an asterisk: $V_{x,j}^*$. A strategy whose expected value is $V_{x,j}^*$ will be denoted by $\{\alpha_{i,\ell}^*, i = x, x - 1, \ldots, 1; \ell = j, j - 1, \ldots, 1\}$.[5]

The Problem. Suppose an operator with X units of capital begins an n move game. What strategy should he follow to achieve $V_{X,n}^*$?

Solution. It will be shown that if $\{\bar{\theta}_n, \bar{\theta}_{n-1}, \ldots, \bar{\theta}_1\}$ are n independent random variables with common measure P_θ and common cumulative distribution function F where $F(\alpha) \equiv P(\bar{\theta}_j < \alpha), j = n, n - 1, \ldots, 1$, then, letting $\beta \equiv \alpha_{x,n}^*$ for notational convenience,

$$V_{x,n}^* = [1 - F(\beta)]V_{x-1,n-1}^* + F(\beta)V_{x,n-1}^*$$

$$+ \int_\beta^\infty y dF(y), \tag{8.3a}$$

and

$$\alpha_{x,n}^* = V_{x,n-1}^* - V_{x-1,n-1}^*. \tag{8.3b}$$

Initial conditions are $V_{x,0}^* = kx$ and $V_{0,n}^* = 0$, for all $x \geq 0$ and all $n \geq 0$.

Lemma 1. Conditional upon knowing $V_{x,j}^*$ for $j < n$ and all x, the optimal cutoff with x units of capital remaining and n deals left to review is

$$\alpha_{x,n}^* = V_{x,n-1}^* - V_{x-1,n-1}^*.$$

Proof. Upon observing θ_n the operator can either accept or reject θ_n. If he accepts θ_n, the expected value of the game becomes $V_{x-1,n-1}^* + \theta_n$. If he rejects θ_n, the expected value of the game becomes $V_{x,n-1}^*$.

---

[5]This implies that the optimal strategy conditional upon having $x \leq X$ capital remaining and $j = n$ deals left to review is the same for all games which commence with $X \geq x$ units of capital and $n \geq j$ deals to review and which have identical boundary conditions and distribution functions F.

To achieve $V^*_{x,n}$ he will accept θ_n if $V^*_{x-1,n-1} + \theta_n > V^*_{x,n-1}$, will reject θ_n if $V^*_{x-1,n-1} + \theta_n < V^*_{x,n-1}$, and will be indifferent between acceptance and rejection if $V^*_{x-1,n-1} + \theta_n = V^*_{x,n-1}$. These inequalities imply that he will

$$\text{accept } \theta_n \text{ if } \quad \theta_n > V^*_{x,n-1} - V^*_{x-1,n-1},$$

$$\text{reject } \theta_n \text{ if } \quad \theta_n < V^*_{x,n-1} - V^*_{x-1,n-1},$$

$$\text{be indifferent if } \quad \theta_n = V^*_{x,n-1} - V^*_{x-1,n-1}.$$

It follows that

$$\alpha^*_{x,n} = V^*_{x,n-1} - V^*_{x-1,n-1}.$$

Lemma 2. Given the boundary conditions $V^*_{0,n} = 0$ and $V^*_{x,0} = kx$, $V^*_{x,n}$ satisfies the following functional equation for all $x > 0$ and $n > 0$.

$$V^*_{x,n} = [1 - F(\beta)]V^*_{x-1,n-1} + \int_\beta^\infty ydF(y) + F(\beta)V^*_{x,n-1} \quad (8.3a)$$

Proof. Suppose the operator follows an optimal strategy

$$\{\alpha^*_{i,j}, i = x, x - 1, \ldots, 1; \; j = n, n - 1, \ldots, 1\}.$$

Then before nature's first move in an n move game, the probability that the operator will accept θ_n at his first move is $1 - F(\beta)$, and the probability that he will reject θ_n is $F(\beta)$, since $\tilde{\theta}_n$ is a random variable before nature's first move.

The expected value of the game conditional upon $\tilde{\theta}_n \geq \alpha^*_{x,n} = \beta$ will be

$$\frac{1}{1 - F(\beta)} \int_\beta^\infty ydF(y) + V^*_{x-1,n-1}$$

before he moves.

The expected value of the game conditional upon $\tilde{\theta}_n < \alpha^*_{x,n} = \beta$ will be $V^*_{x,n-1}$. Weighting these conditional expectations by their respective probabilities and summing, we obtain (8.3a).

An Example

The illustrative example of 8.2 shows how the results of analysis are used. Table 8.2 is a display of the optimal strategy

$$\{\alpha^*_{i,j}, i = 5, 4, 3, 2, 1; \; j = 15, 14, \ldots, 1\}$$

given that the range set of $\tilde{\theta}$ is $\{-1, 3, 4, 7, 10\}$ and that P_θ is as follows:

θ	P_θ
-1	.2
3	.3
4	.3
7	.1
10	.1
	1.0

Table 8.3 displays $V_{i,j}^*$ for $i = 5, 4, 3, 2, 1$ and $j = 15, 14, \ldots, 1$. Boundary conditions are $V_{0,j}^* = V_{i,0}^* = 0$.

8.3.2. Formal Statement of Model II. We again consider the sequential investment problem as a game with adversaries "operator" and "nature," one which, however, has properties different from the game characterized by Model I. In addition to the definitions stated for Model I, there is the following definition.

I_j = the investment chosen by nature at her $(n - j + 1)$st move,

and define the 2×1 random vector

$$\tilde{\underline{r}}_j = \begin{pmatrix} \tilde{\theta}_j \\ \tilde{I}_j \end{pmatrix} \quad \text{the payoff and the investment chosen by nature at her } (n - j + 1)\text{st move.}$$

Let $\{\tilde{\underline{r}}_n, \tilde{\underline{r}}_{n-1}, \ldots, \tilde{\underline{r}}_1\}$ be n independent random vectors with common measure P_r and common cumulative distribution function F.

Moves in the Game. With the specifications above the moves in the game are precisely the same as those in the game of Model I except that nature chooses an $\underline{r}_j$ according to $P_{\underline{r}}$ instead of a θ_j according to P_θ when it is her turn to move.

Payoff Function. Since each $\tilde{I}_j$ can assume one of a number of values, the payoff function for this model must be structured differently than that of Model I, for which each $\tilde{I}_j$ was restricted to be equal to 1.

At the operator's $(n - j + 1)$st move if he has x units of capital, $\underline{r}_j^t = (\theta_j, I_j)$ is realized, $I_j \le x$, and $a_j = 1$, then he invests I_j for a payoff of θ_j and he has $x - I_j$ units of capital available for the remainder of the game. If, on the other hand, $I_j > x$, and $a_j = 1$, then his payoff is $x\theta_j/I_j$, and he has no capital left to invest.

More precisely, a particular realization of a sequence of $r_j s$, $\{r_n, r_{n-1}, \ldots, r_j, \ldots, r_1\}$, results in the operator's possessing capital and payoff in the following amounts: if there is an integer $\epsilon > 0$ such that

$$X - \sum_{j=n}^{\epsilon+1} a_j I_j \geq 0 \quad \text{and} \quad X - \sum_{j=n}^{\epsilon} a_j I_j < 0, \tag{8.4a}$$

then he possesses

$$\sum_{j=n}^{\epsilon+1} a_j \theta_j + \frac{\theta_\epsilon}{I_\epsilon}\left(X - \sum_{j=n}^{\epsilon+1} a_j I_j\right) \quad \text{if } \epsilon > 1 \text{ and } \sum_{j=\epsilon-1}^{1} a_j I_j = 0,$$
$$\text{or if } \epsilon = 1,$$
$$\tag{8.4b}$$
$$0 \qquad \text{if } \epsilon > 1 \text{ and } \sum_{j=\epsilon-1}^{1} a_j I_j < 0.$$

If there is no such $\epsilon > 0$, then he possesses

$$\sum_{j=n}^{1} a_j \theta_j + k(X - \sum_{j=n}^{1} a_j I_j) \tag{8.4c}$$

units of capital and payoff. As does (8.1), (8.4) implies that if for some $\epsilon > 0$,

$$X - \sum_{j=n}^{\epsilon} a_j I_j < 0,$$

then for all $m < \epsilon$, $a_m = 0$ if the operator wishes to possess more than 0 units of capital and payoff at the game's termination.

Operator's Strategy. The operator's strategy in playing this game is more complex than that for Model I. It can be characterized by a sequence of numbers

$$\{\alpha_{i,j}^{(m)}, i = X, X - 1, \ldots, 1; j = n, n - 1, \ldots, 1; m = 1, 2, \ldots \}. \tag{8.5a}$$

Each $\alpha_{i,j}^{(m)}$ is a number such that if $x = i$, $I_j = m$, and the operator is at j (operator move number $n - j + 1$), he chooses

$$\text{act} \quad a_j = 1 \quad \text{if} \quad \theta_j \geq \alpha_{i,j}^{(m)},$$

or

$$\text{act} \quad a_j = 0 \quad \text{if} \quad \theta_j < \alpha_{i,j}^{(m)}.$$

Expected Value of the Game. The expected value of being at the node of nature's move number $n - j$ (j operator moves remaining) with capital x and following a strategy

$$\{\alpha_{i,\ell}^{(m)}, i = x, x - 1, \ldots, 1; \; \ell = j, j - 1, \ldots, 1; \; m = 1, 2, \ldots \}$$
$$(8.5a)$$

will be denoted by $V_{x,j}$. The maximal value of $V_{x,j}$ will be distinguished by an asterisk: $V_{x,j}^*$. A strategy whose expected value is $V_{x,j}^*$ will be denoted by

$$\{\alpha_{i,\ell}^{(m)*}, i = x, x - 1, \ldots, 1; \; \ell = j, j - 1, \ldots, 1; \; m = 1, 2, \ldots \}.$$
$$(8.5b)$$

The Problem. An operator with X units of capital begins an n move game. What strategy should he follow so as to achieve $V_{X,n}^*$?

Solution. It will be shown that if $\{\tilde{r}_n, \tilde{r}_{n-1}, \ldots, \tilde{r}_1\}$ are n independent random vectors with common measure P_r and common cumulative distribution function F where $F(z, y) = P(\tilde{I}_j < z, \tilde{\theta}_j < y)$, $j = n$, $n - 1, \ldots, 1$, then, letting $\zeta(z) = \alpha_{x,n}^{(z)*}$ and $I = I_n$ for notational convenience,

$$V_{x,n}^* = \int_0^x \int_{\zeta(z)}^\infty V_{x-z,n-1}^* dF(z, y) + V_{x,n-1}[1 - \int_0^\infty \int_{\zeta(z)}^\infty dF(z, y)]$$
$$+ \int_0^x \int_{\zeta(z)}^\infty y \, dF(z, y) + x \int_x^\infty \int_{\zeta(z)}^\infty \left(\frac{y}{z}\right) dF(z, y), \qquad (8.6)$$

and

$$\alpha_{x,n}^{(I)*} = \begin{cases} V_{x,n-1}^* - V_{x-I,n-1}^*, & \text{if } x - I \le 0, \\ \dfrac{I}{x} V_{x,n-1}^* & \text{if } x - 1 > 0. \end{cases}$$

Initial conditions are $V_{x,0}^* = kx$ and $V_{0,n}^* = 0$ for all $x \ge 0$ and all $n \ge 0$.

Lemma 3. Conditional on knowing $V_{x,j}^*$ for $j < n$ and for all x, the optimal cutoff with x units of capital remaining and n deals left to review is

$$\alpha_{x,n}^{(I)*} = \begin{cases} V_{x,n-1}^* - V_{x-I,n-1}^* & \text{if } x - I \ge 0, \\ \dfrac{I}{x} V_{x,n-1}^* & \text{if } x - I < 0. \end{cases}$$

Proof. Upon observing $r_n^t = (\theta_n, I_n)$ the operator can either accept or reject θ_n. Four possibilities must be examined to determine the expected value of the game.

1. If $x - I \geq 0$ and he accepts θ_n, the expected value of the game becomes $V_{x-I,n-1}^* + \theta_n$.

2. If $x - I \geq 0$ and he rejects θ_n, the expected value of the game becomes $V_{x,n-1}^*$.

3. If $x - I < 0$ and he accepts θ_n, the expected value of the game becomes $\theta_n x/I$.

4. If $x - I < 0$ and he rejects θ_n, the expected value of the game becomes $V_{x,n-1}^*$.

To achieve $V_{x,n}^*$ if $x - I \geq 0$, he will accept θ_n if $V_{x-I,n-1}^* + \theta_n > V_{x,n-1}^*$, will reject θ_n if $V_{x-I,n-1}^* + \theta_n < V_{x,n-1}^*$ and will be indifferent between acceptance and rejection if $V_{x-I,n-1}^* + \theta_n = V_{x,n-1}^*$. It follows that

$$\alpha_{x,n}^{(I)*} = V_{x,n-1}^* - V_{x-I,n-1}^* \quad \text{if} \quad x - I \geq 0.$$

To achieve $V_{x,n}^*$ if $x - I < 0$, he will accept θ_n if $x\theta_n/I > V_{x,n-1}^*$, will reject θ_n if $x\theta_n/I < V_{x,n-1}^*$, and will be indifferent between acceptance and rejection if $x\theta_n/I = V_{x,n-1}^*$. It follows that

$$\alpha_{x,n}^{(I)*} = \frac{I}{x}V_{x,n-1}^* \quad \text{if} \quad x - I < 0.$$

Lemma 4. Given the boundary conditions $V_{0,n}^* = 0$ and $V_{x,0}^* = kx$, $V_{x,n}^*$ satisfies (8.6) for all $x > 0$ and $n > 0$.

Proof. Suppose the operator follows an optimal strategy

$$\{\alpha_{i,j}^{(m)*}, \ i = X, X - 1, \ldots, 1; \ j = n, n - 1, \ldots, 1; \ m = 1, 2, \ldots \}.$$

Then before nature's first move in an n move game, we must examine four possibilities.

1. If $\tilde{I}_n \leq x$ the probability that he will accept $\tilde{\theta}_n$ at his first move is

$$p_A \equiv \int_0^x \int_{\zeta(z)}^\infty dF(z, y) \bigg/ \int_0^x \int_{-\infty}^\infty dF(z, y).$$

The expected value of the game conditional upon his accepting $\tilde{\theta}_n$ is

$$\frac{1}{p_A}\left[\int_0^x\int_{\zeta(z)}^\infty ydF(z, y) + \int_0^x\int_{\zeta(z)}^\infty V_{x-z, n-1}^* dF(z, y)\right]$$

before he makes his first move.

2. If $\tilde{I}_n \leq x$ the probability that he will reject $\tilde{\theta}_n$ at his first move is p_A and the expected value of the game conditional on his rejection of $\tilde{\theta}_n$ is $V_{x, n-1}^*$.

3. If $\tilde{I}_n > x$ the probability that he will accept $\tilde{\theta}_n$ is

$$p_B = \int_x^\infty\int_{\zeta(z)}^\infty dF(z, y) \bigg/ \int_x^\infty\int_{-\infty}^\infty dF(z, y).$$

The expected value of the game conditional upon his acceptance of $\tilde{\theta}_n$ is

$$\frac{x}{p_B}\int_x^\infty\int_{\zeta(z)}^\infty \left(\frac{y}{z}\right)dF(z, y)$$

before he makes his first move.

4. If $\tilde{I}_n \leq x$ the probability that he will reject $\tilde{\theta}_n$ is $1 - p_B$ and the expected value of the game is $V_{x, n-1}^*$. The unconditional expected value $V_{x, n}^*$ is the sum of the conditional expectations of 1, 2, 3, and 4, weighted by their respective probabilities, as was to be proved.

An Example

To illustrate how the analytical results of Section 8.3.2 are used, suppose that the common measure $P_{\tilde{r}}$ of the mutually independent random vectors $\tilde{\underline{r}}_j$, $j = n, n - 1, \ldots, 1$, where $\tilde{\underline{r}}_j^t = (\theta_j, I_j)$, is as follows

θ \ I	$P_{\tilde{r}}$					P_θ
	1	2	3	4	5	
-1	.04	.08	.02	0	0	.14
3	.08	.08	.02	0	0	.18
4	.06	.12	.08	.02	0	.28
7	.02	.08	.04	.04	.02	.20
10	0	.04	.02	.03	.02	.11
11	0	0	.02	.01	.06	.09
P_I:	.20	.40	.20	.10	.10	1.00

TABLE 8.5. VALUES OF $V^*_{i,j}$ FOR $i = 5, 4, \ldots, 1$ AND $j = 15, 14, \ldots, 1$

i	1	2	3	4	5	6	7	8	9	10	11	12	13	14	15
5	5.150	9.028	11.096	12.449	13.518	14.409	15.200	15.899	16.513	17.049	17.516	17.925	18.290	18.622	18.928
4	4.950	8.007	9.531	10.589	11.450	12.195	12.833	13.374	13.831	14.220	14.563	14.874	15.155	15.410	15.644
3	4.557	6.626	7.704	8.526	9.197	9.742	10.182	10.541	10.852	11.124	11.365	11.592	11.807	12.011	12.205
2	3.805	4.952	5.676	6.219	6.628	6.942	7.199	7.426	7.632	7.822	7.997	8.158	8.306	8.443	8.570
1	2.212	2.763	3.119	3.370	3.562	3.717	3.851	3.969	4.073	4.168	4.258	4.343	4.422	4.497	4.567
0	1	2	3	4	5	6	7	8	9	10	11	12	13	14	15
								j							

TABLE 8.6. VALUES OF $\alpha^{(1)*}_{i,j}$ FOR $i = 5, 4, \ldots, 1$ AND $j = 15, 14, \ldots, 1$

i	1	2	3	4	5	6	7	8	9	10	11	12	13	14	15
5	0	0.200	1.020	1.566	1.860	2.068	2.214	2.366	2.525	2.682	2.829	2.953	3.052	3.136	3.212
4	0	0.392	1.381	1.827	2.063	2.253	2.453	2.652	2.833	2.978	3.096	3.198	3.282	3.348	3.399
3	0	0.752	1.675	2.027	2.308	2.569	2.800	2.982	3.115	3.220	3.302	3.368	3.433	3.500	3.568
2	0	1.592	2.188	2.557	2.848	3.066	3.225	3.348	3.457	3.560	3.654	3.739	3.815	3.884	3.947
1	0	2.212	2.763	3.119	3.370	3.562	3.717	3.851	3.969	4.073	4.168	4.258	4.343	4.422	4.497
0	1	2	3	4	5	6	7	8	9	10	11	12	13	14	15
								j							

TABLE 8.7. VALUES OF $\alpha^{(2)*}_{i,j}$ FOR $i = 5, 4, \ldots, 1$ AND $j = 15, 14, \ldots, 1$

i	1	2	3	4	5	6	7	8	9	10	11	12	13	14	15
5	0	0.592	2.401	3.393	3.923	4.321	4.667	5.018	5.358	5.661	5.925	6.151	6.334	6.483	6.611
4	0	1.145	3.055	3.854	4.370	4.822	5.253	5.634	5.948	6.198	6.398	6.566	6.716	6.848	6.967
3	0	2.345	3.863	4.585	5.156	5.635	6.025	6.331	6.572	6.780	6.956	7.107	7.249	7.385	7.515
2	0	3.805	4.952	5.676	6.219	6.628	6.942	7.199	7.426	7.632	7.822	7.997	8.158	8.306	8.443
1	0	4.425	5.527	6.238	6.741	7.125	7.434	7.702	7.938	8.145	8.336	8.516	8.685	8.844	8.993
0	1	2	3	4	5	6	7	8	9	10	11	12	13	14	15
								j							

TABLE 8.8. VALUES OF $\alpha^{(3)*}{}_{i,j}$ FOR $i = 5, 4, \ldots, 1$ AND $j = 15, 14, \ldots, 1$

i	$j=1$	2	3	4	5	6	7	8	9	10	11	12	13	14	15
5	0	1.345	4.076	5.420	6.230	6.890	7.467	8.001	8.473	8.881	9.227	9.519	9.767	9.984	10.179
4	0	2.737	5.244	6.412	7.219	7.888	8.479	8.983	9.405	9.758	10.052	10.305	10.531	10.732	10.914
3	0	4.557	6.626	7.704	8.526	9.197	9.742	10.182	10.541	10.852	11.124	11.365	11.592	11.807	12.011
2	0	5.707	7.427	8.514	9.328	9.942	10.414	10.799	11.139	11.448	11.733	11.996	12.237	12.460	12.665
1	0	6.637	8.290	9.357	10.111	10.687	11.151	11.553	11.906	12.218	12.505	12.774	13.028	13.266	13.490
0	1														

TABLE 8.9. VALUES OF $\alpha^{(4)*}{}_{i,j}$ FOR $i = 5, 4, \ldots, 1$ AND $j = 15, 14, \ldots, 1$

i	$j=1$	2	3	4	5	6	7	8	9	10	11	12	13	14	15
5	0	2.937	6.264	7.977	9.078	9.956	10.693	11.349	11.930	12.440	12.881	13.258	13.582	13.868	14.125
4	0	4.950	8.007	9.531	10.589	11.458	12.195	12.833	13.374	13.831	14.220	14.563	14.874	15.155	15.410
3	0	6.077	8.835	10.272	11.369	12.263	12.990	13.575	14.055	14.470	14.832	15.154	15.455	15.742	16.015
2	0	7.610	9.903	11.352	12.438	13.256	13.885	14.398	14.852	15.265	15.644	15.994	16.316	16.613	16.887
1	0	8.850	11.053	12.476	13.482	14.249	14.868	15.404	15.875	16.290	16.673	17.032	17.370	17.688	17.987
0	1														

TABLE 8.10. VALUES OF $\alpha^{(5)*}{}_{i,j}$ FOR $i = 5, 4, \ldots, 1$ AND $j = 15, 14, \ldots, 1$

i	$j=1$	2	3	4	5	6	7	8	9	10	11	12	13	14	15
5	0	5.150	9.028	11.096	12.449	13.518	14.409	15.200	15.899	16.513	17.049	17.516	17.925	18.290	18.622
4	0	6.187	10.009	11.913	13.236	14.313	15.244	16.042	16.717	17.288	17.775	18.204	18.592	18.943	19.263
3	0	7.596	11.044	12.839	14.211	15.329	16.237	16.969	17.568	18.087	18.540	18.942	19.319	19.678	20.019
2	0	9.512	12.379	14.190	15.597	16.570	17.356	17.998	18.565	19.081	19.556	19.993	20.395	20.766	21.109
1	0	11.062	13.817	15.595	16.852	17.812	18.585	19.259	19.899	20.363	20.841	21.290	21.713	22.110	22.489
0	1														

and boundary conditions are $V^*_{0,j} = V^*_{i,0} = 0$. Then Table 8.5 is a display of values of $\{V^*_{i,j}, i = 5, 4, \ldots, 1; j = 15, 14, \ldots, 1\}$ for the game and Tables 8.6 through 8.10 display values of

$$\{\alpha^{(m)*}_{i,j}, i = 5, 4, \ldots, 1; \; j = 15, 14, \ldots, 1; \; m = 1, 2, \ldots, 5\}$$

one table for each value of m.

If he is faced with a sequence of choices as shown in Table 8.11 and follows the dictates of Tables 8.6 through 8.10, the result is as displayed in the last two columns of Table 8.11.

TABLE 8.11

An Example

Operator Choice Number	$r^t = (\theta, I)^6$	Payoff of Accepted Deals	Capital Remaining to Invest after Choice
1	(10, 2)	10	3
2	(7, 1)	7	2
3	(4, 4)	—	2
4	(10, 4)	—	2
5	(7, 2)	—	2
6	(3, 2)	—	2
7	(3, 2)	—	2
8	(3, 1)	—	2
9	(4, 3)	—	2
10	(4, 3)	—	2
11	(7, 4)	—	2
12	(11, 5)	—	2
13	(3, 1)	3	1
14	(4, 4)	—	1
15	(3, 1)	3	0
Total payoff		23	
Units of capital uninvested			0

8.3.3. Formal Statement of Model III.

We now consider a third game whose moves differ from those of the preceding two games. The essential difference is that while nature generates a particular realization $\{r_n, r_{n-1}, \ldots, r_j, \ldots, r_1\}$ of a sequence of random vectors $\{\tilde{r}_j, j = n, n - 1, \ldots, 1\}$ as in the game of Model II, she reveals only the I_j component of each r_j before the operator makes his choice of act $a_j = 1$ or $a_j = 0$.

---

[6]Random numbers were used to generate this sequence of r's according to the table of P_r shown in the example of 8.3.2.

Moves in the Game.

Move No. N1a Nature selects an $\underline{r}_n$ according to $P_{\underline{r}}$, but reveals only I_n to the operator.

No. O1 The operator accepts or rejects θ_n, which he does not know with certainty.

No. N1b Nature reveals θ_n to the operator.

No. N2a Nature selects an $\underline{r}_{n-1}$ according to $P_{\underline{r}}$ but reveals only I_{n-1} to the operator.

.

.

.

No. Nnb Nature reveals θ_1 to the operator.

The game terminates, after n complete moves by nature.

Payoff Function. The payoff function is that of (8.4).

Operator Strategy. The operator's strategy is somewhat different than that of the preceding games, as he must select $a_j = 1$ or $a_j = 0$ knowing only the element I_j of $\underline{r}_j$ with certainty. By virtue of our assumption that the $\{\tilde{r}_j, j = n, n - 1, \ldots, 1\}$ are identically distributed, mutually independent random variables, we may define the expected value of $\tilde{\theta}_j$ given $\tilde{I}_j = I_j$ as

$$E_{\theta|I_j} = E_{\theta_j|I_j} \quad \text{for} \quad j = n, n - 1, \ldots, 1.$$

Now the operator's strategy can be characterized by a sequence of numbers like (8.5), where each $\alpha_{i,j}^{(m)}$ is a number such that if $m = I_j$ he chooses

$$\text{act} \quad a_j = 1 \quad \text{if} \quad E_{\theta|I_j} \geq \alpha_{i,j}^{(I_j)},$$

or

$$\text{act} \quad a_j = 0 \quad \text{if} \quad E_{\theta|I_j} < \alpha_{i,j}^{(I_j)}.$$

Expected Value of the Game. The notation for the expected value of the game is the same as that for the game of Model II.

The Problem. An operator with X units of capital begins an n move game. What strategy should he follow so as to achieve $V_{X,n}^*$?

Solution. Define the function

$$\delta_{x,n}^{(I)*} = \begin{cases} 1 & \text{if} \quad E_{\theta|I} \geq \alpha_{x,n}^{(I)*}, \\ 0 & \text{if} \quad E_{\theta|I} < \alpha_{x,n}^{(I)*}, \end{cases} \tag{8.7}$$

where $I \equiv I_n$ for notational simplicity.

It will be shown that if $\{\tilde{r}_n, \tilde{r}_{n-1}, \ldots, \tilde{r}_1\}$ is a sequence of n independent random vectors with common distribution function F and common measure $P_{\tilde{r}}$, then, letting $\delta(z) \equiv \delta_{x,n}^{(z)*}$ for notational convenience,

$$V_{x,n}^* = \int_0^x \int_{-\infty}^{\infty} \delta(z)[E_{\theta|z} + V_{x-z,n-1}^*]dF(z,y)$$

$$+ V_{x,n-1}^* \int_0^{\infty} \int_{-\infty}^{\infty} [1 - \delta(z)]dF(z,y) \tag{8.8a}$$

$$+ x \int_x^{\infty} \int_{-\infty}^{\infty} \delta(z)z^{-1}E_{\theta|z}dF(z,y),$$

and

$$\alpha_{x,n}^{(I)*} = \begin{cases} V_{x,n-1}^* - V_{x-I,n-1}^* & \text{if } x - I \leq 0 \\ \dfrac{I}{x}V_{x,n-1}^* & \text{if } x - I > 0, \end{cases} \tag{8.8b}$$

providing that the Riemann-Stieltjes integrals of (8.8) exist.[7]

Lemma 5. Conditional on knowing $V_{x,j}^*$ for $j < n$ and for all x, the optimal cutoff with x units of capital remaining and n deals left to review is as described in Lemma 3.

Proof. The essential steps in the proof are the same as those in proving Lemma 3.

Lemma 6. Given the boundary conditions $V_{0,n}^* = 0$ and $V_{x,0}^* = kx$, $V_{x,n}^*$ satisfies (8.8) for all $x > 0$ and $n > 0$.

Proof. Suppose that an operator follows an optimal policy (8.5b). As in the proof of Lemma 3, we must examine four possibilities.

1. If $I_n \leq x$ the probability that he will accept $\tilde{\theta}_n$ at his first move is

$$p_A' \equiv \int_0^x \int_{-\infty}^{\infty} \delta(z)dF(z,y) \;\bigg/\; \int_0^x \int_{-\infty}^{\infty} dF(z,y).$$

The expected value of the game conditional upon his accepting $\tilde{\theta}_n$ is

$$\frac{1}{p_A'}\left[\int_0^x \int_{-\infty}^{\infty} \delta(z)E_{\theta|z}dF(z,y) + \int_0^x \int_{-\infty}^{\infty} V_{x-z,n-1}^*dF(z,y) \right]$$

before he makes his first move.

---

[7]We may define $\delta^{(I)*}{}_{x,n}$ so that existence is assured.

2. If $I_n \leq x$ the probability that he will reject $\tilde{\theta}_n$ at his first move is $1 - p'_A$ and the expected value of the game conditional on his rejection of $\tilde{\theta}_n$ is $V^*_{x,n-1}$.

3. If $I_n > x$ the probability that he will accept $\tilde{\theta}_n$ is

$$p'_B \equiv \int_x^\infty \int_{-\infty}^\infty \delta(z) \, dF(z, y) \, \bigg/ \int_x^\infty \int_{-\infty}^\infty dF(z, y).$$

The expected value of the game conditional on his acceptance of $\tilde{\theta}_n$ is

$$\frac{x}{p'_B} \int_x^\infty \int_{-\infty}^\infty z^{-1} E_{\theta|z} dF(z, y)$$

before he makes his first move.

4. If $I_n > x$ the probability that he will reject $\tilde{\theta}_n$ is $1 - p'_B$ and the expected value of the game is $V^*_{x,n-1}$.

The unconditional expected value $V^*_{x,n}$ is the sum of the conditional expectations of 1, 2, 3, and 4, weighted by their respective probabilities. This sum is (8.6) as was to be proved.

8.3.4. *Formal Statement of Model Ia.* The game of Section 8.3.1 may be generalized by assuming that the number of choices $\tilde{n}$ allowed the operator during the game's course is a random variable. We will now analyze a specific example of this type of game under three assumptions about $\tilde{n}$.

1. *Temporal homogeneity.* The probability of $(n \geq 0)$ deals being offered in the time interval s to $s - t > 0$ is independent of s, $s > t$.

2. *Independence.* The probability of n deals being offered in the time interval s to $s - t$ does not depend on the number of deals being offered from s to 0 or on the number of deals offered in any subinterval of s to 0.

3. *Unicity of occurrences.* The probability that in any time interval t to $t - \Delta t$ there will be exactly one deal offered is (neglecting terms depending on Δt which go to 0 faster than Δt) $\lambda \Delta t$ where λ is a constant.

Feller[8] shows that 1, 2, and 3 imply that given a time interval of length $T > 0$,

$$P(\tilde{n} = n) = f_p(n \mid \lambda, T) = \frac{e^{-\lambda T}(\lambda T)^n}{n!}, \qquad \lambda > 0, \qquad (8.9)$$

---

[8]William Feller, *An Introduction to Probability Theory and its Applications*, 2nd. ed. Volume I (New York, John Wiley & Sons, Inc., 1957), pp. 400–402.

and furthermore that the waiting times $\{\tilde{\tau}_\ell, \ell = 1, 2, \ldots, n\}$ between the $(\ell - 1)$st and ℓth operator choices are mutually independent random variables with common exponential density function

$$f_e(\tau \mid \lambda, 1) = \lambda e^{-\lambda \tau} \tag{8.10}$$

and common cumulative distribution function

$$P(\tilde{\tau} \leq t \mid \lambda, 1) = F_e(t \mid \lambda, 1) = 1 - e^{-\lambda t}. \tag{8.11}$$

Moves in the Game. If the game starts at time T and ends at time 0, and we let $\{\tilde{\theta}_{\tilde{n}}, \tilde{\theta}_{\tilde{n}-1}, \ldots, \tilde{\theta}_1\}$ be $\tilde{n}$ independent random variables with common measure P_θ and common distribution function F as before, we may list the moves in the game as follows:

Move No. N1 Nature selects a τ_1 according to f_e and a θ_1 according to P_θ.

No. O1 Operator either accepts or rejects θ_1.

No. N2 Nature selects a τ_2 according to f_e and a θ_2 according to P_θ.

No. O2 Operator either accepts or rejects θ_2.

$$\vdots$$

The game terminates at nature's nth move if

$$\sum_{\ell=1}^{n} \tau_\ell \leq T$$

and

$$\sum_{\ell=1}^{n+1} \tau_\ell > T.$$

Payoff Function. If the game terminates with the operator having had n moves, the payoff function is (8.1).

Operator's Strategy. The operator's strategy in playing the game can be characterized by a sequence of numbers $\{\alpha_i(t), i = X, X - 1, \ldots, 1; T \geq t \geq 0\}$ where t denotes the amount of time left to play the game, and, if it is operator's move number $n - j + 1$, the operator chooses

$$\text{act} \quad a_j = 1 \quad \text{if} \quad \theta_j \geq \alpha_i(t),$$

or

$$\text{act} \quad a_j = 0 \quad \text{if} \quad \theta_j < \alpha_i(t).$$

Expected Value of the Game. The expected value of having time t left to play with capital x and following a strategy $\{\alpha_i(t'),\ i = x,\ x - 1, \ldots, 1;\ t \geq t' \geq 0\}$ will be denoted by $V_x(t)$. As before, the maximal value of $V_x(t)$ will be distinguished by an asterisk: $V_x^*(t)$; and a strategy whose expected value is $V_x^*(t)$ will be likewise distinguished.

The Problem. An operator with X units of capital begins as game of time duration T. What strategy should he follow to achieve $V_X^*(T)$?

Solution. It is easily shown that for each x and for $T \geq t \geq 0$, $V_x^*(t)$ is continuous in t and monotonically decreasing as $t \to 0$. We will show explicitly that the partial derivative of $V_x^*(t)$ with respect to t exists and satisfies

$$\frac{\partial}{\partial t} V_x^*(t) = \lambda G(\eta(t))[V_{x-1}^*(t) - V_x^*(t)] + \lambda \int_{\eta(t)}^{\infty} y dF(y), \quad (8.12a)$$

for $x = X,\ X - 1, \ldots, 1$, and that

$$\alpha_x^*(t) = V_x^*(t) - V_{x-1}^*(t), \quad (8.12b)$$

where in (8.12a) we let $\eta(t) = \alpha_x^*(t)$ and $G(\eta(t)) = 1 - F(\eta(t))$ for notational convenience. Since x is fixed, (8.12a) is a system of *ordinary* differential equations. Boundary conditions are $V_0^*(t) = 0$ and $V_x^*(0) = kx$ for all $x \geq 0$ and $T \geq t \geq 0$.

Lemma 1'. Conditional on knowing $V_x^*(t)$ for all x and for $T \geq t \geq 0$, the optimal cutoff with x units of capital remaining and time t left in the game is

$$\alpha_x^*(t) = V_x^*(t) - V_{x-1}^*(t).$$

Proof. The method of proof of Lemma 1 is used: If the operator has a choice of accepting or rejecting a particular θ at time t, and must make his choice instantaneously, then he will

accept θ if $\theta \geq V_x^*(t) - V_{x-1}^*(t)$,

reject θ if $\theta < V_x^*(t) - V_{x-1}^*(t)$.

Lemma 2'. Given the boundary conditions $V_0^*(t) = 0$ and $V_x^*(0) = kx$, $V_x^*(t)$ satisfies the functional equations (8.12a) for $T \geq t \geq 0$ and $x > 0$.

Proof. Comparing the value of the game at t with the value at $t - \Delta t$, we see that there is probability[9] $^*\lambda\Delta t$ that an operator choice will appear in the interval t to $t - \Delta t$. Conditional upon a choice appearing the argument of the proof of Lemma 1 is applicable, and we have the following conditional expected value of the game at t given x:

$$G(\eta(\xi))V^*_{x-1}(t - \Delta t) + \int_{\eta(\xi)}^\infty ydF(y) + F(\eta(\xi))V^*_x(t - \Delta t),$$

where $t > \xi > t - \Delta t$.

With probability $^*1 - \lambda\Delta t$ an operator choice will not appear in the interval t to $t - \Delta t$, in which case the conditional expected value of the game is $V^*_x(t - \Delta t)$.

Weighting the two conditional expected values of the game derived above by their respective probabilities, and summing, we get

$$V^*_x(t) = \lambda\Delta t \left(G(\eta(\xi))V^*_{x-1}(t - \Delta t) + \int_{\eta(\xi)}^\infty ydF(y) + F(\eta(\xi))V^*_x(t - \Delta t) \right)$$
$$+ (1 - \lambda\Delta t)V^*_{x-1}(t - \Delta t).$$

This equation may be re-expressed as

$$\frac{V^*_x(t) - V^*_x(t - \Delta t)}{\Delta t} = \lambda G(\eta(\xi))V^*_{x-1}(t - \Delta t) + \lambda \int_{\eta(\xi)}^\infty ydF(y)$$
$$- \lambda G(\eta(\xi))V^*_x(t - \Delta t).$$

Letting $\Delta t \to 0$ on both sides of the equation above, we obtain (8.12a) as was to be shown.

8.3.5. Formal Statement of Model IIa.

The assumptions made in Section 8.3.4 about the number of choices $\tilde{n}$ allowed the operator during the course of the game are also made for this game. The assumptions made in Section 8.3.2 about $\{\tilde{r}_j, j = \tilde{n}, \tilde{n} - 1, \ldots, 1\}$ are also assumed to hold.

Moves in the Game. The moves in the game are the same as those in the Model Ia game except that nature chooses an $\underline{r}_j$ according to $P_{\underline{r}}$ instead of a θ_j according to P_θ when it is her turn to move.

Payoff Function. If the game terminates with the operator having had n moves, the payoff function is (8.4).

---

[9]We shall distinguish by an asterisk probability statements that neglect terms $0(t)$ which go to 0 faster than $\lambda\Delta t$ as $\Delta t \to 0$.

Operator's Strategy. The operator's strategy in playing the game can be characterized by a sequence of numbers

$$\{\alpha_i^{(m)}(t), \ i = x, x - 1, \ldots, 1; \ m = 1, 2, \ldots; \ T \geq t \geq 0\}. \qquad (8.13)$$

If there is time t left to play the game and if it is operator's move number $n - j + 1$, the operator chooses

$$\text{act} \quad a_j = 1 \quad \text{if} \quad \theta_j \geq \alpha_i^{(m)}(t),$$

or

$$\text{act} \quad a_j = 0 \quad \text{if} \quad \theta_j < \alpha_i^{(m)}(t).$$

Expected Value of the Game. The expected value of having time t left to play with capital x and following a strategy (8.13) will be denoted by $V_x(t)$. As before, the maximal value of $V_x(t)$ will be distinguished by an asterisk: $V_x^*(t)$; and a strategy whose expected value is $V_x^*(t)$ will be likewise distinguished.

The Problem. An operator with X units of capital begins a game of time duration T. What strategy should he follow so as to achieve $V_X^*(T)$?

Solution. As for Model Ia, it is easily proved that for each x and for $T \geq t \geq 0$, $V_x^*(t)$ is continuous in t and monotonically decreasing as $t \to 0$. We will show explicitly that if $\{\tilde{r}_{\tilde{n}}, \tilde{r}_{\tilde{n}-1}, \ldots, \tilde{r}_1\}$ is a sequence of $\tilde{n}$ mutually independent random vectors with common cumulative distribution function F and common measure P_r, then the partial derivative of $V_x^*(t)$ with respect to t exists and, letting $\phi(z, t) \equiv \alpha_x^{(z)*}(t)$ and $I \equiv I_n$ for notational convenience, satisfies

$$\frac{\partial}{\partial t} V_x^*(t) = \lambda \left[\int_0^x \int_{\phi(z,t)}^\infty V_{x-z}^*(t) dF(z, y) - V_x^*(t) \int_0^\infty \int_{\phi(z,t)}^\infty dF(z, y) \right.$$

$$\left. + \int_0^x \int_{\phi(z,t)}^\infty y dF(z, y) + x \int_x^\infty \int_{\phi(z,t)}^\infty \left(\frac{y}{z}\right) dF(z, y) \right], \qquad (8.14a)$$

for $x = X, X - 1, \ldots, 1$, and that

$$\alpha_x^{(I)*}(t) = \begin{cases} V_x^*(t) - V_{x-I}^*(t) & \text{if} \quad x - I \leq 0 \\ \dfrac{I}{x} V_x^*(t) & \text{if} \quad x - I > 0 \end{cases}. \qquad (8.14b)$$

Since x is fixed, (8.14a) is a system of *ordinary* differential equations. Boundary conditions are $V_0^*(t) = 0$ and $V_x^*(0) = kx$ for all $x \geq 0$ and $T \geq t \geq 0$. The system of differential equations (8.14a) may alternatively be expressed as a system of integral difference equations. However, little insight is gained into the structure of the problem by this re-expression for the result does not substantially simplify (8.14a).

Lemma 3'. Conditional on knowing $V_x^*(t)$ for all x and for $T \geq t \geq 0$ the optimal cutoff with x units of capital remaining and time t left in the game is

$$\alpha_x^{(I)*}(t) = \begin{cases} V_x^*(t) - V_{x-I}^*(t) & \text{if } x - I \geq 0, \\ \dfrac{I}{x}V_x^*(t) & \text{if } x - I < 0. \end{cases}$$

Proof. The method of proof of Lemma 3 is used in the same fashion as the method of proof of Lemma 1 was used to prove Lemma 1'.

Lemma 4'. Given the boundary conditions $V_0^*(t) = 0$ and $V_x^*(0) = kx$, $V_x^*(t)$ satisfies the functional equations (8.14a) for $T \geq t \geq 0$ and all $x > 0$.

Proof. Comparing the value of the game at t with the value at $t - \Delta t$ we see that there is probability $*\lambda\Delta t$ that an operator choice will appear in the interval t to $t - \Delta t$. Conditional upon a choice appearing, the argument of the proof of Lemma 3 is applicable and we have the following conditional expected value of the game at t given x:

$$\int_0^x \int_{\phi(z,\xi)}^\infty V_{x-z}^*(t - \Delta t)dF(z, y) + V_x^*(t - \Delta t)\left[1 - \int_0^\infty \int_{\phi(z,\xi)}^\infty dF(z, y)\right]$$

$$+ \int_0^x \int_{\phi(z,\xi)}^\infty ydF(z, y) + x\int_x^\infty \int_{\phi(z,\xi)}^\infty \left(\frac{y}{z}\right)dF(z, y)$$

where $t > \xi > t - \Delta t$.

With probability $*1 - \lambda\Delta t$ an operator choice will not appear in the interval t to $t - \Delta t$ in which case the conditional expected value of the game is $V_x^*(t - \Delta t)$.

Weighting the two conditional expected values of the game derived above by their respective probabilities of occurrence and summing, we get

$$V_x^*(t) = \lambda\Delta t\left[\int_0^x \int_{\phi(z,\xi)}^\infty V_{x-z}^*(t - \Delta t)dF(z, y)\right.$$

$$\left. + V_x^*(t - \Delta t)\left[1 - \int_0^\infty \int_{\phi(z,\xi)}^\infty dF(z, y)\right]\right.$$

$$+ x \int_{x}^{\infty} \int_{\phi(z,\xi)}^{\infty} \left(\frac{y}{z}\right) dF(z, y) + \int_{0}^{x} \int_{\phi(z,\xi)}^{\infty} x dF(z, y) \Bigg]$$

$$+ V_{x}^{*}(t - \Delta t)[1 - \lambda \Delta t].$$

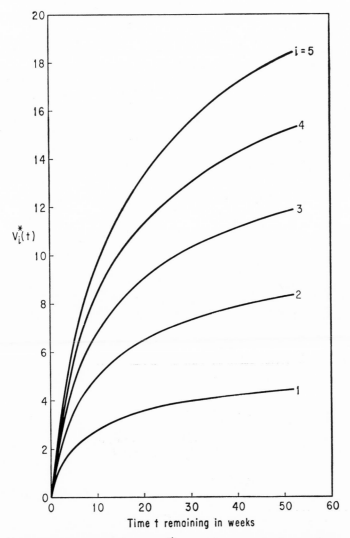

Graph 8.1. Expected values $V_{i}^{*}(t)$ of following optimal strategies for illustrative model IIa game given i units of capital to invest and time t remaining in planning period for $i = 5, 4, \ldots, 1$ and $52 \geq t \geq 0$ weeks

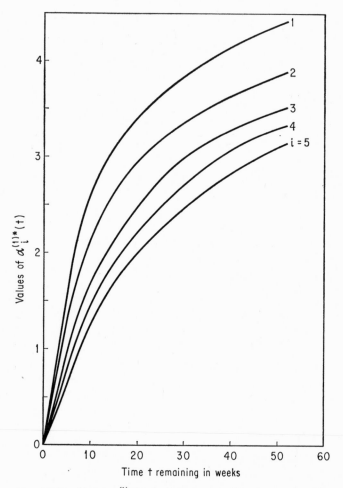

Graph 8.2. Values $\alpha_i^{(1)*}(t)$ of minimum payoff for acceptance of a deal requiring 1 unit of investment which appears when t weeks remain in the planning period and the operator has i units of investable capital for $52 \geq t \geq 0$ and $i = 5, 4, \ldots, 1$

This equation may be re-expressed as

$$\frac{V_x(t) - V_x^*(t - \Delta t)}{\Delta t} = \lambda \int_0^x \int_{\phi(z,\xi)}^\infty V_{x-z}^*(t - \Delta t) dF(z, y)$$

$$- \lambda V_x^*(t - \Delta t) G(0, \phi(z, \xi)) + \lambda \int_0^\infty \int_{\phi(z,\xi)}^\infty y dF(z, y)$$

$$+ \lambda x \int_x^\infty \int_{\phi(z,\xi)}^\infty \left(\frac{y}{z}\right) dF(z, y).$$

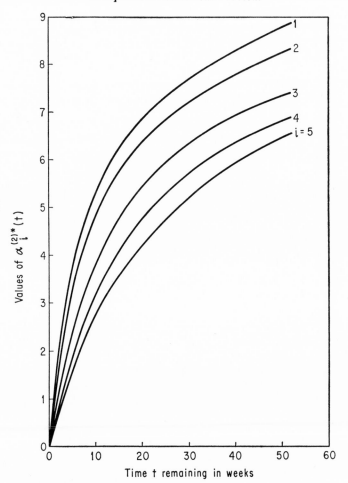

Graph 8.3. Values of $\alpha_i^{(2)}*(t)$ of minimum payoff for acceptance of a deal requiring 2 units of investment which appears when t weeks remain in the planning period and the operator has i units of investable capital for $52 \geq t \geq 0$ and $i = 5, 4, \ldots, 1$

Letting $\Delta t \to 0$ on both sides of the equation, we obtain (8.14a) as was to be shown.

An Example[10]

Suppose P_r is as stated in the example of 8.3.2 and also that

1. the operator's planning period is 52 weeks; i.e., $T = 52$ weeks;

---

[10]This example, as well as the two examples cited earlier, is based on data presented in the experiment reviewed in Chapter 9.

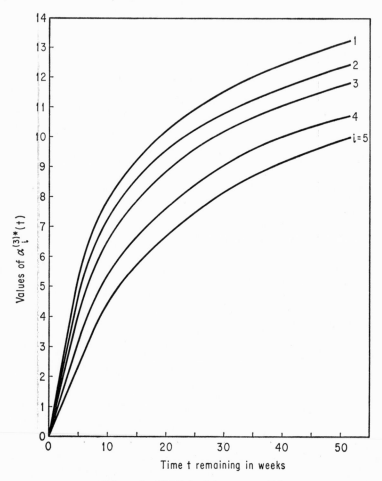

Graph 8.4. Values of $\alpha_i^{(3)*}(t)$ of minimum payoff for acceptance of a deal requiring 3 units of investment which appears when t weeks remain in the planning period and the operator has i units of investable capital for $52 \geq t \geq 0$ and $i = 5, 4, \ldots, 1$

2. the expected waiting time between deals is 3.47 weeks;

3. he has five units of capital to invest during the planning period; i.e., $X = 5$.

4. boundary conditions are $V_0^*(t) = V_x^*(0) = 0$ for $x > 0$ and $T \geq t \geq 0$.

Then Graph 8.1 displays values of $\{V_j^*(t), j = 5, 4, 3, 2, 1; 52 \geq t \geq 0\}$

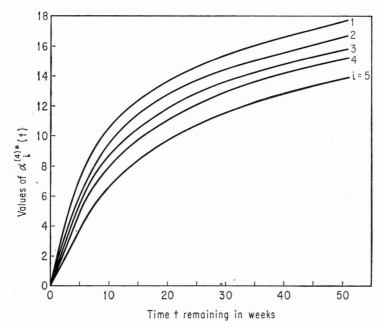

Graph 8.5. Values of $\alpha_i^{(4)}*(t)$ of minimum payoff for acceptance of a deal requiring 4 units of investment which appears when t weeks remain in the planning period and the operator has i units of investable capital for $52 \geq t \geq 0$ and $i = 5, 4, \ldots, 1$

and Graphs 8.2 through 8.6 display values of $\{\alpha_j^{(m)}*(t), j = 5, 4, 3, 2, 1;$ $52 \geq t \geq 0\}$, for $m = 1, 2, 3, 4, 5$.

If he is faced with a sequence of choices as shown in Table 8.12 and follows the dictates of Graphs 8.2 through 8.6, the result is as displayed in the last two columns of Table 8.12.

8.3.6. Formal Statement of Model IIIa. We retain the assumptions about $\tilde{n}$ made in 8.3.4 and also make the assumptions about $\{\tilde{r}_j, j = \tilde{n}, \tilde{n} - 1, \ldots, 1\}$ presented in Section 8.3.3.

Moves in the Game.

Move No. N1a   Nature selects a τ_1 according to f_e and a r_n according to P_r, but reveals only I_n to the operator.

No. O1   The operator accepts or rejects θ_n, which he does not know with certainty.

No. N1b   Nature reveals θ_n to the operator.

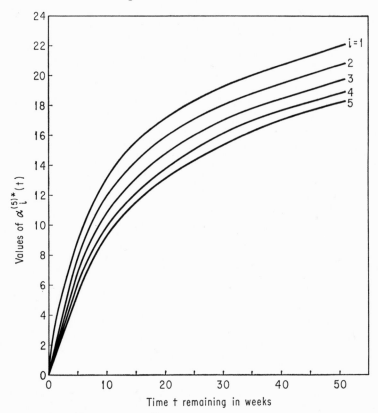

Graph 8.6. Values of $\alpha_i^{(5)*}(t)$ of minimum payoff for acceptance of a deal requiring 5 units of investment which appears when t weeks remain in the planning period and the operator has i units of investable capital for $52 \geq t \geq 0$ and $i = 5, 4, \ldots, 1$

No. N2a   Nature selects a τ_2 according to f_e and a $\underline{r}_{n-1}$ according to $P_{\underline{r}}$ but reveals only I_{n-1} to the operator.

.

.

.

The game terminates at nature's nth move if

$$\sum_{\ell=1}^{n} \tau_\ell \leq T,$$

and

$$\sum_{\ell=1}^{n+1} \tau_\ell > T.$$

TABLE 8.12

Operator Choice	Remaining Time[a] t (Weeks) (1)	Payoff-Investment Pairs $[r^t = (\theta, I)]^b$ (2)	Payoff of Accepted Deals (3)	Capital Remaining To Invest after Choice (4)
1	51	(10, 2)	10	3
2	47	(7, 1)	7	2
3	32	(4, 4)	—	2
4	25	(10, 4)	—	2
5	21	(7, 4)	—	2
6	16	(7, 3)	—	2
7	15	(4, 4)	—	2
8	12	(4, 3)	—	2
9	6	(7, 4)	$3\frac{1}{2}$	0
10	5	(11, 5)	—	0
11	2	(3, 1)	—	0
12	1	(3, 1)	—	0
Total payoff			$20\frac{1}{2}$	
Units of capital uninvested				0

[a]Exponential random deviates were used to generate the waiting time between deals. Waiting times were rounded off to the nearest week. Mean waiting time was 3.47 weeks.

[b]Random numbers were used to generate this sequence of r's according to the table of P_r shown in the example of 8.3.2.

Payoff Function. The payoff function is that of (8.4).

Operator's Strategy. We may characterize the operator's strategy by a sequence of numbers like (8.13) where each $\alpha_i^{(m)}(t)$ is a number such that if $m = I_j$ he chooses

act $a_j = 1$ if $E_{\theta|I_j} \geq \alpha_i^{(I_j)}(t)$,

act $a_j = 0$ if $E_{\theta|I_j} < \alpha_i^{(I_j)}(t)$.

Expected Value of the Game. The notation for the expected value of the game is the same as that for the Model IIa game.

The Problem. An operator with X units of capital begins a game of time duration T. What strategy should he follow so as to achieve $V_X^*(T)$?

Solution. Define the function

$$\delta_x^{(I)*}(t) = \begin{cases} 1 & \text{if} \quad E_{\theta|I} \geq \alpha_x^{(I)*}(t) \\ 0 & \text{if} \quad E_{\theta|I} < \alpha_x^{(I)*}(t) \end{cases} \qquad (8.15a)$$

It will be shown that if $\{\tilde{\underline{r}}_{\tilde{n}}, \tilde{\underline{r}}_{\tilde{n}-1}, \ldots, \tilde{r}_1\}$ is as equence of $\tilde{n}$ mutually independent random vectors with common cumulative distribution function F and common measure $P_{\underline{r}}$, then, letting $\delta(z, t) \equiv \delta_x^{(I)}*(t)$ for notational convenience,

$$\frac{\partial}{\partial t}V_x^*(t) = \lambda \int_0^x \int_{-\infty}^{\infty} \delta(z, t)[E_{\theta|z} + V_{x-z}^*(t)]dF(z, y)$$

$$- \lambda V_x^*(t) \int_0^{\infty} \int_{-\infty}^{\infty} \delta(z, t)dF(z, y) \qquad (8.15b)$$

$$+ \lambda x \int_x^{\infty} \int_{-\infty}^{\infty} \delta(z, t)z^{-1}E_{\theta|z}dF(z, y),$$

for $x = X, X - 1, \ldots, 1$, and

$$\alpha_x^{(I)}*(t) = \begin{cases} V_x^*(t) - V_{x-I}^*(t) & \text{if } x - I \geq 0 \\ \dfrac{I}{x}V_x^*(t) & \text{if } x - I < 0 \end{cases} \qquad (8.15c)$$

Lemma 5′. Conditional on knowing $V_x^*(t)$ for $T \geq t \geq 0$ and for all $x > 0$ the optimal cutoff with x units of capital remaining and time t left in the game is as described in Lemma 3′.

Proof. The essential steps in the proof are the same as those in proving Lemma 3′.

Lemma 6′. Given the boundary conditions $V_x^*(0) = kx$ and $V_0^*(t) = 0$, $V_x^*(t)$ satisfies (8.15b) for all $x > 0$ and for $T \geq t \geq 0$.

Proof. Comparing the value of the game at t with the value at $t - \Delta t$ we see that there is probability $*\lambda\Delta t$ that an operator choice will appear in the interval t to $t - \Delta t$. Conditional on a choice appearing the argument of the proof of Lemma 3 is applicable, and we have the following conditional expected value of the game at t given x:

$$\int_0^x \int_{-\infty}^{\infty} \delta(z, \xi)[E_{\theta|z} + V_{x-z}^*(t - \Delta t)]dF(z, y)$$

$$+ V_x^*(t - \Delta t) \int_0^{\infty} \int_{-\infty}^{\infty} [1 - \delta(z, \xi)]dF(z, y)$$

$$+ x \int_x^{\infty} \int_{-\infty}^{\infty} \delta(z, \xi)z^{-1}E_{\theta|z}dF(z, y),$$

where $t > \xi > t - \Delta t$.

With probability $*1 - \lambda\Delta t$ an operator choice will not appear in the interval t to $t - \Delta t$ in which case the conditional expected value of the game is $V_x^*(t - \Delta t)$.

Weighting the two conditional expected values of the game derived above by their respective probabilities of occurrence and summing, we get

$$
V_x^*(t) = \lambda\Delta t \left[\int_0^x \int_{-\infty}^\infty \delta(z, \xi)[E_{\theta|z} + V_{x-z}^*(t - \Delta t)]dF(z, y) \right.
$$
$$
+ V_x^*(t - \Delta t) \int_0^\infty \int_{-\infty}^\infty [1 - \delta(z, \xi)]dF(z, y)
$$
$$
\left. + x \int_x^\infty \int_{-\infty}^\infty \delta(z, \xi)z^{-1}E_{\theta|z}dF(z, y) \right]
$$
$$
+ V_x^*(t - \Delta t)[1 - \lambda\Delta t].
$$

This equation may be re-expressed as

$$
\frac{V_x^*(t) - V_x^*(t - \Delta t)}{\Delta t} = \lambda \int_0^x \int_{-\infty}^\infty \delta(z, \xi)[E_{\theta|z} + V_{x-z}^*(t - \Delta t)]dF(z, y)
$$
$$
- \lambda V_x^*(t - \Delta t) \int_0^\infty \int_{-\infty}^\infty \delta(z, \xi)dF(z, y)
$$
$$
+ \lambda x \int_x^\infty \int_{-\infty}^\infty \delta(z, \xi)z^{-1}E_{\theta|z}dF(z, y).
$$

Letting $\Delta t \to 0$ on both sides of the equation above, we obtain (8.15b) as was to be shown.

8.4. Computer Program for Calculating Optimal Strategies

8.4.1. Computational Method.

Given boundary conditions on $V_{0,j}^*$ and $V_{i,0}^*$ for $i = X, X - 1, \ldots, 1$ and $j = n, n - 1, \ldots, 1$, the optimal strategy for games like those of Model I, II, or III may be found by backward induction.

To illustrate, assume that we are playing the game of Model I, and let

$$
k = 0, \quad V_{0,j}^* = V_{i,0}^* = 0, \quad \text{all} \quad i, j \geq 0,
$$
$$
X = 5, \quad n = 15,
$$

If we are given the information that

θ	P_θ
-1	.2
3	.3
4	.3
7	.1
10	.1
	1.0

then we may use Lemmas 1 and 2 to determine the optimal strategy $\{\alpha^*_{i,j}, i = 5, 4, \ldots, 1; j = 15, 14, \ldots, 1\}$ and the expected values $\{V^*_{i,j}, i = 5, 4, \ldots, 1; j = 15, 14, \ldots, 1\}$.

Our procedure is first to calculate $\alpha^*_{i,j}$ from the knowledge of $V^*_{i-1,j-1}$ and $V^*_{i,j-1}$, building up two tables, one column at a time:

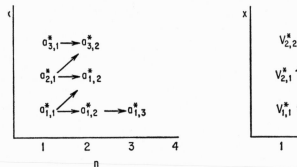
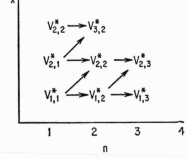

1. From (8.3b), we have

$$\alpha^*_{1,1} = V^*_{1,0} - V^*_{0,0} = 0$$

and thus

$$V^*_{1,1} = [1 - F(0)]V^*_{0,0} + F(0)V^*_{i,0} + \int_0^\infty y\,dF(y)$$

$$= \int_0^\infty y\,dF(y) = 3.8,$$

from (8.3a).

2. We may calculate

$$V^*_{2,1} = V^*_{3,1} = V^*_{4,1} = V^*_{5,1} = 3.8$$

in a similar fashion.

3. It is now possible to compute

$$\alpha_{1,2}^* = V_{1,1}^* - V_{0,1}^* = 3.8$$

and

$$V_{1,2}^* = [1 - F(3.8)]V_{0,1}^* + F(3.8)V_{1,1}^* + \int_{3.8}^{\infty} y \, dF(y)$$
$$= 4.8;$$

$$\alpha_{2,2}^* = V_{2,1}^* - V_{1,1}^* = 0$$

and

$$V_{2,2}^* = [1 - F(0)]V_{1,1}^* + F(0)V_{2,1}^* + \int_{0}^{\infty} y \, dF(y)$$
$$= 7.6;$$

etc.

The basic procedure for computing the α's and $\overset{.}{V}{}^*$'s of Models II and III is similar, although more complicated.

8.4.2. Discussion of the Program. Although hand computation is easy when X and n are small, it rapidly becomes impractical as X and n both become large. To facilitate computation of optimal strategies and their expected values, a general purpose computer program was written, one which would service Models I, Ia, II, IIa, and with slight modification, III and IIIa. A FORTRAN statement of the program is presented as Exhibit 8.3. Without going into detail, here is a list of some of the program's more important properties.[11]

1. Initial conditions:

$$\alpha_{0,j}^*, \quad \text{all} \quad j \geq 0 \qquad \text{AINIT}$$

$$V_{0,j}^*, \quad \text{all} \quad j \geq 0 \qquad \text{VINIT}$$

$$V_{i,0}^* \quad \text{all} \quad i \geq 0 \qquad \text{XK(IX)}[12]$$

max of j	IA
max of i	IB
max of I	IC
max of θ	ID
λ	DENS

2. The program accepts P_r only as a probability mass function with the constraint $(\text{IC} \times \text{ID}) \leq 5000$, where IC and ID are fixed

---

[11]Detailed instructions for running the program are available from the writer on request.

[12]Omitted in Exhibit 8.3.

point integers. Probability density functions must be approximated.

3. To use the program for Model I, set DENS = 1.0, IC = 1.

4. To use it for Model II, set DENS = 1.0.

5. Models Ia, IIa, and IIIa are analyzed on the computer as special cases of Models I, II, and III, respectively; i.e., the time interval T is divided into n intervals of equal length in each of which there is probability λ of an operator choice occurring.

Exhibit 8.3.

```
 1 DIMENSION XPROB(50, 100), THETA(50), SUM(100), FOUR
   (100), W(100), V(100, 1100)
 2 READ INPUT TAPE 4, 3, IA, IB, IC, ID, VINIT, AINIT, ITEST
 3 FORMAT (4I3, 2F10.2, I2)
   READ INPUT TAPE 4, 99, (THETA(L), L = 1, ID)
99 FORMAT (6F4.1)
   READ INPUT TAPE 4, 98, ((XPROB(L, M), L = 1, ID),
   M = 1, IC)
98 FORMAT (6F3.2)
   IF(4-ITEST)4, 4, 200
 4 WRITE OUTPUT TAPE 2, 96, IA, IB, IC, ID, VINIT, AINIT
96 FORMAT (40H IA, IB, IC, ID, VINIT AND AINIT EQUAL 4I5,
   2F10.2)
   WRITE OUTPUT TAPE 2, 95, (THETA(L), L = 1, ID)
95 FORMAT (15H THETAS EQUAL 6F5.1)
   WRITE OUTPUT TAPE 2, 93, ((XPROB(L, M), L = 1, ID),
   M = 1, IC)
93 FORMAT (22H PROBABILITIES EQUAL 6F6.2)
200 DENS = .28846153
 5 DO 6 N = 1, IA
   DO 6 IX = 1, IB
 6 V(IX, N) = 0.0
 7 DO 66 N = 1, IA
 8 DO 66 IX = 1, IB
 9 DO 10 M = 1, IC
   FOUR (M) = 0.0
   SUM (M) = 0.0
```

```
10 W(M) = 0.0
   ONE = 0.0
   TWO = 0.0
   THREE = 0.0
   FIVE = 0.0
   SIX = 0.0
   DO 100 I = 1, IC
11 ALPHA = 0.0
   R = I
   S = IX
12 IF (N − 1)13, 13, 15
13 ALPHA = AINIT
   GO TO 22
15 IF (IX − I)19, 21, 17
17 M1 = IX − I
18 ALPHA = V(IX, N − 1) − V(M1, N − 1)
   GO TO 22
19 CONTINUE
20 ALPHA = (R/S)*V(IX, N − 1)
   GO TO 22
21 ALPHA = V(IX, N − 1) − VINIT
22 WRITE OUTPUT TAPE 2, 23, N, IX, I, ALPHA
23 FORMAT (28H          ALPHA(14, 14, 14, 4H) = F8.3)
   IF (THETA(ID) − ALPHA)24, 24, 29
24 SUM(I) = 0.0
   FOUR(I) = 0.0
   GO TO 43
29 DO 30 K = 1, ID
   IF (THETA(K) − ALPHA)30, 30, 36
30 CONTINUE
36 IF (4 − ITEST)31, 31, 35)
31 WRITE OUTPUT TAPE 2, 91, K
91 FORMAT (10H K EQUALS 15)
35 DO 38 L = K, ID
37 SUM(I) = SUM(I) + XPROB(L, I)
38 FOUR(I) = FOUR(I) + THETA(L) *XPROB(L, I)
39 IF (4 1 ITEST)41, 41, 43
41 WRITE OUTPUT TAPE 2, 42, SUM(I), FOUR(I)
42 FORMAT (21H SUM AND FOUR EQUAL 2F7.3)
43 IF (IX − I)45, 45, 44
44 IF (N − 1)45, 45, 46
```

```
 45  W(I) = VINIT
     GO TO 50
 46  M2 = IX − 1
 47  W(I) = V(M2, N − 1)
 50  IF (IX − I)52, 51, 51
 51  ONE = ONE + W(I) * SUM(I)
 52  TWO = TWO + SUM(I)
 53  IF (N − 1)54, 54, 55
 54  THREE = VINIT * TWO
     GO TO 89
 55  THREE = V(IX, N − 1) * TWO
 89  IF (IX − I)58, 56, 56
 56  FIVE = FIVE + FOUR (I)
 57  GO TO 100
 58  SIX = SIX + (S/R * FOUR(I)
100  CONTINUE
 59  IF (4 − ITEST)60, 60, 61
 60  WRITE OUTPUT TAPE 2, 94, ONE, TWO, THREE, FIVE, SIX
 94  FORMAT (39H ONE, TWO, THREE, FIVE AND SIX EQUAL
     5F8.3)
 61  IF (N − 1)62, 62, 64
 62  WX = VINIT
 63  GO TO 66
 64  WX = V(IX, N − 1)
 66  V(IX, N) = (DENS*(ONE − THREE + FIVE + SIX)) + WX
     DO 68 N = 1, IA
 67  DO 68 IX = 1, IB
 68  WRITE OUTPUT TAPE 2, 69, N, IX, V(IX, N)
 69  FORMAT (28H                   V(14, 14, 4H) = F8.3)
     END FILE 2
     CALL EXIT
     END
```

The program was debugged, tested, and run on the MIT Computation Center's IBM 709 computer. No attempt has been made as yet to estimate the error in approximations to optimal strategies caused by features (2) and (5) above, but they are undoubtedly of second or third order importance in most problems.

Run time for small problems is negligible. Calculation of the tables of α's and V's took .6 minute for the Model I example cited in Section 8.3.1, and 4.8 minutes for the Model II example of Section 8.3.2. A

Model IIa example of magnitude similar to the Model II example just cited took 5.7 minutes to run. The latter two times *include* program compilation, so that when compilation is omitted, run time should be on the order of 1 to 1.5 minutes in these two instances.

8.5. Comments on Extensions of the Models

8.5.1. A Generalization of Model III. To increase the realism of Model III we may allow the operator the option of purchasing information about the expected payoff of a deal before he makes a decision to accept or reject it.

The essential idea of the change is this: Suppose the operator looks at the $(n - j + 1)$st deal, and nature reveals that the required investment is I_j. In accordance with the assumptions of Model III, he also has partial information on θ_j; i.e., he knows the expected value $E_{\theta_j | I_j}$ of $\tilde{\theta}_j$ conditional on $\tilde{I}_j = I_j$. However, we now assume that the operator may for a price purchase information about the "quality" of the deal. This information is assumed to be in a form such that he will have more than full information on just I_j but less than full information on θ_j; e.g., the deal may be categorized as "good," "bad," or "excellent" in geological quality.

We may formalize this idea as follows: Suppose, without loss of generality, that the cost of information about the quality of a deal is one unit of capital available for investment, and define the acts

$A_j = 1$ the operator decides to purchase information on the quality of the $(n - j + 1)$st deal,

$A_j = 0$ the operator does not purchase this information.

Also assume that each deal falls within one of k quality categories and define the random variables

$\tilde{q}_j =$ the quality category of the $(n - j + 1)$st deal.

Define in addition the random vector

$$(\tilde{\underline{r}}'_j)^t = (\tilde{\theta}_j, \tilde{I}_j, \tilde{q}_j), \qquad j = n, n - 1, \ldots, 1.$$

We assume that $\{\tilde{\underline{r}}'_j, j = n, n - 1, \ldots, 1\}$ is a sequence of mutually independent, identically distributed random vectors with common measure $P_{\underline{r}'}$ and common cumulative distribution function $F_{\underline{r}'}$.

Moves in the Game.

Move No. N1a Nature selects an $\underline{r}'_n$ according to $P_{\underline{r}'}$, but reveals only I_n to the operator.

Move No. O1a The operator purchases information about the first deal ($A_n = 1$) at a cost of 1 unit of capital; alternatively the operator decides not to purchase information ($A_n = 0$).

No. N1b If $A_n = 1$, nature reveals q_n to the operator.

No. O1b The operator accepts θ_n, ($a_n = 1$), which he does not know with certainty, or rejects θ_n ($a_n = 0$).

No. N1c If $a_n = 1$, nature reveals θ_n to the operator.

.

.

.

No. Nnc Nature reveals θ_1 to the operator.

Payoff Function. Following the pattern of the argument leading to (8.4), a particular realization of a sequence of $\underline{r}'_j$s, $\{\underline{r}'_n, \underline{r}'_{n-1}, \ldots, \underline{r}'_1\}$ results in the operator possessing capital and payoff in the following amount: If there is an integer $\epsilon > 0$ such that

$$X - \sum_{j=n}^{\epsilon+1} (a_j I_j + A_j) \geq 0 \quad \text{and} \quad X - \sum_{j=n}^{\epsilon} (a_j I_j + A_j) < 0, \tag{8.16a}$$

then he possesses

$$\sum_{j=n}^{\epsilon+1} a_j \theta_j + \frac{\theta_\epsilon}{I_\epsilon} [X - \sum_{j=n}^{\epsilon+1} (a_j I_j + A_j)]$$

$$\text{if } \epsilon > 1 \text{ and } \sum_{j=\epsilon-1}^{1} (a_j I_j + A_j) = 0,$$

$$\text{or if } \epsilon = 1, \tag{8.16b}$$

$$0 \qquad \text{if } \epsilon > 1 \text{ and } \sum_{j=\epsilon-1}^{1} (a_j I_j + A_j) > 0,$$

units of capital and payoff. If there is no such $\epsilon > 0$ then he possesses

$$\sum_{j=n}^{1} a_j \theta_j + k \left[X - \sum_{j=n}^{1} (a_j I_j + A_j) \right]. \tag{8.16c}$$

units of capital and payoff.

Operator's Strategy. The operator's strategy can be characterized by a combination of two sequences of numbers:

$$\{\alpha_{i,j}^{(I,q)}, i = X, X - 1, \ldots, 1; j = n, n - 1, \ldots, 1; I = 1, 2, \ldots;$$
$$q = 1, 2, \ldots, k\}$$

is a sequence such that if, after observing $\tilde{I}_j = I$, the operator chooses act $A_j = 1$ and $\tilde{q}_j = q$ obtains, then he takes act

$$a_j = 1 \quad \text{if} \quad E_{\theta|q,I} \geq \alpha_{i,j}^{(I,q)}$$

$$a_j = 0 \quad \text{if} \quad E_{\theta|q,I} < \alpha_{i,j}^{(I,q)};$$

in addition,

$$\{\beta_{i,j}^{(I)}, i = X, X - 1, \ldots, 1; j = n, n - 1, \ldots, 1; I = 1, 2, \ldots\}$$

is a sequence such that if, after observing $\tilde{I}_j = I$, the operator chooses act $A_j = 0$, then he takes act

$$a_j = 1 \quad \text{if} \quad E_{\theta|I} \geq \beta_{i,j}^{(I)}$$

$$a_j = 0 \quad \text{if} \quad E_{\theta|I} < \beta_{i,j}^{(I)}$$

Then a generic strategy may be regarded as a sequence of ordered pairs of numbers

$$\{(A_j\alpha_{i,j}^{(I,q)}, [1 - A_j]\beta_{i,j}^{(I)}), i = X, X - 1, \ldots, 1; j = n, n - 1, \ldots, 1;$$
$$I = 1, 2, \ldots; q = 1, 2, \ldots, k\}$$

for which we adopt the convention that at nature's $(n - j + 1)$st move, the appropriate cutoff number is the non-zero element of the ordered pair if one exists, or is zero if both numbers are zero.

Expected Value of the Game. The expected value of being at the node of nature's move number $(n - j + 1)$ with capital x and following an *optimal* strategy will be denoted as before by $V_{x,j}^*$. A strategy whose expected value is $V_{x,j}^*$ will also have its cutoff numbers distinguished by an asterisk.

The Problem. An operator with X units of capital begins an n move game. What strategy should he follow so as to achieve $V_{X,n}^*$?

Solution. Let $\{\tilde{r}'_n, \tilde{r}'_{n-1}, \ldots, \tilde{r}'_1\}$ be a sequence of n independent random vectors with common measure $P_{r'}$.
Define

$$\delta_{x,n}^{(I,q)*} = \begin{cases} 1 & \text{if} \quad E_{\theta|I,q} \geq \alpha_{x,n}^{(I,q)*} \\ 0 & \text{if} \quad E_{\theta|I,q} < \alpha_{x,n}^{(I,q)*} \end{cases}$$

and

$$\rho_{x,n}^{(I)*} = \begin{cases} 1 & \text{if} \quad E_{\theta|I} \geq \beta_{x,n}^{(I)*} \\ 0 & \text{if} \quad E_{\theta|I} < \beta_{x,n}^{(I)*} \end{cases}$$

and for notational convenience let

$$u(w) = \delta_{x,n}^{(I,w)*} \quad \text{and} \quad v(I) = \rho_{x,n}^{(I)*}.$$

We also make the following definitions.

$W_0^{(n)}(I)$ = The expected value of following an optimal strategy when n deals remain to review, conditional on $I_n = I$ and $A_n = 0$.

$W_1^{(n)}(I)$ = The expected value of following an optimal strategy when n deals remain to review, conditional on $I_n = I$ and $A_n = 1$.

In terms of $W_0^{(n)}(I)$ and $W_1^{(n)}(I)$ it is clear that

$$V_{x,n}^* = E_I \max \{W_0^{(n)}(\tilde{I}), W_1^{(n)}(\tilde{I})\}. \tag{8.16d}$$

The functions $W_0^{(n)}(I)$ and $W_1^{(n)}(I)$ are in turn defined as follows:
if $I \leq x$,

$$W_0^{(n)}(I) = v(I)\{E_w[E_{\theta|I,\tilde{w}}] + V_{x-I,n-1}^*\} + [1 - v(I)]V_{x,n-1}^* \tag{8.16e}$$

and if $I > x$,

$$W_0^{(n)}(I) = v(I)\left\{\frac{x}{I}E_w[E_{\theta|I,\tilde{w}}]\right\} + [1 - v(I)]V_{x,n-1}^*; \tag{8.16f}$$

if $I \leq x - 1$,

$$W_1^{(n)}(I) = E_w[u(\tilde{w})\{E_{\theta|I,\tilde{w}} + V_{x-I-1,n-1}^*\}] + V_{x-1,n-1}^*E_w[1 - u(\tilde{w})] \tag{8.16g}$$

and if $I > x - 1$,

$$W_1^{(n)}(I) = \left(\frac{x-1}{I}\right)E_w[u(\tilde{w})E_{\theta|I,\tilde{w}}] + E_w[1 - u(\tilde{w})]V_{x-1,n-1}^*. \tag{8.16h}$$

Furthermore,

$$\beta_{x,n}^{(I)*} = \begin{cases} V_{x,n-1}^* - V_{x-I,n-1}^* & \text{if } x - I \geq 0 \\ \dfrac{I}{x}V_{x,n-1}^* & \text{if } x - I < 0 \end{cases} \quad (8.16\text{i})$$

and

$$\alpha_{x,n}^{(I)*} \equiv \alpha_{x,n}^{(I,q)*} = \begin{cases} V_{x-1,n-1}^* - V_{x-I-1,n-1}^* & \text{if } x - I \geq 0 \\ \dfrac{1}{x-1}V_{x-1,n-1}^* & \text{if } x - I < 0 \end{cases} \quad (8.16\text{j})$$

Initial conditions are $V_{x,0}^* = kx$ and $V_{0,n}^* = 0$ for all $x \geq 0$ and all $n \geq 0$.[13]

The results above follow from the lemmas proven below.

Lemma 7. Conditional on knowing $V_{x,j}^*$ for $j < n$ and for all x, the optimal cutoff with x units of capital remaining and n deals left to review is

$$\beta_{x,n}^{(I)*} = \begin{cases} V_{x,n-1}^* - V_{x-I,n-1}^* & \text{if } x - I \geq 0, \\ \dfrac{I}{x}V_{x,n-1}^* & \text{if } x - I < 0 \end{cases}$$

when $A_n = 0$, and is

$$\alpha_{x,n}^{(I)*} = \begin{cases} V_{x-1,n-1}^* - V_{x-I-1,n-1}^* & \text{if } x - I - 1 \geq 0 \\ \dfrac{I}{x-1}V_{x-1,n-1}^* & \text{if } x - I - 1 < 0 \end{cases}$$

when $A_n = 1$, and $\tilde{q} = q$.

Proof. The essential steps in the proof are the same as those followed in proving Lemma 3.

Lemma 8. Given the boundary condition $V_{0,n}^* = 0$ and $V_{x,0}^* = kx$, $V_{x,n}^*$ satisfies (8.16d) for all $x > 0$ and $n > 0$.

Proof. Suppose that the operator follows an optimal strategy. If $\tilde{I}_n = I$, then by the argument used in proving Lemma 6, the expected value of the game may be shown to be $W_0^{(n)}(I)$ if the optimal act as operator move number 1a is $A_n = 0$, or $W_1^{(n)}(I)$ if the optimal act it

---

[13]Note that the superscript q on $\alpha^{(I,q)*}_{x,n}$ may be dropped once we show that the optimal cutoff given $A_n = 1$ is a function of I, x, and n alone, as shown in (8.16j).

$A_n = 1$, i.e., conditional on observing $\tilde{I}_n = I$ the expected value of the game is

$$\max \{W_0^{(n)}(I), W_1^{(n)}(I)\}.$$

Taking the expectation of the above quantity with respect to I yields (8.16d) as was to be proven.

8.5.2. A Problem in Ranking Presently Available Investment Opportunities.

Suppose that the operator has a limited amount of capital X available for investment, and that he has the option of either

1. retaining all of X and using it to play an investment game like that of Model IIa, say,

or

2. investing a fraction of X in a subset S of a set D of deals presently available to him, then playing the game with what remains of X.

If he knows the θ and the I of each of the presently available deals, what strategy should he follow so as to maximize the sum of the expected value of playing the game plus the sum of θ's of the presently available deals which he accepts?

Phrasing the problem differently, how should he choose among the presently available deals, given the goal just stated?

To state the problem more precisely, make the following definitions.

$d_\ell = $ the ℓth element of D, $\ell = 1, 2, \ldots, k$,

$\theta^{(\ell)} = $ the payoff of d_ℓ,

$I^{(\ell)} = $ the investment required in d_ℓ if accepted,

$V_x^*(T) = $ the expected value of playing a game of duration T with capital x, using an optimal strategy, $0 \le x \le X$,

$S_n = $ a set of n presently available deals accepted by the operator; i.e., $S_n \subseteq D$, $1 \le n \le k$.

Payoff Function. Assuming that the game will be of duration T irrespective of what choices the operator makes from D, we may simplify notation by writing $V_x^*(T)$ as $V^*(x)$. Now if the operator selects a subset S_n of D, his expected payoff g_n is

$$\sum_{d_\ell \epsilon S_n} \theta^{(\ell)} + V^*(X - \sum_{d_\ell \epsilon S_n} I^{(\ell)}) \quad \text{if} \quad X - \sum_{d_\ell \epsilon S_n} I^{(\ell)} \ge 0$$

and

$$0 \quad \text{if} \quad X - \sum_{d_\ell \epsilon S_n} I^{(\ell)} < 0.$$

(8.17)

We assume further that *presently* available deals are infinitely divisible; i.e., he can either accept or reject each of the presently available deals as they stand or can accept a fraction of a deal. If he accepts a fraction f, $0 < f < 1$ of d_l, he recovers a payoff $f\theta^{(l)}$ from d_l. We will denote the maximum of g_n by g_n^* and the maximum of g_n^* with respect to n by g^*.

Solution.

$$g_1^* = \max_{d_l \epsilon D} [\theta^{(l)} + V^*(X - I^{(l)}), V^*(X)], \qquad (8.18a)$$

and for $n > 1$,

$$g_n^* = \max_{d_l \neq S_{n-1}} [\theta^{(l)} + V^*(Z_{n-1} - I^{(l)}) - V^*(Z_{n-1}), 0] + g_{n-1}^* \quad (8.18b)$$

where

$$Z_{n-1} = X - \sum_{d_l \epsilon S_{n-1}} I^{(l)}. \qquad (8.18c)$$

In addition, we will demonstrate that if $V^*(\omega)$ is concave for $0 \leq \omega \leq \infty$ there exists a (not necessarily unique) subset S^* of D which achieves g^*, one of which may be found by the following simple procedure.

1. If there is a $d_l \epsilon D$ such that

    $$\theta^{(l)} + V^*(X - I^{(l)}) \geq V^*(X),$$

    accept that deal; i.e., $d_l \epsilon S_1$.

2. If a single deal is accepted and if there remains one or more deals not in S_1 such that $Z_1 - I^{(l)} > 0$ and

    $$\theta^{(l)} + V^*(Z_1 - I^{(l)}) \geq V^*(Z_1),$$

    accept that one for which the quantity $\theta^{(l)} + V^*(Z_1 - I^{(l)}) - V^*(Z_1)$ is greatest.

    If, on the other hand, the best of acceptable deals requires an investment $I^{(l)}$ such that $Z_1 - I^{(l)} < 0$, accept a fraction $Z_1/I^{(l)}$ of it, exhausting the capital X and terminating the procedure.

    If there are no such deals, accept no more deals from D and begin the game with capital

    $$Z_1 = X - \sum_{d_l \epsilon S_1} I^{(l)}.$$

3. Continue the procedure of 2 until either
   a. the game begins
   b. or, if

$$X - \sum_{\ell=1}^{k} I^{(\ell)} \leq 0,$$

   the capital X is exhausted by investing in presently available deals
   c. or, if

$$X - \sum_{\ell=1}^{k} I^{(\ell)} > 0,$$

   all presently available deals D are accepted, in which case the game begins with the remaining capital

$$Z_k = X - \sum_{\ell=1}^{k} I^{(\ell)}.$$

To prove the optimality of the foregoing procedure, we first prove two lemmas. The first lemma shows that the procedure outlined above has a nondecreasing expected value, and the second guarantees its optimality.

Lemma 1. If $V^*(\omega)$ is concave for $0 \leq \omega \leq \infty$, then

$$g_1^* \leq g_2^* \leq \ldots \leq g_n^* \leq \ldots \leq g_k^*.$$

Proof. If

$$\sum_{\ell=1}^{k} I^{(\ell)} \leqslant X,$$

then by virtue of the concavity of $V^*(\omega)$, the *relative* ordering by magnitude of the quantities

$$\theta^{(1)} + V^*(Z_n - I^{(1)}),$$

$$\vdots$$

$$\tag{A}$$

$$\theta^{(k)} + V^*(Z_n - I^{(k)}),$$

will not change as $n \to k$. It then follows from the definition of g_n^* that

$$g_1^* \leq g_2^* \leq \ldots \leq g_n^* \leq \ldots \leq g_k^*.$$

(Furthermore, the argument above implies that if a deal is to be accepted, as large a fraction of it as possible should be accepted.)

If on the other hand

$$\sum_{\ell=1}^{k} I^{(\ell)} > X,$$

then there will be one or more deals, say the δth in particular, such that for some $n \leq k$ and given that $d_\delta \epsilon S_{n+1}$,

$$\sum_{d_\ell \epsilon S_n} I^{(\ell)} \leq X \quad \text{and} \quad \sum_{d_\ell \epsilon S_n} I^{(\ell)} + I^{(\epsilon)} > \delta.$$

Since by (8.17) the payoff equals 0 if $d_\delta \epsilon S_{n+1}$, at most a fraction of the δth deal can be accepted if the payoff of all accepted deals is to be greater than zero. As the relative ordering in (A) does *not* change with changes in the magnitude of Z_n even as $Z_n \to 0$ (by virtue of the concavity of $V^*(\omega)$), the argument of the previous paragraph holds in this case also.

Lemma 2. If $g_n^* = g_{n+1}^*$, then $g_n^* = g_{n+j}^*$, $1 < j \leq k = n$ and $g^* = \max\limits_{\ell} g_\ell^* = g_n^*$.

Proof. We will prove the lemma by showing that the assumption, if $g_n^* = g_{n+1}^*$ then there exists at least one j, $1 < j \leq k - n$, for which $g_n^* < g_{n+j}^*$, is a contradiction.

For suppose

$$g_n^* = g_{n+1}^*, \qquad n > 1, \tag{A}$$

and

$$g_n^* < g_{n+j}^* \tag{B}$$

for one or more j, $1 < j \leq k - n$. Proposition (A) is true if and only if there are no deals d_m in D but not in S_n such that $\theta^{(m)} + V^*(Z_n - I^{(m)}) - V^*(Z_n) > 0$. However, since $V^*(\omega)$ is concave for $\omega \epsilon [0, \infty)$, it follows that for any deal d_m in D but not in S_n,

$$\theta^{(m)} + V^*(Z_{n+j} - I^{(m)}) - V^*(Z_{n+j}) \leq 0$$

for $1 \leq j \leq k - n$ which implies that if Proposition (A) is true, Proposition (B) must be false.

CHAPTER 9

A Sequential Investment
Experiment

Chapter 9 reports on a pilot experiment designed to test the degree to which sequential decision rules like those of Chapter 8 can aid a decision maker to achieve a preassigned goal. The experiment was prompted by the following questions which consideration of the analysis of Chapter 8 raised:

1. Within the assumptions underlying Models I, II, and IIa of Chapter 8, how much more effective than unaided judgement are mathematical decision rules in maximizing expected payoff?

2. Do formal decision rules become increasingly effective as the complexity of the decision-making situation increases?

3. How do people make decisions in a sequential decision-making situation?

4. Are decision rules like those of Chapter 8 administratively practical in a highly complex real-world situation?

For purposes of the experiment, effectiveness is measured in terms of the difference between the performance of experimental subjects and the optimal decision rule's performance in playing games like those of Model I, II, or IIa. That is, the total payoff achieved by the optimal decision rule on a single replication of a game like that of Model II, say, is subtracted from the average of the total payoff achieved by the experimental subjects on the game replication. This difference is calculated for several

260

replications of each game and then plotted (see Graphs 9.1 to 9.3) to see whether there is any systematic change in its value. As an example, large negative differences at the outset which rapidly diminish to differences fluctuating about zero after a small number of replications of the game imply that the group improved its performance very rapidly — they "learned" the game.

The link between the effectiveness of mathematical decision rules in a highly artificial experimental environment and their effectiveness when imbedded in the decision-making fabric of a real firm is highly tenuous. Nevertheless, the writer's point of view is that the experiment is useful in two respects. First, subject to certain obvious qualifications, it provides an example of the kind of experiment that if appropriately modified can be used to test the effectiveness of decision rules in an actual business environment; second, it helps us to refine our probability judgements about what the effectiveness of rules like those of Chapter 8 will be in a business environment.

We will discuss the design of the experiment in Section 9.1, present the results in Section 9.2., and draw conclusions in Section 9.3.

While not providing answers to all of the questions which prompted it, the experiment does clarify some aspects of these questions; namely:

1. The optimal decision rules total payoff per play of a game when averaged over all (42) replications of three games is only 2 per cent greater than the average per play achieved by the experimental subjects; i.e., within the assumptions of these games, the decision rules are not a substantial improvement over intuitive judgement.

2. Within the scope of the Model I, II, and IIa games, there is some indication that the optimal decision rules become more effective as the complexity of the game increases. However, the data does not firmly establish this conclusion.

3. Experience in playing these games enables the player substantially to improve his judgement of the expected value of a single play of a game, even without doing any mathematical analysis.

4. The improvement in judging the expected value of the game indicates that mathematical decision rules can be useful in deciding whether or not to undertake a game at all, for the analysis of one game immediately carries over to *all* games with similar rules even though the numbers in the game change. Intuition is not as adaptable.

The experiment was not designed to deal effectively with the third question and yields very little information in answer to it. Chapter 10 discusses some aspects of the administrative practicability of the decision rules.

9.1. The Design

The experiment was made in two parts, a pilot study and a main study. The results of both were used in arriving at the conclusions set forth above, even though the pilot study was primarily intended to act as a feedback device on the adequacy of the initial design.

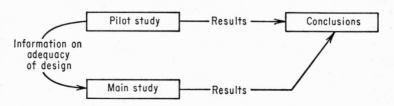

Both studies were administered in the following steps:

1. The subjects were given a pamphlet describing the problem which motivated the experiment, and the experimental procedure. The description of the experimental procedure was divided into three parts, one for each model treated. Each part stated the goal the subject was to try to achieve, the rules of the game for that portion of the experiment, the amount of capital available for investment, the number of deals to review, and the probability distributions of relevant random variables, plus presenting a numerical example to illustrate how the rules of the game are applied.[1]

2. The experiment was administered to all objects in the same room at the same time.

3. The games represented by Models I, II, and IIa were replicated several times. A replication consisted of a complete play of a game. The games were presented in order of decision-making difficulty — the replications of the game of Model I were followed by those of Model II and then Model IIa.

4. Subjects recorded their results on a data sheet passed out at the beginning of the experiment.

---

[1] Questions about the value of the game were omitted in the pilot study. The main study pamphlet is reproduced in Appendix A to Chapter 9.

5. They were asked to "revalue" each game on the basis of their experience.

9.1.1. The Pilot Study. The purpose of the pilot study was to debug the experiment's design, to provide clues as to the outcome of the main study, and to serve as a control in the particular sense explained in 9.1.2.

The persons who participated in the pilot study were all doctoral candidates at the Harvard Business School. (This is, of course, a most atypical group from the viewpoint of the oil executive!)

Eight replications of each of three games were performed.

The numbers on which the subjects based their choices were generated using random number tables and the probability distributions given in the experimental pamphlet.

9.1.2. The Main Study. After analyzing the results of the pilot study, three minor changes were made in the experiment.

1. Since the main study group was larger than the pilot study group, and the time to administer the experiment was limited to one and a half hours, the number of replications of each game was reduced to six.

2. A graph of the probability distribution of $\tilde{n}$, the number of deals that will appear in a replication of the Model IIa game, was replaced with a table of waiting time probabilities.

3. Questions pertaining to the value of the game were added.

The numbers used within each replication were the same as those used in a particular replication of the pilot study. However, the order of presentation of sequences of numbers representing payoff, investment, and number of deals remaining was completely reversed so that any trend effect in results wholly due to the peculiarities of the number sequences could be ferreted out: e.g.,

MODEL I GAME.

Replication Number	Pilot Study Sequence Number	Main Study Sequence Number
1	1	8
2	2	7
3	3	5
4	4	3
5	5	2
6	6	1
7	7	—
8	8	—

As indicated above, two replications of each game played in the pilot study were eliminated in the main study. Those sequences which were least effective in discriminating between subjects were dropped; e.g., if everyone scored exactly the same as the optimal decision rule on a given replication, then it is highly likely that the "best" strategy is obvious:

TABLE 9.1

Game	Pilot Study Replications Dropped
Model I	4, 6
Model II	4, 5
Model IIa	2, 5

The participants in the main study were nineteen professors of business administration who were attending a year-long program in mathematics for business administration at Harvard University.

9.1.3. Comments on the Design. Several aspects of the design bear comment. First, the order of presentation. The subjects had to make decisions on data of monotonically increasing complexity; Model I data was followed by Model II data, which in turn was followed by Model IIa data. A progression from least to most difficult seemed to be a natural way to cope with the *irreversible* changes in the subjects' behavior — learning[2] — that took place during performance of the experiment. This ordering was conjectured to allow learning to take place more rapidly than if, say, data was presented in order of monotonically decreasing complexity, for the rational evaluation of Model IIa according to the expected value criterion is so complicated as to thoroughly confuse some subjects with no "experience" in making such decisions.

Classical analysis of variance designs are clearly not applicable in view of the statistical instability of the learning process; i.e., we expect to find a transient effect due to the impact of feedback of information from the outcome of early replications on the subjects' behavior patterns, which will die out as the subjects evolve statistically stable strategies for playing the game. In particular one would expect the rate of improvement in a subject's performance to diminish as his performance (averaged over replication) approaches the expected value of the game.

Second, while it would have been possible to split the group into two

[2]"Learning" here means learning as defined by Bush and Mosteller in *Stochastic Models for Learning* (New York: John Wiley & Sons, Inc., 1955), p. 3, "... any systematic change in behavior ... whether or not the change is adaptive, desirable for certain purposes or in accordance with any other such criteria. We consider learning to be complete when certain kinds of [statistical] stability — not necessarily stereotypy — obtain."

or three blocks and to administer the data to each of these blocks in a different order, this could be done only at a sacrifice of replications with a given ordering of sequences of data. (Three blocks allow only one third the number of replications per block achieved when the group is regarded as a single block.) The sole reason for such a restriction is that the time for administering the experiment was limited to one and a quarter hours. It was judged that the experiment could best be done by regarding the group as a single block so as to increase the replications per block to the maximum for two reasons. First, by increasing the number of subjects per replication of each game, the variance of the group performance per replication averaged over subjects might be decreased, and second, tracing the behavior of transient effects due to an initially rapid rate of learning which slows down as subjects evolve statistically stable strategies may be easier. Even so, the replications per game are insufficient in number to allow a truly accurate judgement of the relative effectiveness of the subjects versus the decision rules. The experiment could be improved by expanding the time allotted to perform it so that more replications are possible with a given ordering, and so that the effects of varying the order in which the games are presented can be explored.

Third, while there was no control group within the pilot study, the pilot study itself was used as a control on the main study. As mentioned in Section 9.1.2, this was accomplished by reversing the order in which the number sequences representing payoff and investments were presented to the subjects. Thus if there is an observable upward linear trend in the measure of effectiveness due *solely* to peculiarities of the number sequences when presented in the order 1 through 8, it will be observable as a downward linear trend of opposite and equal slope when sequences are presented in the order 8 through 1. There is no guarantee that such a trend is linear, but we may visually interpret Graphs 9.1 to 9.3 to see whether there are any gross slope reversals in the trends of the plotted points.

Fourth, the experiment was administered to the subjects en masse in order to minimize the time needed to perform it. No attempt was made to isolate each subject from the comments and exclamations of his fellow subjects. If one of the experiment's objectives was to gain insight into the learning process of each subject as an individual this interaction would seriously distort the results. However, the objective was to compare the average performance of the subjects *as a group* with that of optimal decision rules, and subject to subject interaction did not appear extensive enough to substantially affect the performance of the group as a whole. If a more detailed investigation of the objectives of this experiment is undertaken, interaction can easily be eliminated at the expense of more time and money.

Fifth, in any future experiment of this type, the measure of effectiveness described subsequently would more accurately pinpoint differences between subject group and decision rule behavior if the range sets of the random variables "payoff" and "investment" specified in the experiment were expanded by *increasing both the range and number of values the subject must consider*. This suggestion follows directly from the tentative conclusion that when the payoff of a deal is either very high or very low with respect to the investment required in it, the better choice — accept or reject — is obvious. In less extreme cases, the cost of irrationality is low.

Sixth, an attempt was made to restrict the effect of individual preferences in risk taking (utility considerations) on the results by giving the subjects *explicit goals* as set forth in the experimental pamphlet rather than allowing them to choose their own goals. However, personal preferences in risk taking strongly influence the strategies chosen by an individual and undoubtedly affect his rate of learning the games so that our measure of effectiveness, while ostensibly composed only of "expected values," is strongly tainted by an amalgam of such preferences.

More insight into the nature of the learning process could have been garnered by asking the subjects to write down the strategies they followed in playing the games, and then carefully studying the results. This was judged to be beyond the limited aims of the present experiment but should be done in any future experiments which attempt to explore the learning process in playing sequential games against nature.

9.2. Results

The results of both the main and the pilot studies are summarized in Graphs 9.1 through 9.6. The following definitions are made.

Δ_{ij} = [average payoff of all subjects on the ith replication of the jth game]

— [payoff achieved by the optimal decision rule on the ith replication of the jth game],

$$i = 1, 2, \ldots, 8, \qquad j = 1, 2, 3.[3]$$

---

[3] The subscript $j = 1$ refers to the Model I game, $j = 2$ to the Model II game, and $j = 3$ to the Model IIa game.

$\dot{x}_{ij}$ = the deviation of the total payoff achieved by the optimal decision rule on the ith replication of the jth game from the expected value V^* of the rule.

Graphs 9.1, 9.2, and 9.3 are plots of two sequences of numbers
$\{\Delta_{ij}, i = 1, 2, \ldots, 8\}$ and $\{\Delta'_{ij}, i = 1, 2, \ldots, 8\}$, where we distinguish
the main study sequence of Δ's from that of the pilot study by a prime.
Graphs 9.4, 9.5, and 9.6 compare the total payoff per replication

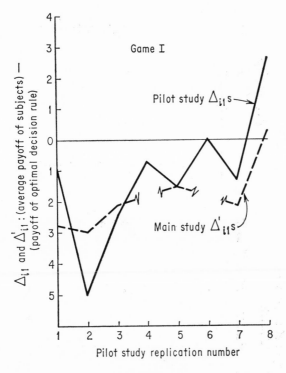

Graph 9.1.

achieved by the decision rules with total payoff per replication (averaged
over subjects) achieved by the pilot and main study groups in the Model
I, II, and IIa games. All plots are to the same scale so that the order of
magnitude of differences between the decision rules' performance and
that of the groups may be compared with the absolute magnitude of the
total payoffs.

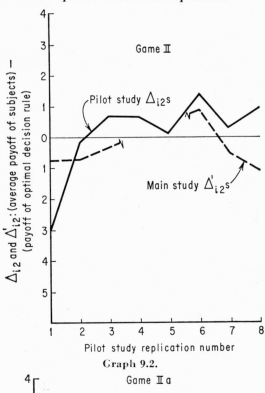

Graph 9.2.

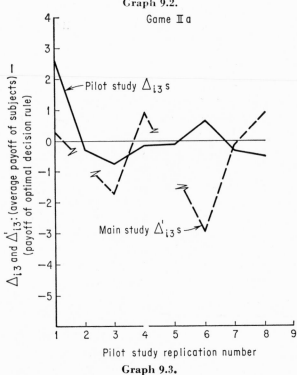

Graph 9.3.

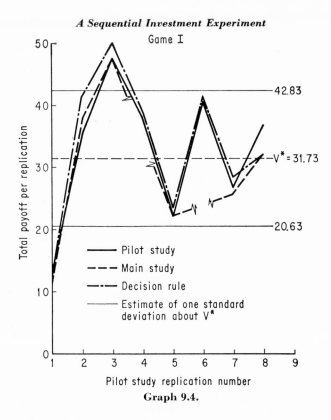

Graph 9.4.

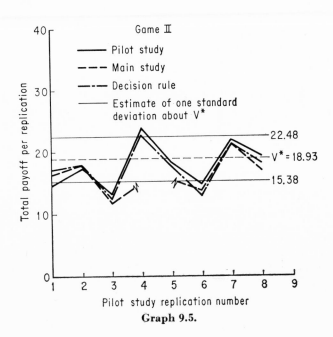

Graph 9.5.

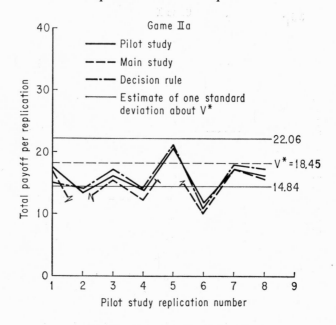

Graph 9.6.

Tables 9.2 and 9.3 conveniently summarize the data from which these graphs were drawn. The raw data underlying Tables 9.2 and 9.3 is presented in Tables B.1 through B.6 of Appendix B to this chapter.

TABLE 9.2. PILOT STUDY RESULTS.

Replication	(1) Averages Over Subjects			(2) Payoffs Achieved By Optimal Strategy			Averages Minus Payoffs		
	I	II	IIa	I	II	IIa	Δ_{i1}	Δ_{i2}	Δ_{i3}
1	13.09	14.67	17.53	14.00	17.67	15.00	− .91	−3.00	2.53
2	36.00	17.82	13.73	41.00	18.00	14.00	−5.00	− .18	− .27
3	47.54	13.01	16.32	50.00	12.25	17.00	−2.46	+ .76	− .68
4	37.36	23.73	13.91	38.00	23.00	14.00	− .64	+ .73	− .09
5	21.54	18.09	20.91	23.00	18.00	21.00	−1.46	+ .09	− .09
6	41.00	14.95	12.64	41.00	13.50	12.00	0	+1.45	.64
7	26.73	21.82	17.35	28.00	21.50	17.67	−1.27	+ .32	− .32
8	34.64	19.46	16.52	32.00	18.50	17.00	+2.64	+ .96	− .48
Averages over replications and subjects.	32.24	17.94	16.10	33.38	17.80	15.96	−1.14	+ .14	+ .14

TABLE 9.3. MAIN STUDY RESULTS.

Replication	(1) Averages Over Subjects			(2) Payoffs Achieved By Optimal Strategy			Averages Minus Payoffs		
	I	II	IIa	I	II	IIa	Δ'_{i1}	Δ'_{i2}	Δ'_{i3}
1	32.21	17.37	15.96	32	18.50	15.00	.21	−1.13	+ .96
2	25.84	21.08	17.07	28	21.50	17.00	−2.16	− .42	− .07
3	21.53	14.46	11.05	23	13.50	14.00	−1.47	+ .96	−2.95
4	47.95	11.89	12.97	50	12.25	12.00	−2.05	− .36	+ .97
5	38.05	17.95	15.98	41	18.00	17.67	−2.95	− .65	−1.69
6	11.26	16.94	17.35	14	17.67	17.00	−2.74	− .72	+ .35
Averages over replications and subjects.	29.47	16.61	15.07	31.33	16.90	15.44	−1.86	− .29	− .37

Interpretation of each graph can be made in terms of three attributes:

1. trends due to the peculiarities of the number sequences;
2. trends due to improvement in the subjects' average performance;
3. trends in the difference in performance between the main and pilot study groups.

We can also explore the behavior of the decision rule itself. Since each decision rule remains invariant over all replications, as do the underlying probability distribution functions which generate the numbers to which it is applied, we may look upon $\{\dot{x}_{ij}, i = 1, 2, \ldots, 8\}$ given j as being a particular sample realization of a stationary stochastic process $\{\ddot{x}_{ij}, i = 1, 2, \ldots \}$, so that unbiased estimates of the mean $E(\ddot{x}_{ij})$ and variance $V(\ddot{x}_{ij})$ of $\ddot{x}_{ij}$ for $i = 1, 2, \ldots$ are

$$\dot{\bar{x}}_{.j} \equiv \frac{1}{8}\sum_{i=1}^{8}\dot{x}_{ij} \quad \text{and} \quad s^2_{.j} \equiv \frac{1}{7}\sum_{i=1}^{8}(\dot{x}_{ij} - \dot{\bar{x}}_{.j})^2$$

respectively. Table 9.4 displays $\bar{x}_{.j} \equiv \dot{\bar{x}}_{.j} + V^*$ and $s^2_{.j}$ for $j = 1, 2, 3$.

TABLE 9.4. TABLE OF ESTIMATED MEANS AND VARIANCES OF OPTIMAL DECISION RULES.[a]

	V^*	Sample Mean $\bar{x}_{.j}$ $\equiv \dot{\bar{x}}_{.j} + V^*$	Estimated Variance of $\Delta_{.j}$ (about Sample Mean)	Estimated Variance of $\Delta_{.j}$ (about V^*)
Model I	31.73	33.38	132.18	123.29
Model II	18.93	17 80	13.04	12.60
Model IIa	18.45	15.96	7.79	13.05

[a]Sample means and variances calculated from the data in Tables 10 and 11.
[b]Calculated from the formula

$$\frac{1}{8}\sum_{i=1}^{8}(\dot{x}_{ij})^2.$$

Some general observations which can be made about the results are

1. The deviations Δ_{ij} and Δ'_{ij} are very small compared with the fluctuations of $\hat{x}_{ij}$. This can be seen in Graphs 9.4, 9.5, and 9.6.

2. Trends due to learning appear strongest in the Model I game and are least visible in the Model IIa game (see Graphs 9.1, 9.2, and 9.3).

3. The estimated variance of $\hat{x}_{i1}$ is about ten times that of $\hat{x}_{i2}$ and $\hat{x}_{i3}$.

The first observation implies that the general nature of an optimal strategy — set a high cutoff initially and lower it as the time remaining to invest shortens — may be obvious to the subjects. Informal discussions with pilot study subjects revealed that in fact at least six of eleven subjects did adopt strategies of this type at some point during the experiment.

Although the essence of the best decision rule may be obvious, a specification of the numerical value of an optimal cutoff point at a given point in a game is not so obvious. Here is where experience counts.

Of particular interest is the observation that in all three games the ability of the main study subjects to judge the expected value of the game greatly improved after playing. As shown in Table 9.5 most subjects initially tended to undervalue the game in all three instances:[4]

9.2.1. Model I Game. The pilot study subjects appear to have learned this game quite rapidly, as the positive slope of the trend in Δ_{i1} from $i = 1$ to $i = 8$ indicates. However, tracing Δ'_{i1} from $i = 8$ to $i = 1$, we see that the slope of its trend is slightly negative, implying that there probably is some effect due to the ordering of the number sequences. This latter conclusion is strengthened by observing that there is a *relative* improvement in the main study group's performance. Note that it did at least as well as or better than the pilot study group on three of its *last* four replications — numbers 5, 3, and 2 on the graph — which were the pilot study's *first* four replications. Such relative comparisons must be gross since we are judging the performance of the pilot study group on the basis of eight replications of each game, as against six for the main study group.

There was a substantial upward revision in the average of values assigned to the game by the main study group from 22.56 before playing to 29.52 after playing. The expected value of the optimal decision rule is $V^* = 31.73$.

---

[4]See Table B.7 in Appendix B to this chapter for the raw data underlying Table 9.5.

TABLE 9.5

	Change in Value of Game Assignments After Completion of Experiment			Average of Values Assigned		Average of Values Achieved by Optimal Decision Rule			Expected Value of Game
	Increase	No Change	Decrease	Before	After	Pilot Study	Main Study		
Game I, Part (1)	15	2	1	22.56	29.52	33.38	31.33		31.73
Game II, Part (2)	11	2	5	14.33	17.22	17.80	16.90		18.93
Game IIa, Part (3)	11	2	5	13.36	15.12	15.96	15.44		18.45

9.2.2. Model II Game. Again a positive trend in Δ_{i2} from $i = 1$ to $i = 8$ indicates that the pilot study group improved its performance as it gained experience, but the trend is less pronounced than that of Δ_{i1} in Graph 9.1, probably due to a combination of two circumstances: First, the estimate $s^2_{.2}$ of the variance of $\mathring{x}_{i2}$ is only one tenth that of $s^2_{.1}$, implying that fluctuations of the magnitude of those of $\mathring{x}_{i1}$ are much less likely, so that one would expect the absolute magnitude of any trend due to peculiarities of the number sequences to be smaller in magnitude than for the Model I game; second, the pilot study group outperformed the decision rule on three out of the first five replications, attaining total payoffs greater than V^* in two instances; hence their opportunity for improvement was considerably diminished by virtue of the high level of their initial performance.

Just as in the Model I game, the main study group did not display as much ability to improve their performance as the pilot study group. This group did not display the same degree of improvement relative to the pilot study group shown in the Model I game.

The average of value of game assignments by the main study group changed upward from 14.33 before playing to 17.22 after playing the game, closer to $V^* = 18.93$.

9.2.3. Model IIa Game. The Model IIa results offer little evidence of learning or improvement of performance on the part of either the pilot study groups or the main study group. In terms of the absolute magnitude of Δ_{i3} and Δ'_{i3} as compared with the total payoffs achieved by the optimal decision rule, the groups again performed almost as well as the decision rule; there are no discernable trends.

One would expect learning to be much slower than in the earlier, simpler games, yet the experience of playing the game brought the average of values assigned to the game much closer to $V^* = 18.45$ than the average of values assigned before playing the game: 13.36 before and 15.12 after.

9.3. Summary

Whereas in Section 9.1.3, comments on the experiment's design, several ways of improving the experiment are suggested, there are some conclusions implied by the results that a more sophisticated experiment would undoubtedly confirm:

1. The optimality conditions for games like those of Chapter 8 are very broad; i.e., when the payoff of a deal is either very high or

very low with respect to the investment required in it, the better choice — accept or reject — is obvious. In less extreme cases, the cost of irrationality is low, and the final outcome of the game is not substantially affected. Thus intuition is almost as good as optimal decision rules in the obvious cases, and is improved upon only in the marginal choices so that the outcome (total payoff per replication of a game) of the optimal decision rule cannot be expected to differ greatly from the outcome of a smart player with some experience in playing the games.

2. The decision maker's unaided judgement about the value of the game *before he has experience in playing it* is poor. The real worth of formal analysis of a game is to aid the decision maker in his *initial evaluation* of it. The analysis will help him to decide whether or not he should begin the game at all.

We may argue by analogy that the prime usefulness of formal analysis of problems like those of Chapter 8 does not lie in its ability to tell the operating executive how to behave once he has made a major policy decision to "play the game," so to speak. Rather, it lies in the *immediate* insight it gives into the value of making such a policy decision, a value which he may be ill equipped to judge intuitively without experience in "playing the game." Since he cannot gain this experience unless he makes the decision "to play," without formal analysis he is faced with a dilemma akin to that of the sophist of Hegel who wished to learn how to swim without entering the water.

In addition, formal analysis based on a sound conceptualization of the real-world problem allows us to judge the effect of *changes* in numerical values of the problem's parameters on the "value of the game" more accurately than can be done with unaided judgement. For when the numerical value of a parameter is changed significantly, the operator is "playing a new game" and so finds himself in the dilemma just mentioned Once the formal solution to a class of problems has been found, however, it is a solution for all problems in that class, and the algorithm for finding the numbers which characterize the optimal strategy is the same for all problems in the class *provided that the structure* of the problem remains invariant under changes in the numerical values of its parameters.[1]

In sum, the administrative practicability of a formal decision model is

---

[1] Even when faced with a "new game" that cannot be formally analyzed, the operator may be able to use simulation to provide artificial experience and then use the experience to help him to decide whether or not to play.

not wholly dependent on a comparison of its performance with that of human decision makers. It would not be surprising to find that purely intuitive decision methods work well enough in the hands of experienced oil and gas operators to leave little or no advantage to more sophisticated analyses and computations of the kind to be described. Even if this were true, these models might still have substantial value as an aid in training inexperienced personnel in the art of informal decision-making, by providing them with benchmarks against which to judge their performance. In addition, they can serve as vehicles for the generation and testing of hypotheses about the relationship between uncertainty and optimal investment criteria in specific decision-making situations such as the oil and gas operator's problem.

The Experimental Pamphlet

Subject: An Experiment in Investment Behavior

To: Participants in the Experiment

From: Gordon M. Kaufman

1. I would appreciate your participation in an experiment in investment behavior. This experiment is motivated by some petroleum exploration problems which I have been investigating for my doctoral thesis, whose title is:

   *Statistical Decision and Related Techniques In
   Petroleum Exploration.*

2. The purpose of the experiment is described on the bottom of the first page of the attached pamphlet.

3. Please read the pamphlet so that when you get to class you will be prepared to participate, but *do not* attempt to do any formal (mathematical) analysis of the problems.

4. After reading the pamphlet, but *before* coming to class to participate in the experiment, please answer the questions on the last page of the pamphlet.

Thank you,

Gordon M. Kaufman

Harvard Business School

AN OIL AND GAS EXPLORATION INVESTMENT PROBLEM†

During the fiscal year, many independent oil and gas operators review between 60 to 250 investment opportunities, or "deals" as I shall call them. The *number* of deals which will appear during the year and the *value* (in a sense to be defined later) of each deal when it does appear are usually unknown to the operator at the beginning of the year. In spite of these uncertainties he must decide whether to accept or reject each deal after he has reviewed the information about it that is available to him.

Uncertainty about the value of future deals and about the number that will appear is not the only complicating factor. The decision problem is further complicated by income tax considerations: an operator can avoid income taxes on revenue from oil and gas properties which he owns if he invests this revenue in oil and gas deals. Any revenue uninvested at the end of the fiscal year is taxable as ordinary income. Intuitively it is easy to see that:

1. if the operator sets his acceptance criteria too high he may end the fiscal year with a substantial tax penalty;

2. if he sets his acceptance criteria too low, he may have committed his capital early in the year and be unable to participate in a very good deal which may appear towards the end of the year.

The two possible outcomes cited above are indeed extreme, but they emphasize the fact that truly effective *decision rules* may be difficult to design.

Having given you a brief sketch of the nature of the real problem, I would now like to discuss the experiment itself.

I. *Purpose*

The purpose of my experiment is to reach some tentative conclusions about the "effectiveness" of some formal (mathematical) decision rules. These formal rules have been derived for three mathematical analogues, or models, of the sequential investment problem outlined above. One of the research questions that I am posing is:

Within the assumptions underlying sequential investment models 1, 2, and 3, how much more effective than unaided judgment are formal mathematical decision rules in maximizing expected payoff?

Since I am testing how you behave without the benefit of any formal aids to decision making I will not acquaint you with the structure of the models, the decision rules which are derived from them, or the measure of effectiveness that I will use. You are asked to proceed with the experiment on your own, and to

---

†Copyright © 1960 by the President and Fellows of Harvard College

make the decisions required in the experiment in any fashion you desire within the bounds of the procedure discussed below.

II. *Goals*

The experiment is divided into three parts. You will be asked to proceed with a specific goal in mind. This goal will be specified for each part of the experiment.

III. *Procedure*

The manner in which the experiment will be carried out is described below.

Part (1) of Three Parts

Goal

In carrying out Part (1) you are to assume that your ultimate objective is to maximize the number of blue poker chips in your possession at the end of each replication of the experiment. The blue chips can be thought of as the *payoff* from an investment in a deal.

Procedure for Part (1)

A. You will be given 5 white poker chips. These chips can be imagined to be the capital available to you for investment in deals at the beginning of the year. Any deal which you *accept* will require an "investment" of one white poker chip. You will *not* be allowed to "invest" the payoff from deals that you accept. Thus you can accept at most five deals out of those presented to you for a decision.

B. The following process will be repeated 15 or less times:

1. A random number is drawn from a table of random numbers. Each number from 0 to 9 represents a payoff in blue chips according to the following scheme:

Random Number	Payoff in Blue Chips	Probability of Payoff
0,1	−2	.2
2,3,4	3	.3
5,6,7	4	.3
8	7	.1
9	10	.1
		1.0

2. You will be offered the payoff in blue chips corresponding to the random number which has been drawn; e.g., if the random number "4" occurs you will be offered a payoff of 3 blue chips.

3. You must now decide whether or not to accept the payoff that is offered. If you *accept* the payoff (which is equivalent to accepting the deal it represents) you give me one white chip. This is the "investment" that

you must make in order to receive the payoff. If you *reject* the payoff you of course do not receive any blue chips, and you do not need to pay me a white chip. You cannot change your decision with respect to this particular deal at a later point in the experiment.

4. Steps 1, 2, and 3 will be repeated 15 times. The process terminates for you when either:

        a. you have exhausted your supply of white chips; or
        b. steps 1, 2, and 3 have been repeated 15 times.

C. Steps 1, 2, 3, and 4 will be repeated 6 times.

Discussion

To facilitate your understanding of the experiment I have drawn a flow chart of the steps outlined in B above.

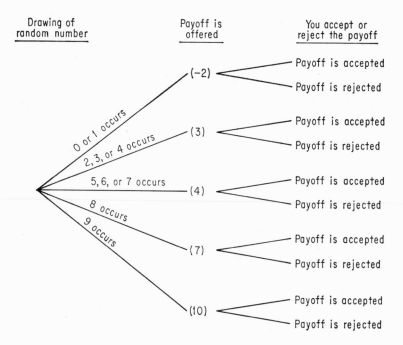

The next page contains further information about Part (1). It displays the results of a single repetition of Part (1) when a hypothetical subject adopted the strategy:

        Accept deals with payoffs of 7 or 10 blue
        chips. Reject all other deals.

The tally sheet is simply intended to give you a "feel" for the numbers and does *not* imply that *you* must choose a *fixed* level of acceptance, as the hypothetical subject has done.

TALLY SHEET

Deal No.	Random Number Drawn	A = Accept R = Reject	Payoff	Remaining Capital
1	6	R	—	5
2	4	R	—	5
3	2	R	—	5
4	4	R	—	5
5	9	A	10	4
6	6	R	—	4
7	3	R	—	4
8	6	R	—	4
9	6	R	—	4
10	4	R	—	4
11	3	R	—	4
12	9	A	10	3
13	6	R	—	3
14	5	R	—	3
15	2	R	—	3

Total Payoff   20 blue chips
Uninvested Capital   3 white chips
No. Deals Accepted   2

Part (2) of Three Parts

Goal

The goal is the same as for Part (1): you are to assume that your ultimate objective is to maximize the number of blue poker chips in your possession at the end of each replication of the experiment. As in Part (1), these chips can be thought of as the *payoff* from an investment in a deal.

Procedure for Part (2)

A. You will be given 5 white poker chips. As in Part (1) they can be imagined to be capital available for investment. Part (2) differs from Part (1) in that a deal which you decide to accept may require anywhere from one to five white poker chips of investment.

B. The following process will be repeated 15 or less times:
   1. Random numbers will be used to generate a sequence of payoff-investment pairs according to the following probabilities:

JOINT PROBABILITIES OF PAYOFF AND INVESTMENT

Payoffs	Investments 1	2	3	4	5	Marginal probability of Payoff
−2	.04	.08	.02	0	0	.14
3	.08	.08	.02	0	0	.18
4	.06	.12	.08	.02	0	.28
7	.02	.08	.04	.04	.02	.20
10	0	.04	.02	.03	.02	.11
11	0	0	.02	.01	.06	.09
Marginal Probability of Investment:	.20	.40	.20	.10	.10	1.00

All relevant probabilities are summarized for you in the above table. In each cell is the joint probability of an investment-payoff combination: e.g.,

P (payoff of 4 blue chips *and* an investment of 3 white chips) = .08.

2. After each random number is drawn, you will be offered a payoff in blue chips and told the number of white chips that you must invest to receive the payoff.

3. Same as point 3 in Part (1). You must now decide whether or not to accept the payoff that is offered. If the investment required is greater than the number of white chips you have left, you may accept the deal under these conditions:

   a. you must invest all of your remaining white chips;

   b. you will receive a payoff proportional to your investment.

   For example, suppose you have 2 chips left, and the deal being offered has a payoff of 10 blue chips for an investment of 5 white chips. If you wish to accept the deal you would invest your 2 white chips for a payoff of $(2/5 \times 10) = 4$ blue chips.

4. Steps 1, 2, and 3 will be repeated 15 times. The process terminates for you when either:

   a. you have exhausted your supply of white chips; or

   b. Steps 1, 2, and 3 are repeated 15 times.

C. Steps 1, 2, 3, and 4 will be repeated 6 times.

Part (3) of Three Parts

Part (3) differs from Part (2) in only one respect: you will not know for certain how many deals will be offered for review during each replication of the experiment. Imagine that the period during which you will be allowed to invest is one year. The average waiting time between deals is 3.47 weeks. That is, during the 52 weeks of the year the expected number of deals that you will see is (52/3.47 = 15. A table of waiting time probabilities is displayed below:

TABLE OF WAITING TIME PROBABILITIES*

Waiting Time Between Deals: t	Probability that Waiting Time Between Deals Equals t	Probability that Waiting Time Between Deals Is Greater Than t
0	.14	.86
1	.22	.64
2	.16	.48
3	.12	.36
4	.09	.27
5	.07	.20
6	.05	.15
7	.04	.11
8	.03	.08
9	.02	.06
10	.02	.04
11	.01	.03
12	.01	.02
13	.01	.01
14	.01	—
15	—	—
	1.00	

*Time t is discretized into units of one week, and probabilities are rounded to the nearest 1/100.

Procedure for Part (3)

A. Same as Part (2).

B. Same as Part (2) only the number of times the procedure will be repeated is governed by a random mechanism: exponential random deviates were used to generate the waiting times between deals. To simplify the experimental procedure, time was discretized into units of one week. As each deal is announced, you will be told the number of weeks remaining in the year, so that you will know how much time is left for investing. Since time has been discretized into units of one week, it may be that two (or more) deals will occur in "one week"; for example, you may receive instructions of the following kind:

There are 37 weeks remaining and the deal which has just appeared requires an investment of 3 white chips for a payoff of 11 blue chips.

(You make a decision on this deal and then the next deal is announced):

There are *still* 37 weeks remaining and the deal which has just appeared requires an investment of 2 white chips for a payoff of 10 blue chips.

The process terminates for you when:
a. you have exhausted your white chips; or
b. the year ends.

C. This part of the experiment will be replicated 6 times.

QUESTION SHEET

Suppose I were to give you one dollar for each blue chip in your possession at the end of the experiment. This would surely be a desirable experiment in which to participate!

1. How much would you be willing to pay for an opportunity to participate in one replication of Part (1) of the experiment?

$ _____

2. How much would you be willing to pay for an opportunity to participate in one replication of Part (2) of the experiment?

$ _____

3. How much would you be willing to pay for an opportunity to participate in one replication of Part (3) of the experiment?

$ _____

TALLY SHEET FOR PART (1)

Payoffs of accepted deals

Replicate No.	1	2	3	4	5	6	7	8
Deal 1								
" 2								
" 3								
" 4								
" 5								
" 6								
" 7								
" 8								
" 9								
" 10								
" 11								
" 12								
" 13								
" 14								
" 15								
Total payoff:								

A. Each column is for one replicate of the experiment of Part (1). *If and only if* you accept a deal, enter the *payoff* of that deal opposite the appropriate deal number in the column representing the replicate being performed.

B. You may, if you wish, enter the total payoff of each replicate at the bottom of the column.

C. Remember, you cannot accept more than 5 deals, so there should *never* be more than five entries in any one column.

TALLY SHEET FOR PART (2)

Investments in and payoffs of accepted deals

Replicate No.:	1		2		3		4		5		6		7		8	
	I	P	I	P	I	P	I	P	I	P	I	P	I	P	I	P
Deal 1																
" 2																
" 3																
" 4																
" 5																
" 6																
" 7																
" 8																
" 9																
" 10																
" 11																
" 12																
" 13																
" 14																
" 15																
Total payoff:																
Amount of investment :																

A. This sheet is to be filled in just as the tally sheet for Part (1). The I column is for entering the number of white chips you invest in an accepted deal. The P column is for entering the payoff of an accepted deal.

B. Remember, the *sum* of the entries in any I column cannot exceed 5.

C. After each application you may, if you wish, enter the total payoff and the number of white chips invested at the bottom of each column.

TALLY SHEET FOR PART (3)

A. Make your entries as on the Part (2) Tally Sheet, opposite the number of weeks remaining when the deal is accepted.

Investments in and payoffs of accepted deals

Replicate No.:	1		2		3		4		5		6		7		8	
Weeks remaining	I	P	I	P	I	P	I	P	I	P	I	P	I	P	I	P
52																
51																
50																
49																
48																
47																
46																
45																
44																
43																
42																
41																
40																
39																
38																
37																
36																
35																
34																
33																
32																
31																
30																
29																
28																
27																
26																
25																
24																
23																
22																
21																
20																
19																
18																
17																
16																
15																
14																
13																
12																
11																
10																
9																
8																
7																
6																
5																
4																
3																
2																
1																
Total payoff :																
Amount of investment :																

Raw Data Underlying Graphs 9.1 Through 9.6 and Tables 9.4 and 9.5

TABLE B.1. PILOT STUDY. RESULTS FOR MODEL I — PAYOFFS.

		Replication Number								Average over Replications
		1	2	3	4	5	6	7	8	
Subject Number	1	15	35	47	32	23	41	28	39	32.50
	2	14	32	47	38	18	41	27	32	31.12
	3	14	32	47	37	22	41	28	35	32.00
	4	12	35	47	38	20	41	28	39	32.50
	5	13	37	50	38	22	41	27	35	32.88
	6	14	41	47	38	22	41	27	35	33.12
	7	10	35	47	38	23	41	27	35	32.00
	8	11	35	47	38	22	41	27	32	31.62
	9	11	41	47	38	22	41	23	35	32.00
	10	14	41	50	38	23	41	24	32	32.88
	11	16	32	47	38	20	41	28	32	32.00
Averages over Subjects		13.09	36.00	47.54	37.36	21.54	41.00	26.73	34.64	GRAND AVERAGES: 32.24
Payoff Achieved by Optimal Strategy		14.00	41.00	50.00	38.00	23.00	41.00	28.00	32.00	33.38
Δ_{i1}		−.91	−5.00	−2.46	−.64	−1.46	0	−1.27	+2.64	−1.14

TABLE B.2. PILOT STUDY. RESULTS FOR MODEL II — PAYOFFS.

Subject Number	Replication Number								Average over Replications
	1	2	3	4	5	6	7	8	
1	13	18	11	24	18	17	22	21	18.00
2	17	18	$12\frac{1}{3}$	24	18	$13\frac{1}{2}$	22	20	18.08
3	$14\frac{1}{3}$	21	$15\frac{1}{2}$	24	18	13	22	21	18.57
4	10	18	15	24	10	17	22	20	18.00
5	13	11	11	23	19	17	22	20	17.00
6	14	18	$12\frac{1}{4}$	24	18	13	$21\frac{1}{2}$	20	17.94
7	18	18	$13\frac{3}{4}$	24	18	$12\frac{1}{2}$	22	18	17.91
8	$11\frac{2}{3}$	14	$12\frac{1}{4}$	22	18	$12\frac{1}{2}$	$21\frac{1}{2}$	18	16.43
9	18	18	$15\frac{1}{4}$	24	18	17	22	20	18.66
10	$14\frac{1}{3}$	21	$15\frac{1}{4}$	24	18	13	$21\frac{1}{2}$	18	18.14
11	18	21	$15\frac{1}{4}$	24	18	$13\frac{1}{2}$	$21\frac{1}{2}$	18	18.66
Averages over Subjects	14.67	17.82	13.01	23.73	18.09	14.95	21.82	19.46	GRAND AVERAGES: 17.94
Payoff Achieved by Optimal Strategy	17.67	18.00	12.25	23.00	18.00	13.50	21.50	18.50	17.80
Δ_{i2}	−3.00	−.18	+.76	+.73	+.09	+1.45	+.32	+.96	+.14

TABLE B.3. PILOT STUDY. RESULTS FOR MODEL IIa — PAYOFFS.

Subject Number	Replication Number								Average over Replications
	1	2	3	4	5	6	7	8	
1	$14\frac{1}{2}$	14	$16\frac{1}{2}$	15	21	12	$17\frac{1}{2}$	17	15.94
2	$18\frac{1}{3}$	14	$16\frac{1}{2}$	12	21	12	$17\frac{2}{3}$	17	16.07
3	$18\frac{1}{3}$	11	$16\frac{1}{2}$	$14\frac{1}{2}$	21	14	16	17	16.04
4	18	14	16	$14\frac{1}{2}$	21	13	17	17	16.31
5	11	14	$16\frac{1}{2}$	$11\frac{1}{2}$	20	10	18	17	14.75
6	19	14	17	13	21	13	$17\frac{2}{3}$	16	16.33
7	$18\frac{1}{3}$	14	$16\frac{1}{2}$	15	21	13	$17\frac{1}{3}$	14	16.14
8	$18\frac{1}{3}$	14	16	15	21	13	$17\frac{1}{3}$	17	16.46
9	19	14	17	14	21	13	$17\frac{2}{3}$	17	16.58
10	19	14	15	$14\frac{1}{2}$	21	13	$17\frac{1}{3}$	$15\frac{2}{3}$	16.06
11	19	14	16	14	21	13	$17\frac{1}{3}$	17	16.42
Averages over Subjects	17.53	13.73	16.32	13.91	20.91	12.64	17.35	16.52	GRAND AVERAGES: 16.10
Payoff Achieved by Optimal Strategy	15.00	14.00	17.00	14.00	21.00	12.00	17.67	17.00	15.96
$\Delta_{.3}$	2.53	−.27	−.68	−.09	−.09	.64	−.32	−.48	+.14

TABLE B.4. MAIN STUDY. RESULTS FOR MODEL I — PAYOFFS.

Subject Number	Replication Number						Average over Replications
	1	2	3	4	5	6	
1	32	27	23	47	41	11	30.17
2	32	28	22	47	35	11	29.13
3	35	27	22	50	41	10	30.73
4	32	24	22	47	35	13	28.83
5	29	28	22	50	41	14	30.67
6	35	24	22	47	41	10	29.83
7	35	27	22	47	41	13	30.73
8	32	24	18	47	37	10	28.00
9	30	24	21	47	35	10	27.83
10	35	27	22	50	37	10	30.17
11	32	24	21	47	41	10	29.13
12	35	27	22	50	41	10	30.73
13	32	23	21	47	35	13	28.50
14	32	27	18	47	35	10	28.13
15	32	24	22	47	41	10	29.33
16	29	27	22	50	35	13	29.33
17	32	27	22	47	35	10	28.83
18	29	28	23	50	35	16	30.17
19	32	24	22	47	41	10	29.33
Averages over Subjects	32.21	25.84	21.53	47.95	38.05	11.26	GRAND AVERAGES: 29.47
Payoff Achieved by Optimal Strategy	32	28	23	50	41	14	31.33
Δ_{ii}	.21	−2.16	−1.47	−2.05	−2.95	−2.74	−1.86

TABLE B.5. MAIN STUDY. RESULTS FOR MODEL II — PAYOFFS.

Subject Number	Replication Number						Average over Replications
	1	2	3	4	5	6	
1	18	22	13	11	21	$17\frac{1}{3}$	17.06
2	20	22	17	$8\frac{1}{3}$	18	17	17.06
3	$18\frac{1}{2}$	$21\frac{1}{2}$	13	$15\frac{1}{4}$	18	$17\frac{2}{3}$	17.32
4	$18\frac{1}{2}$	22	14	11	18	17	16.75
5	$18\frac{1}{2}$	$21\frac{1}{2}$	13	$12\frac{1}{4}$	18	17	16.71
6	18	25	14	$12\frac{1}{4}$	18	15	17.06
7	20	22	13	$12\frac{1}{4}$	21	18	17.38
8	21	22	17	11	18	17	17.67
9	18	22	14	$15\frac{1}{4}$	18	$17\frac{2}{3}$	17.49
10	18	22	13	$15\frac{1}{4}$	18	18	17.38
11	20	22	21	$8\frac{1}{3}$	11	17	16.56
12	18	$21\frac{1}{2}$	17	$12\frac{1}{4}$	18	$16\frac{1}{3}$	17.18
13	11	19	$9\frac{2}{3}$	$12\frac{1}{4}$	18	$13\frac{1}{5}$	13.85
14	18	$21\frac{1}{2}$	17	11	21	18	17.75
15	$18\frac{1}{2}$	$21\frac{1}{2}$	17	11	18	18	17.33
16	11	15	$13\frac{1}{2}$	$12\frac{1}{4}$	16	18	14.29
17	18	$21\frac{1}{2}$	13	11	18	15	16.08
18	11	15	$12\frac{1}{2}$	13	14	$17\frac{1}{3}$	13.87
19	18	$21\frac{1}{2}$	13	11	21	$17\frac{1}{3}$	16.97
Averages over Subjects	17.37	21.08	14.46	11.89	17.95	16.94	GRAND AVERAGES: 16.61
Payoff Achieved by Optimal Strategy	18.50	21.50	13.50	12.25	18.00	17.67	16.90
$\Delta._{2}$	-1.13	-.42	+.96	-.36	-.65	-.72	-.29

TABLE B.6. MAIN STUDY. RESULTS FOR MODEL II*a*.

		Replication Number						Averages over Replications
		1	2	3	4	5	6	
Subject Number	1	17	$17\frac{1}{2}$	13	$14\frac{1}{2}$	16	$18\frac{1}{3}$	16.06
	2	17	18	10	13	$16\frac{1}{2}$	19	15.58
	3	16	18	10	13	17	19	15.50
	4	10	$17\frac{2}{3}$	10	13	17	19	14.44
	5	17	$17\frac{2}{3}$	10	13	$16\frac{1}{2}$	$18\frac{2}{3}$	15.47
	6	17	$17\frac{2}{3}$	10	14	14	14	14.44
	7	$17\frac{2}{3}$	$17\frac{2}{3}$	9	15	16	$18\frac{1}{3}$	15.61
	8	13	14	13	$16\frac{1}{2}$	$16\frac{1}{2}$	$18\frac{2}{3}$	15.28
	9	13	18	7	10	15	14	12.83
	10	17	$17\frac{2}{3}$	13	10	$16\frac{1}{2}$	19	15.53
	11	17	18	10	13	17	19	15.67
	12	17	$17\frac{1}{3}$	10	13	17	19	15.56
	13	12	$13\frac{2}{3}$	10	3	16	$18\frac{1}{3}$	12.17
	14	$17\frac{2}{3}$	18	13	15	16	$18\frac{1}{3}$	16.33
	15	17	18	10	$14\frac{1}{2}$	$13\frac{1}{2}$	11	14.00
	16	17	$17\frac{1}{2}$	13	13	$16\frac{1}{2}$	11	14.67
	17	17	$17\frac{1}{3}$	13	15	16	$18\frac{1}{3}$	16.11
	18	17	$13\frac{1}{3}$	13	13	$14\frac{2}{3}$	$18\frac{1}{3}$	14.88
	19	17	$17\frac{1}{3}$	13	15	16	$18\frac{1}{3}$	16.11
Averages over Subjects		15.96	17.07	11.05	12.97	15.98	17.35	GRAND AVERAGES: 15.07
Payoff Achieved by Optimal Strategy		15.00	17.00	14.00	12.00	17.67	17.00	15.44
	$\Delta_{.3}$	+.96	−.07	−2.95	+.97	−1.69	+.35	−.37

TABLE B.7. MAIN STUDY. VALUE OF GAME ASSIGNMENTS.

Subject Number	Part (1) Before	After	Part (2) Before	After	Part (3) Before	After
1	$33	$33	$20	$20	$20	$20
2	18	25	8	20	8	15
3	$22\frac{1}{2}$	31	$22\frac{1}{2}$	17	$22\frac{1}{2}$	15
4	20	29	$17\frac{1}{2}$	$16\frac{1}{2}$	$17\frac{1}{2}$	13
5	25	32	12	17	12	15
6	30	34	12	17	12	16
7	30	30	15	17	15	15
8	34	32	10	19	8	$17\frac{1}{2}$
9	25	30	12	20	10	15
10	25	30	20	$17\frac{1}{2}$	20	16
11	20	29	12	15	10	15
12[a]	—	—	—	—	—	—
13	27	31	20	18	20	16
14	4	30	6	17	5	14
15	20	28	17	17	$16\frac{1}{2}$	13
16	$23\frac{1}{2}$	$29\frac{1}{3}$	20	15	10	$14\frac{2}{3}$
17	15	28	10	15	5	12
18	20	30	10	17	5	15
19	14	20	14	15	14	15
Averages:	22.56	29.52	14.33	17.22	13.36	15.12

[a]This subject misunderstood the instructions.

CHAPTER 10

Future Research Problems and Conclusions

To put this research in perspective, we will cite some future research problems that it suggests and then discuss the administrative practicability of the results in Chapters 6, 7, and 8.

10.1. Future Research Problems

Problems which may be fruitful subjects for future research fall into two broad classes: those concerned with the extension of quantitative analysis into other aspects of petroleum exploration and those concerned with the administrative implications of quantitative techniques.

Several interesting problems of the first kind are extensions of the research presented here. For example, the Yule distribution was found to fit some of the histograms of Chapter 6 better than the Lognormal distribution in the extreme right tail. Can a reasonable stochastic model of the discovery process be built which leads to the Yule functional form?[1] Are there functional forms among the class of stable probability distributions discussed in 6.1.3 that are more appropriate? Can the distribution theory of these functional forms be developed as was done for the Lognormal distribution in Chapter 7?

---

[1] The writer has constructed a model from assumptions similar to those used by H. Simon to build a model of the frequency histogram of words in prose samples by their frequency of occurrence; cf., *Models of Man*, Chapter 9 (New York: John Wiley & Sons, Inc., 1957).

There are many questions raised by the sequential investment models of Chapter 8, one of the most important being "How can these models be revised to render them more realistic?" For example, how might the constraint that only a given amount X of capital is available for investment be revised to allow for fluctuations in X as the fortunes of the firm rise and fall? What would be the effect of such a revision on the optimal decision rule?

In addition, statistical decision and related techniques might be applied to several exploration problems that have not been emphasized in this research. Representative ones are:

1. A typical problem faced by an operator is how should he allocate his funds among $n(> 0)$ petroliferous areas which he may be interested in exploring. If the ith area, $1 \leq i \leq n$, is characterized by a generic parameter θ_i which is not known with certainty, then an interesting analogy can be drawn with a famous unsolved problem called the "two-armed bandit" problem.[2] Suppose we have a slot machine with two arms. When either arm is pulled the machine pays off either one unit or nothing. The probability of winning with the left arm is p_ℓ and that of winning with the right, p_r. Neither p_ℓ nor p_r is known with certainty, but $\tilde{p}_\ell$ and $\tilde{p}_r$ are random variables with a known (joint) prior distribution function F_{p_ℓ, p_r}. If the player is allowed n plays, and there is no cost per play, what sequential strategy should he follow so as to maximize the expected value of the n plays? An interesting research problem is to determine:

   (a) to what extent the analogy is valid;

   (b) how the two-armed bandit problem should be modified to make it more like the exploration problem mentioned above; e.g., make it an n-armed bandit problem;

   (c) if the modified problem can be solved analytically, and if not, how to simulate solutions.

2. The use of polynomial regression schemes to isolate regional from local effects on any contour-type map has recently come into vogue among geologists and geophysicists.[3] Thus far the technique has

---

[2] R. N. Bradt, S. M. Johnson, and S. Karlin, "On Sequential Designs for Maximizing the Sum of n Observations," *Annals of Mathematical Statistics*, Vol. 27 (March–December, 1956), pp. 1060–1074.

[3] An excellent article on this subject is "Trend Surface Analysis of Contour-type Maps with Irregular Control-point Spacing" by W. C. Krumbein in the *Journal of Geophysical Research*, Vol. 64, No. 7 (July, 1959). Additional references are cited in this article.

been regarded as a technical tool to enable the expert to under-stand the geological nature of an area where well control is fairly good. However, the map — be it a gravity, magnetic, seismic, isopach, or facies map — is also one of the chief types of informa-tion the operator has available to aid him in economic decision making, the real purpose motivating understanding of the purely technical (geological) aspects of an area. In a majority of in-stances, the yield in barrels of oil or in MCF of gas is directly pro-portional to the sand thickness of the strata containing hydro-carbon deposits. Sand thickness is portrayed on an isopach (equal thickness) map. Clearly, a regression scheme can be used to predict the expected value of sand thickness that may be en-countered in a borehole within the limits of the area analyzed. One might also wish to know whether further experimentation is warranted before proceeding with a test well.

3. The devices used to gather information in reconnaissance explora-tion are highly imperfect predictors in two senses. First, there is a possibility that the device will yield misleading information; e.g., a seismograph may indicate a "structural high" where there is none. Second, and perhaps more subtle, geological and geophysi-cal experimentation give information pertaining to *conditions favorable to the accumulation* of oil and gas — they NEVER tell whether oil or gas is present. Only the drill can confirm the exist-ence or non-existence of oil or gas. At the time same, these devices are expensive; e.g., seismic crew can cost up to $5,000 per day. A natural question that arises in the operator's mind is:

Given the costs of the experiments which can give me added in-formation about this area, what subset of available experiments should I choose, and in what order should I use them?

4. Bidding for leases is oftentimes fiercely competitive. What insight does a game theoretical analysis of the bidding problems faced by operators offer into the structure of the problem and its solution?

Ideally, the development of analytical techniques for decision making in business will be accompanied by a careful consideration of how businessmen are to be educated to use them. The successful introduction of new aids to decision making into an organization depends on an educa-tional process which is especially delicate in its early stages. The basic parts of such a process consist of:

making the goals of the method and its relation to present ways of making decisions clear to the potential user,

showing the user how to use the method and how to interpret the results,

seeing that the method is properly used.

Speaking in broad generality, the educational effort cannot be effective unless, first, the administrative environment in which the method will be used is favorable to technical innovation in decision making; second, the goals which are to be achieved by using the method are made explicit and are understood and accepted by the potential user; and third, policies and procedures for introducing the method are carefully planned in advance.

An administrative environment receptive to innovation is a necessity. If management has developed a habit of holding post-mortems for the purpose of putting blame on those who made "poor" decisions *as judged after the fact*, then decision-making innovations have little chance of being effective. The decision maker in such an environment is tempted to avoid approval of any commitment of funds or personnel which has a high element of risk or which is not clearly far above his superior's standards. The bending of the subordinate's utility curve by such an environment can result in excessive cash balances, inefficiently used capital, and subordinates who are unwilling to take even "reasonable" risks. Statistical decision techniques will prove to be of little aid in such an environment.

Even if the administrative environment is favorable to change in decision-making methods, a program aimed at introducing a new method cannot be properly implemented unless the goals of the program are clearly specified. The expert or consultant and the executive who will be responsible for goal achievement must arrive at an understanding of precisely what they wish to accomplish and how best to communicate this; e.g., the specialist and the executive might decide that the initial training will have as a goal the development of a sensitivity to the meaning of a decision rule rather than an understanding of the complex formal rationale which generated it.

Once the goals are specified, the question of how to achieve them arises. Policies and procedures are so strongly dependent upon the particular organization concerned that, from a more general point of view, we can only suggest questions that the executive and the specialist might ask each other:

1. How can we make our people aware of the usefulness of this technique?

2. How do we teach them its limitations:
   What are the built-in assumptions?
   What important variables may be excluded?
   How wide is the technique's applicability?

3. How do we teach the mechanics of the technique?

4. Do we maintain present methods of analysis and simply integrate this technique, or do we replace a way of doing things?

5. How do we measure the effectiveness of our program?

6. How do we provide for continual feedback on the manner in which the technique is being used?

7. Who will have continuing responsibility to see that this program is carried out?

A second class of research problems of a different nature than the mathematically oriented problems stated earlier arise from these considerations:

What guides to action, or policies, can be established that will be useful in helping the expert introduce tools for quantitative analysis into the decision process in the small independent? In the major?

What is the effect on organizational structure of weaving these techniques into the fabric of the decision process?

What kind of training of operating personnel is needed to implement such techniques? How should this be done?

These broad problems are the administrative complement to the model-building type of problems first mentioned. One can forecast with little error that the introduction of mathematical analysis into the everyday decision-making routine of a management unaccustomed to thinking in a mathematical fashion will accent the already acute problem of how the technical specialist who introduces the mathematics should communicate his ideas. Two premises which are too broad to be of great help in a specific instance but are narrow enough to guide our thinking about the general problem area are:

1. New methods of analysis should be presented as a complement to existing ways of weighing and analyzing decision problems. Phrased differently, the prospective user must see these techniques as an added dimension in perception, like spectacles for the nearsighted. "Rational" desirability of a new technique is not enough.

2. The *process* of introducing such methods must proceed so that the prospective user does not view them as a "threat" — if he does, a reversion to familiar methods of analysis is highly likely to occur, or some other non-cooperative reaction on his part will appear.

10.2 Administrative Considerations

We can place the main contents of this research — development of the Lognormal functional form as an appropriate form for the distribution of "size of petroleum deposit" in problems where this is a key random variable and determination of optimal decision rules for certain sequential investment problems — in better perspective by discussing its administrative practicability. The reader will remember that we termed a mathematical aid to decision making "administratively practical" if it:

1. includes the important variables in the problem area being analyzed;

2. provides relations among these variables which accurately characterize the problem;

3. yields a solution or strategy which is easily interpretable in terms of managerial action, and which can *informally* be justified as a "best" course of action within the limits of the assumptions underlying the technique;

4. improves upon competitive methods of analysis.

What functional form to use for the random variable "size of deposit" is a problem of statistical methodology more than a business-oriented decision problem under uncertainty. It is concerned with creation of appropriate mathematical underpinnings for a particular class of decision problems under uncertainty rather than with solutions to this class of problems. Nevertheless, this methodological problem is of practical importance, for the administrative practicability of a mathematical decision rule preferred as a solution to a decision problem under uncertainty is strongly influenced by the particular functional form chosen for the distribution function of the key random variable(s) in the problem. The choice usually affects the *relations between* the variables of the problem and therefore falls within the domain of 2 above.

As the discussion of future research problems indicates, the Lognormal functional form may not be the sole useful form to use for the distribution of field sizes or petroleum deposits, but its usefulness has been established on several grounds. Besides being a good empirical fit to histograms of reported field sizes and being in concordance with concepts of how mineral deposits are formed, it can be derived from simple but acceptable assumptions about the discovery process. Furthermore, it is rich enough to capture most reasonable oilmen's probability judgements about random variables such as reported field size and is analytically tractable.

By contrast with a solution to the methodological problem just discussed, the optimal decision rules of Chapter 8 are mathematical guides to decision making in the full sense. The formulation of Model IIIa in particular captures the essence of the real-world problem faced by oil and gas operators, for it includes the important economic variables in the real problem and provides reasonably realistic relations between them. The decision rules which follow from this formulation of the problem are easily interpretable in common sense terms and in some firms might improve on competitive methods of analysis if used.

Such improvement can be achieved in several ways. For example, one technique can be considered more effective than another if it allows a manager to delegate a decision-making activity with no loss in the degree to which the activity's goal is achieved. An example of this kind of effectiveness is cited in an article by A. Henderson and R. O. Schlaifer. They mention the use of linear programming by the H. J. Heinz Company for the scheduling of ketchup shipments to branch warehouses, stating that:

> One of the most important advantages gained by the H. J. Heinz Company from the introduction of linear programming was relief of the senior members of the distribution department from the burden of preparing shipping programs. Previously the quarterly preparation of the program took a substantial amount of their time; now they pay only as much attention to this problem as they believe necessary to keep the feel of the situation, while the detailed development of the program has been handed over to clerks. Freed from the burden of working out what is after all only glorified arithmetic, they have this much more time to devote to matters which really require their experience and judgement.

> An equally important gain, in the opinion of these officials themselves, is the peace of mind which results from being sure that the program IS the lowest cost program possible.[4]

[4]A. Henderson and R. O. Schlaifer, "Mathematical Programming: Better Information for Better Decision Making," *Harvard Business Review*.

Although they do not relieve the manager from the burden of a great deal of arithmetic, in large organizations where the evaluation of a deal or prospect must filter through several organizational layers before a final decision to accept or reject is made, decision rules like those of Chapter 8 would provide a clear, explicit criterion for use at all levels in judging the economic value of the deal or prospect. In other words, it can be effective as a device for communicating a management policy and, if management desires, as an aid in delegating authority.

One of the more important results of the analysis of the particular class of sequential decision problems we have chosen to investigate is the insight it gives into the structure of these problems. The good manager is always trying to improve his performance by learning from his experiences and those of others, a process which can be accelerated if he thoroughly understands the structure of the problems he faces. As Jerome S. Bruner states it in another context:[5]

> There are two ways in which learning serves the future. One is through its specific applicability to tasks that are highly similar to those we originally learned to perform. A second way in which earlier learning renders later performance more efficient is through what is conveniently called nonspecific transfer or, more accurately, the transfer of principles and attitudes. In essence, it consists of learning initially not a skill but a general idea, which can then be used as a basis for recognizing subsequent problems as special cases of the idea originally mastered. This type of transfer is at the heart of the educational process — the continual broadening and deepening of knowledge in terms of basic and general ideas.
>
> The continuity of learning that is produced by a second type of transfer, transfer of principles, is dependent upon mastery of the structure of the subject matter. . . . That is to say, in order for a person to be able to recognize the applicability or inapplicability of an idea to a new situation and to broaden his learning thereby, he must have clearly in mind the general nature of the phenomenon with which he is dealing. The more fundamental or basic is the idea he has learned, almost by definition, the greater will be its breadth of applicability to new problems.

Utilization of hypothetical games against nature such as those of

---

[5]Jerome S. Bruner, *The Process of Education* (Cambridge: Harvard University Press, 1960), pp. 17–18.

Chapter 8 is a cheap way of providing experience, which, while not equal to experience in making real decisions (about oil and gas ventures, for example), does give the player a feeling for the structure of the real decision problem. Such games can also serve as a testing ground for rules of thumb which a player may have evolved using intuition:

> . . . the intellectual technique of arriving at plausible but tentative formulations without going through the analytic steps by which such formulations would be found to be valid or invalid conclusions . . . the shrewd guess, the fertile hypothesis, the courageous leap to a tentative conclusion — these are the most valuable coin of the thinker at work, whatever his line of work.[6]

The use of mathematical games in this fashion typifies the role which mathematics will play in shaping the way future executives will deal with decision problems under uncertainty of the kind presented in this monograph.

---

[6]*Op. Cit.*, pp. 13–14.

BIBLIOGRAPHY

Petroleum Exploration and Related Topics

Arps, J. J., and T. G. Roberts, "Economics of Drilling for Cretaceous Oil Production on the East Flank of the Denver-Julesburg Basin," unpublished paper (April 3, 1958).

Arrington, J. R., "Size of Crude Reserves is Key to Evaluating Exploration Programs," *The Oil and Gas Journal*, Vol. 58, No. 9 (February 29, 1960), pp. 130–132.

Barton, D. C., "Petroleum Geophysics," *The Science of Petroleum*, New York: Oxford University Press, 1938.

Dix, C. H., *Seismic Prospecting For Oil*, New York: Harper & Row, Publishers, 1952.

Dugan, C. J., "Incidence of Oil Occurrence," *Mines*, Petroleum Number for 1959, p. 127.

The Financial Post, Vol. XV, Toronto: MacLean-Hunter Publishing Co., Ltd., 1959.

Forgotson, J. J., Jr., "Review and Classification of Quantitative Mapping Techniques," *Journal of the American Association of Petroleum Geologists*, Tulsa, Oklahoma, Vol. 44, No. 1 (January, 1960).

Grayson, C. J., Jr., *Decisions Under Uncertainty: Drilling Decisions by Oil and Gas Operators*, Boston: Division of Research, Harvard Business School, 1960.

Hager, D., *Practical Oil Geology*, 6th ed. New York: McGraw-Hill Book Company, Inc., 1951.

Haun, J. D., and L. W. LeRoy (editors), *Subsurface Geology in Petroleum Exploration*, Golden, Colorado: Colorado School of Mines, 1957.

The Independent Petroleum Association of America, "Drilling in the Face of Nine to One Odds," *The IPAA Monthly* (August, 1959).

Jakosky, J. J., *Exploration Geophysics*, 2nd ed. Los Angeles: Trija Publishing Company, 1950.

Krumbein, W. C., "Regional and Local Components in Facies Maps," *Bulletin of the American Association of Petroleum Geologists*, Vol. 40 (1956), pp. 2163–2194.

Krumbein, W. C., "Measurement and Error in Regional Stratigraphic Analysis," *Journal of Sedimentary Petrology* (June, 1958).

Krumbein, W. C., "Trend Surface Analysis of Contour-type Maps With Irregular Control-point Spacing," *Journal of Geophysical Research*, Vol. 64, No. 7 (July, 1959).

Landes, K. K., *Petroleum Geology*, New York: John Wiley & Sons, Inc., 1961.

Levorsen, A., *Geology of Petroleum*, New York: McGraw-Hill Book Company, Inc., 1956.

Megill, R. E., "The Cost of Finding Oil," *Oil and Gas Journal*, Vol. 57, No. 14 (March 30, 1959).

National Oil Scouts and Landsmen's Yearbook — Review of 1957, Vol. XXVIII, Austin, Texas: National Scouts and Landsmen's Association, 1958.

National Petroleum Council, *Submerged Lands Productive Capacity*, Washington 6, D. C.: Report of the National Petroleum Council, 1953.

Oldham, C. H. G., and D. B. Sutherland, "Orthogonal Polynomials: Their Use in Estimating the Regional Effect," *Geophysics*, Vol. 20 (1956).

Vistelius, A. B., "The Skew Frequency Functions and the Fundamental Law of the Geochemical Processes," *The Journal of Geology*, Vol. 68, No. 1 (January, 1960), pp. 1–23.

Statistics, Probability, and Related Topics

Aitchison, J., and J. A. C. Brown, *The Lognormal Distribution*, New York: Cambridge University Press, 1957.

Allais, M., "Method of Appraising Economic Prospects of Mining Exploration Over Large Territories: Algeria Sahara Case Study," *Management Science*, Baltimore (July, 1957).

Bradt, R. N., S. M. Johnson, and S. Karlin, "On Sequential Designs for Maximizing the Sum of N Observations," *The Annals of Mathematical Statistics*, Vol. 27 (1956).

Bruner, J. S., *The Process of Education*, Cambridge: Harvard University Press, 1960.

Cramer, H., *Mathematical Methods of Statistics*, Princeton: Princeton University Press, 1958.

Curtis, H. J., "On the Distribution of a Quotient of Two Chance Variables," *The Annals of Mathematical Statistics*, Vol. 12 (1941), p. 42.

Epstein, B., "The Mathematical Description of Certain Breakage Mechanisms Leading to the Logarithmico-normal Distribution," *Journal of the Franklin Institute*, Vol. 224, p. 471.

Feller, W., *An Introduction to Probability Theory and Its Applications*, 2nd ed. Vol. I, New York: John Wiley & Sons, Inc., 1957.

Fisher, J., "A Class of Stochastic Investment Problems," *Operations Research*, Vol. 9, No. 1 (Jan.–Feb., 1961) pp. 53–65.

Gibbs, J. W., *Elementary Principles of Statistical Mechanics*, New York: Charles Scribner's Sons, 1902.

Gnedenko, B. V., and A. N. Kolmogoroff, *Limit Distributions for Sums of Independent Random Variables*, Cambridge, Mass.: Addison-Wesley Publishing Co., Inc., 1954.

Gumbel, E. J., *Statistics of Extremes*, New York: Columbia University Press, 1958.

Henderson, A. O., and R. O. Schlaifer, "Mathematical Programming: Better Information for Better Decision Making," *Harvard Business Review*, Vol. 32, No. 3 (1954).

Khinchin, A. I., *Mathematical Foundations of Information Theory*, New York: Dover Publications, Inc., 1957.

Krige, D. C., "A Statistical Approach to Some Basic Mine Valuation Problems on the Witwatersrand," *Journal of the Chemical, Metallurgical, and Mining Society of South Africa*, Johannesburg (December, 1951).

MacGregor, D. H., "Pareto's Law," *Economic Journal* (March, 1936).

Mandelbrot, B., "The Pareto-Levy Random Functions and the Multiplicative Variation of Income," Yorktown Heights, New York: I.B.M. Research Center Report, October, 1960.

Matheron, G., "Application des Méthodes Statistiques à L'évaluation des Gisements," *Annales des Mines*, Paris (December, 1955).

Raiffa, H., and R. O. Schlaifer, *Applied Statistical Decision Theory*, Boston: Division of Research, Harvard Business School, 1961.

Rhodes, E. C., "The Pareto Distribution of Income," *Economica* (February, 1944).

Savage, L. J., *The Foundations of Statistics*, New York: John Wiley & Sons, Inc., 1954.

Scarborough, J. B., *Numerical Mathematical Analysis*, 4th ed. Baltimore: The Johns Hopkins Press, 1958.

Shannon, C. D., and W. Weaver, *The Mathematical Theory of Communication*, Urbana, Ill.: University of Illinois Press, 1949.

Simon, H., *Models of Man*, New York: John Wiley & Sons, Inc., 1957.

Solomon, Ezra (editor), *The Management of Corporate Capital*, New York: The Free Press of Glencoe, 1959.

Thebault, J. Y., "Distribution Lognormale de Certains Caractères de Quelques Phénomènes Géologiques et ses Applications," *Revue de Statistique Appliquée*, Paris, Vol. IX, No. 2 (1961).

Wiener, N., *The Extrapolation, Interpolation, and Smoothing of Stationary Time-Series With Engineering Applications*, New York: John Wiley & Sons, Inc., 1949.